RINA

THE RAPID MARINE TRANSPORT GROUP

INTERNATIONAL SYMPOSIUM
& SEMINAR

THE SAFETY OF HIGH SPEED CRAFT

LONDON

6 & 7 February 1997

D
629.3
INT

THE ROYAL INSTITUTION OF NAVAL ARCHITECTS
10 Upper Belgrave Street,
London, SW1X 8BQ

Telephone: 0171-235-4622
Fax: 0171-245-6959

ISBN No: 0903055 26 0

NAMES AND ADDRESSES OF AUTHORS

Michael Schindler
Danish Maritime Institute
Skibsteknisk Laboratorium
Hjortekoersvej 99
DK - 2800 Lyngby
Denmark

Fax: 45 45 87 9333

John Lewthwaite
IMAA Consultancy Ltd
35 Knights Bank Road
Hill Head
Fareham Hants PO14 3HX
UK

Fax: 44 1329 668176

S L Toxopeus
MARIN
2 Haagstaag
PO Box 28
6700 AA Wageningen
Netherlands

Fax: 31 317 493 245

Rob Bryce
Hart Fenton and Co. Ltd
Norman House, 1st Floor,
Kettering Terrace
Portsmouth
Hants PO2 7AE
UK

Fax: 44 1705 875280

Tony Armstrong
Australian Shipbuilders Corporation
3 Warambui Avenue
Baulkham Hills
NSW 2153
Australia

Fax: 61 296 74 1552

Nigel Warren
FBM Marine Ltd
Cowes Shipyard
Cowes
Isle of Wight
UK

Fax: 44 1983 299642

Jim Peachey
Bay 3/21a
The Marine Safety Agency
Spring Place, 105 Commercial Rd
Southampton   SO15 1EG
UK

Fax: 44 1703 329251

J Forestier
Bureau Veritas
17 Bis Place Des Reflets la
Defensez Courbevoie
92400
FRANCE

Fax: 33 1 4291 5320

Vincenzo Farinetti
Fincantieri   Naval   Shipbuilding
Division
Via Cipro 11
16129 Genova
Italy

Fax: 39 10 599 5379

Tormod Eidal
Det Norske Veritas AS
Veritasveien 1
N 1322 Høvik
Norway
UK

Fax: 47 67579911

Professor Jastrebski
Technical University of Szczecin
Faculty of Maritime Engineering
Al. Plastów 41
Szczecin
71065
POLAND

Fax: 48 91 34 0946

David Taylor
Clifford Chance
200 Aldersgate Street
London
EC1A 4JJ
UK

Fax: 44 171 600 5555

W Graham
Bay 3/01 B, Spring Place
105 Commercial Road
Southampton
SO15 1EG
UK

Fax: 44 1703 329 161

Karl Wiklund
Det Norske Veritas
Veritasveien 1
N-1322 Høvik
NORWAY

Fax: 47 67 57 9911

Per Werenskiold
Marintek
Otto Nielsens veg 10
PO Box 4125 Valentinlyst
N-7002 Trondheim
Norway

Fax: 47 73 59 57 76

A Marchant
CETEC Consultancy Ltd
Six Oaks House
Rudds Lane, Upper Timsbury
Romsey, Hants SO51 0NU
UK

Fax: 44 1794 368 967

R Curry
ABS Europe Ltd
ABS House
No 1 Frying Pan Alley
London E1 7HR
UK

Fax: 44 171 247 3053

Stephen Phillips
Seaspeed Technology
2 City Business Centre
Basin Road
Chichester
Sussex PO10 2DU
UK

Fax: 44 1243 783 333

Geoff Billington
ML Lifeguard Equipment Ltd
Canol-y-dre
Ruthen, Denbighshire
LL15 1TU
UK

Fax: 44 1824 705 701

John Gifford
Griffon Hovercraft Ltd
Carlton House
Ringwood Road, Woodlands
Southampton SO40 7HT
UK

Fax: 44 1703 81 3698

CONTENTS

STABILITY

SAFETY IN DESIGN AND OPERATION

SAFETY APPROACHES

SEMINAR/STRUCTURED DISCUSSION

OPENING ADDRESS
by W A Graham, Director, Marine Standards Division, Marine Safety Agency   (UK)

SEMINAR AGENDA

SESSION I - DESIGN ACCELERATIONS

SESSION II - STRUCTURES & FIRE

SESSION III - STABILITY & SUBDIVISION

SESSION IV - LIFESAVING & EVACUATION

SUMMARY OF SEMINAR ACTION POINTS

SUMMARY REPORT OF DISCUSSIONS ON PAPERS PRESENTED IN SHANGHAI

PAPER NO.1.

DAMAGE STABILITY TESTS OF A MODEL REPRESENTING A FAST RO-RO PASSENGER FERRY

by M Schindler, Danish Maritime Institute, Lyngby, Denmark

Paper presented at the

International Symposium & Seminar

THE SAFETY OF HIGH SPEED CRAFT

6 - 7 FEBRUARY 1997 LONDON

DAMAGE STABILITY TESTS OF A MODEL REPRESENTING A FAST RO-RO PASSENGER FERRY

Michael Schindler
Danish Maritime Institute, Lyngby, Denmark

SUMMARY

For the first time a model of a damaged high-speed mono-hull Ro-Ro ferry has been built and tested in rough seas. This paper focuses on DMI's eight years experience in the field of model testing of damaged Ro-Ro ferry models exposed to rough seas. It outlines some of the design principles applied during construction of the DMI models and finally it summarises the most important trends in model behaviour in relation to the results obtained from damage stability calculations.

AUTHOR'S BIOGRAPHY

Mr Michael Schindler has taken part in Danish Maritime Institute's activities related to damage stability problems since 1989. He has been involved in damage calculations for several dry cargo vessels and more recently for existing Ro-Ro passenger ferries with respect to upgrading procedures related to the SOLAS 90 regulations.

He has been responsible for all phases of model testing, and for a great part of the reporting work concerning the UK Department of Transport investigation of stability standards for existing Ro-Ro passenger ferries and a Nordic Co-operation on the Safety of Passenger Ro-Ro Vessels. Mr Schindler has also been involved in the maintenance of existing, and the development of new computer programs to cope with the more and more complex stability rules. He gained his M.Sc. Eng. in Hydrodynamics in 1980.

1. INTRODUCTION

Annex 2 to the Agreement on New Damage Stability Requirements for Ro-Ro Passenger Ships Undertaking Regular Scheduled International Voyages between or to or from Designated Ports in North West Europe and the Baltic Sea, provides 'Stability Requirements' which shall be satisfied by passenger ships with Ro-Ro cargo space as defined in regulation II-2/3 of the International Convention for Safety of Life at Sea. Alternatively to this calculation method, which includes some amount of additional water on Ro-Ro deck, the model test procedure complying with the Appendix 'Model Test Method', SOLAS/CONF. 3/46, Annex is regarded as an equivalent method to prove the capability of the ship to withstand the required seastate in the worst damage case.

Gradually, several conventional Ro-Ro ferries, which do not apply to MSC.36(63) HSC-code have been model tested. Some of them with respect to the SOLAS/CONF. 3/46 agreement above and others subjected to intensive government-controlled and commercial research programmes aimed for better understanding of their behaviour. No model of a fast (HSC) mono-hull Ro-Ro ferry has so far been investigated seriously by model testing in the damaged condition.

On this background, Fincantieri C.N.I. Yard in Genoa as a private venture, has authorised the Danish Maritime Institute to undertake model tank testing of their fast passenger Ro-Ro ferry - "Superseacat" with the objective of investigating her ability to survive in rough seas in regard to the two worst damage positions.

The entire test programme was divided into two phases:

- **Phase One** was dedicated to the investigation of survivability of the ferry 'as is', i.e. generally in accordance with prescriptions in the 'Agreement'

- The objectives of **Phase Two** were to find the limits for survivability in terms of three decisive parameters, regardless of the fact that they may lie beyond the limits of the existing design.

The entire scope of work has been performed on the basis of information provided by the Yard, who also performed the damage stability analyses forming basis for selecting the critical damage cases which should be subjected to testing.

The whole test series was performed in the period between 13th June and 21st August, 1996.

2. PROBLEM FORMULATION

The water ingress into a damaged Ro-Ro ferry is a complex process which depends on a wide range of parameters describing the Ro-Ro ferry characteristics, the damage characteristics and the environmental conditions.

In a calm sea, the damaged Ro-Ro ferry, which is designed according to present regulations, will find an equilibrium condition which is characterised by the whole Ro-Ro deck being well above the waterline. Adherence to present regulations will assure that for a given 'standard' damage the Ro-Ro ferry shall survive with a certain margin of safety against capsize. To demonstrate the fulfilment of the safety margin the still water stability calculations shall be made for the Ro-Ro ferry in the damaged condition. This calculation includes the effect of water flowing freely onto the Ro-Ro deck at higher angles of heel. For the Ro-Ro ferries under the SOLAS resolution, an assumed amount of water on the Ro-Ro deck has to be included by calculation, as required by the 'Agreement'.

Exposure of the damaged Ro-Ro ferry to waves, particularly beam seas, may have the effect that water flows in and out of the damaged opening. This water flow is caused by the varying water head inside and outside the Ro-Ro deck, the relative wave elevation, the ship motions and the motion of water trapped on the Ro-Ro deck.

The overall effect of the waves is that a net increase of water on the Ro-Ro deck can occur. An additional amount of water trapped on the Ro-Ro deck will cause an increase in the mean heel of the Ro-Ro ferry. Unless the forces acting on the Ro-Ro ferry are in balance, she will capsize.

Based on experience, the net water ingress on the Ro-Ro deck of a free floating ferry will depend on the following parameters:

- **Ro-Ro ferry Characteristics:**

  - Size / dimensions / displacement / freeboard
  - Loading condition
    (KG, radii of gyration, GZ-characteristics)
  - Subdivision below Ro-Ro deck
  - Cross-flooding capability
  - Arrangement on Ro-Ro deck

- **Damage Characteristics:**

  - Size
  - Location
  - Damaged freeboard

- **Environmental Conditions:**

  - Sea state (H_s , T_p)
  - Relative wave direction
  - Wind forces and direction

The importance of these parameters has been investigated on previous occasions using models of different Ro-Ro ferries. Therefore, Phase II of the present investigation concentrated on the three most important. They are listed in the following chapter.

3. TEST PROGRAMME

Phase I of the present investigation was formulated to demonstrate the ability of the tested ferry to survive in conditions prescribed in the 'Agreement' but with the following differences:

- According to the 'Agreement', the requirement for additional water on the Ro-Ro deck need not be complied with if the residual (damaged) freeboard is 2.0m or more. In the case of Damage (b) at frame 32 the resulting freeboard at equilibrium according to calculations is 2.06m. The model was tested in this condition.

- The model was tested in both damage cases using H_s = 4m (significant wave height), regardless of the fact that the 'Agreement' makes an allowance for reduction of the applied wave height if the residual freeboard is more than 0.3 m.

- The 'Agreement' prescribes testing of the damaged model using sea states with two peak periods. As consequently demonstrated during previous tests, the survivability of the models is considerably worse in steep waves having a short spectral peak period. The present investigation concentrated on tests in the waves having a short spectral peak period.

- The 'Agreement' prescribes testing of the damaged model in five wave realisations of at least 30 min duration in full-scale time. The model was tested in one wave realisation, but of more than 60 min duration in full-scale time.

Phase II of the present investigation was formulated to demonstrate the ability of the tested ferry to survive in conditions outside the range of the actual design and concentrated on the worst damage case with regard to the amount of water collected on the Ro-Ro deck during the initial part of this phase (runs 301 and 302). The investigated parameters were:

1) Displacement / Damaged Freeboard.
2) Intact GM.
3) Significant Wave Height.

The model was tested in one realisation of the short spectral peak period waves. Phase II testing included 2 different displacements, 3 damaged freeboards, 5 values of intact GM and 5 values of significant wave height. An initial heel angle towards the damaged side of the model was applied prior to some of the runs. Each run lasted more than 60 min in full-scale time. The entire test Programme is specified in Table 3.1.

4. MODEL DESIGN AND CONSTRUCTION

4.1 DESIGN BASIS

The intention behind the present model was to use the concept of a new design of fast mono-hull ferry - Superseacat, now under construction at the Yard. The existing model, recently used for the still-water and wave testing at DMI was a natural basis for construction of the damage stability model. The still-water model, which was built of foam was used as a form for casting the GRP damage stability model. The scale of both models is the same. All model work is based on the documents received from the Yard.

TABLE 3.1   The Entire Test Programme

Phase I						
Run No	Displ.	GM$_{int}$ (m)	Damage Position	Dam. Freeb. (m)	Init. Heel Angle (deg)	Sign. Wave ht. (m)
201	design	5.158	Mid	1.48	0.0	4.0
202	design	5.158	Aft	2.06	0.0	4.0
Phase II						
Run No	Displ. (m^3)	GM$_{int}$ (m)	Damage Position	Dam. Freeb. (m)	Init. Heel Angle (deg)	Sign. Wave Height (m)
301	+25.6%	3.990	Mid	1.06	0.0	4.0
302	+25.6%	3.990	Aft	0.99	0.0	4.0
421	+25.6%	3.800	Mid	0.67	0.0	3.2
422	+25.6%	3.800	Mid	0.67	1.0	3.2
411	+25.6%	3.800	Mid	0.67	0.0	3.5
412	+25.6%	3.800	Mid	0.67	1.0	3.5
401	+25.6%	3.800	Mid	0.67	0.0	4.0
402	+25.6%	3.800	Mid	0.67	1.0	4.0
403	+25.6%	3.680	Mid	0.67	0.0	4.0
404	+25.6%	3.680	Mid	0.67	1.0	4.0
461	+25.6%	3.680	Mid	0.67	1.0	2.0
501	+31.1%	3.490	Mid	0.58	0.0	4.0
502	+31.1%	3.490	Mid	0.58	1.0	4.0
503	+31.1%	3.490	Mid	0.58	3.0	4.0
504	+31.1%	3.490	Mid	0.58	5.0	4.0
601	+31.1%	3.490	Mid	0.34	0.0	4.0

TABLE 4.1 Full Scale and Model Main Dimensions

	Ship	Model
Scale		1 : 20.0
Length, L_{pp}	88.00 m	440.0 cm
Breadth, B	17.10 m	85.5 cm
Draught, T	2.61 m	13.1 cm
Depth to bulkhead deck - aft	5.90 m	29.5 cm
Depth to bulkhead deck - fore	4.50 m	22.5 cm
Height to top of side	10.70 m	53.5 cm
Length of aft ship damage	23.00 m	115.0 cm
Length of fore ship damage - 'as is'	18.00 m	90.0 cm
Length of fore ship damage - max.	29.20 m	146.0 cm
Displacement (intact)	design	

4.2 MODEL HULL AND CONSTRUCTION

The hull of the model is primarily made of GRP with two side damage areas. The longitudinal watertight subdivision below the main Ro-Ro deck is also mainly of GRP with the exception of two transverse bulkheads which from the very early stage of construction work were intended to be removed during Phase II of the project for variation of the damaged freeboard. They were made of transparent polycarbonate material. The whole Ro-Ro deck, including the upper deck in the fore-ship, as well as the ramps were made of the same material. As the model is open from above, the choice of transparent material is important for inspection for water in case of leaking to undamaged compartments during the tests. The sides of the model above the Ro-Ro deck were mainly made of 1 mm thick aluminium plates. The fore-ship part is of GRP.

For bending strength, one stainless steel wire (4 mm) is cast into the GRP-structure just below the Ro-Ro deck in the starboard (damaged) side of the model. This wire passes through the side damage opening unbroken. Two 50 mm wide metal strips are formed and cast into the GRP-structure from side to side through the bottom of the model around two GRP transverse bulkheads. At the top they are used as lifting points of the model.

Undamaged compartments, typically tanks within B/5 below the Ro-Ro deck are modelled by foam blocks. Foam is also used for modelling the port side, undamaged side-casing in the aft part of the Ro-Ro deck, while the corresponding damaged, starboard side-casing is made of thin polycarbonate plates. Ventilation of damaged areas below the Ro-Ro deck is provided in the undamaged side of the model through ventilation tubes of a length corresponding to the model side height above the Ro-Ro deck.

Above the Ro-Ro deck, a main ballast weight lift is provided in the centre line of the model. This lift, a u-shaped aluminium bar, can be moved up and down by means of two 'spindles' cast into two GRP transverse bulkheads below the Ro-Ro deck. The 'spindles' are fixed to the model sides by transverse u-shaped aluminium bars, used for holding small ballast weights for the transverse control of equilibrium. Miscellaneous aluminium profiles were fitted between the top of model sides to provide sufficient stiffness of the model.

Upon completion of the model building, check measurements were made and minor deviations - within 2 mm from the basic design were found. All values presented and used in this report correspond to the model as built.

4.3 SELECTION OF DAMAGE CASES

The damage stability analyses provided by the Yard identify the critical damage cases as prescribed in the Appendix of Annex 2 to the 'Agreement Concerning Specific Stability Requirements for Ro-Ro Passenger Ships Undertaking Regular Scheduled International Voyages between or to or from Designated Ports in North West Europe and the Baltic Sea. For the intact condition corresponding to the tests of Phase I, the following two damages are chosen:

- The damage giving the least area under the GZ-curve up to the maximum lever is Damage No. 2.

- The damage corresponding to the midship damage resulting in the lowest damaged freeboard is Damage No. 5.

Table 4.2 summarises the characteristics of Damage No. 2 and of Damage No. 5.

TABLE 4.2 Damage Stability Characteristics - corresponding to the intact condition of Phase I

CASE	Comp.	GZ max. (m)	Area to Max. Lever (Dynamic Stability) (m rad)	Range (deg)	Min Freeb (m)	Heel at Equili- brium
2	102,103, 201-209, 6,7 and 12	>0.982	>0.231	>40	2.06	0
5	105, 201-209, 1,2 and 12	>1.136	>0.334	>40	1.48	0

The length of the damage openings in the model side corresponds to SOLAS 74 damage length, which in ship scale is 3m + 3% of subdivision length, Ls.

The longitudinal limits of the openings are vertical and the openings are 'unlimited' from above. The inboard extension of the openings in the bottom of the model is to B/5. The damage openings in the Ro-Ro deck plates are equal-sided triangles penetrating inboard to B/5.

In the aft-ship, the damage penetrates the inner side of the side casing in the form of a rectangle with proportionally reduced width.

4.4   THE AFT-SHIP DAMAGE AREA

The model was tested at two different damage freeboards, each at one corresponding displacement and permeability factor. For the model simulating the ship 'as is', two tanks in the centre line of the damaged engine room compartments remained intact. The equivalent of 15% permeability was simulated by means of foam blocks placed in the damaged compartments of both engine rooms. For the condition of reduced damaged freeboard, the foam blocks simulating the intact tanks and the permeability of 15% were removed. In combination with 25.6% increase of displacement in this condition, it resulted in reduction of damaged freeboard by more than 1m.

The main details are presented in Table 4.3.

TABLE 4.3 The Aft-Ship Damaged Compartment.

Length of Damaged Compartment (m)	Displacement (m³)	Intact GM (m)	Damaged GM (m)	Damaged Freeboard (m)
23.0	design	5.158	4.52	2.06
23.0	design + 25.6%	3.990	3.12	0.99

All figures in Table 4.3 correspond to initial (equilib.) condition in water ρ=1000.0 kg/m³.

4.5   THE MIDSHIP DAMAGE AREA

The model was tested at five different damage freeboards; they were obtained by combination of three different displacements, two different extents of damage below the Ro-Ro deck and an adjustment for permeability. For the model simulating the ship 'as is', one tank between frame 102 and frame 110 in the centre line of the damaged compartment remained intact. The equivalent of 5% permeability was simulated by means of foam blocks placed in the damaged compartments. For all of the conditions of reduced damaged freeboard, the foam blocks simulating the intact tank and the permeability of 5% were removed. In combination with up to 31.1% increase of displacement and maximum increase of the damaged space below the Ro-Ro deck, it resulted in the maximum reduction of damaged freeboard by more than 1.1m.

As a matter of special interest it should be noted, that the damage resulting in the lowest freeboard is a three-compartment damage which included an 8-frame long compartment aft of frame 64. Frame 64 was the limit for the extended two compartment damage. In the case of three compartment damage, the space aft of frame 64 was filled with water up to sea level and it was not penetrated from the outside.

TABLE 4.4   The Midship Damaged Compartment at no Initial Heel Angle

Length of Damaged Compartment (m)	Displacement (m³)	Intact GM (m)	Damaged GM (m)	Damaged Freeboard (m)
18.0	design	5.158	4.36	1.48
18.0	design + 25.6%	3.990	3.08	1.06
25.2	design + 25.6%	3.800-3.680	2.48-2.36	0.67
25.2	design + 31.1%	3.490	2.28	0.58
29.2	design + 31.1%	3.490	1.68	0.34

All figures in Table 4.4 correspond to initial (equilib.) condition in water $\rho = 1000.0$ kg/m³.

Figures 4.1 and 4.2 show the 18.0m and 29.2m long damaged compartments

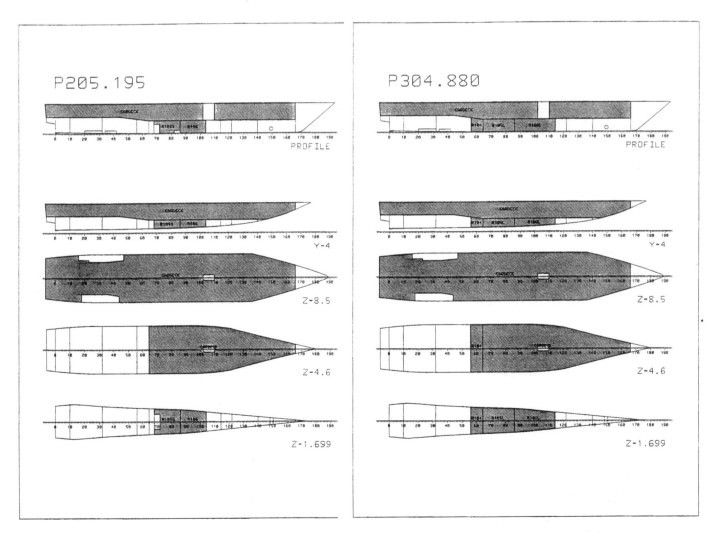

Fig 4.1   The 18.0m long damaged compartments   **Fig 4.2**   The 29.2m long damaged compartment

4.6 LOADING AND DOCUMENTATION OF LOADING CONDITIONS

The information provided by the Client specified the following loading condition for the intact ship to be used in the Phase I of the tests:

Draught - mean	:	2.608 m
Trim	:	-0.188 m
Displacement	:	design
KG_f	:	6.517 m
GM_f	:	5.158 m
KM	:	11.675 m
Roll period	:	5.6 sec

Prior to the tests of Phase I, the model weight was controlled and the model was loaded such that it lay on the appropriate draught marks. The ballast elevator position was adjusted to a position, such that the intact GM 5.16m (ship scale), was controlled by the inclining test. A part of the ballast, which was not placed on the elevator, was shifted such that the roll period of 5.66 sec (ship scale value including added mass effects) was confirmed by a roll decay test. These figures represent the loading condition of the model in Phase I of the tests. Prior to the survivability tests, the damages one by one were opened to sea.

Correct permeability in all damaged compartments was simulated by dummy blocks of limited height, placed symmetrically about the centre line. Volumes of the blocks were calculated based on volumes (up to equilibrium water line) of the corresponding damaged compartments. Permeability above the Ro-Ro deck was not simulated and the model was tested without modelling of vehicles or similar.

The loading of the model during the tests of Phase II was achieved by shifting the ballast in vertical direction and by adjustments of elevator position. Additional ballast was used to create heavier loading conditions. New KG-values were calculated based on the actual state of loading, which in combination with calculated KM-values were used for determination of resulting GM-values. Prior to the tests in each damaged condition it was checked that the model lay on the pre-calculated draught marks.

5. ENVIRONMENTAL CONDITIONS

5.1 DEFINITION OF SEA STATES

As the sea state should not be a limiting factor for ferry operations, model testing in Phase I was performed in the severest waves according to the 'Agreement', i.e. $H_s = 4$ m. In Phase II, the sea state was one of the decisive parameters which should be investigated as a possible limiting factor for survivability. For this purpose, 9 sea states ranging from 1.44 to 4.0m significant wave height H_s were prepared in advance. All of them had short spectral peak period:

$$T_p = 4\sqrt{H_s} ,$$

corresponding to wave steepness of 4%. A narrow band Jonswap spectrum with peakedness factor $\gamma = 3.3$ was used. The following sea states were used during the whole test programme:

TABLE 5.2 Sea States used During the whole Test Programme

Identification	H_s(m)	T_p(s)	Spectrum
C1	2.0	5.7	Jonswap $\gamma = 3.3$
G1	3.2	7.2	Jonswap $\gamma = 3.3$
H1	3.5	7.5	Jonswap $\gamma = 3.3$
A6	4.0	8.0	Jonswap $\gamma = 3.3$

Figure 5.1 shows the comparison of the recorded vs. target spectra of A-waves.

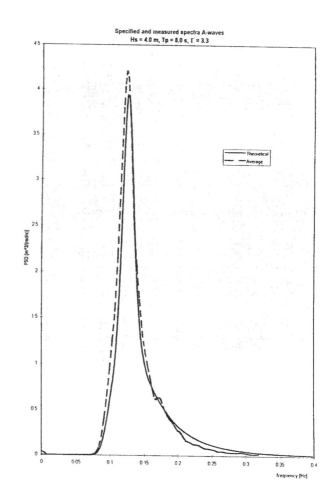

Fig 5.1 Spectrum of Target and Obtained A-Waves

6. INSTRUMENTATION AND CALIBRATION

6.1 DESCRIPTION OF SENSORS AND SENSOR POSITIONS

The complete instrumentation consists of 6 channels:

- Wave mobile
- Carr. speed
- Pitch angle
- Roll angle
- Acc. fore
- Acc. aft

The wave sensor was of the capacitance type. The mobile wave recorder having a measurement accuracy better than 2% was mounted on the towing tank carriage in line with the drifting model.

The unit containing the pitch and roll gyro was mounted on the Ro-Ro deck forward of the collision bulkhead. Absolute accuracy of the gyro measurements is within 0.5°.

Two accelerometers recording heave accelerations in the fore and aft ship were mounted close to the model's centre line. The accuracy of the accelerometers is better than 0.3%.

All sensor signals were recorded on DMI's PC data-acquisition system GPLPC using a logging frequency of 50 Hz and signal filtering at 12 Hz, using a 5th order Butterworth filter.

One video recorder continuously focusing on particular areas of interest was operated during the tests.

7. TEST PROCEDURE

An inclining test in water with model in intact condition corresponding to ship 'as is' was made in order to check the intact GM.

Roll decay test with model in the same intact condition was made in order to check the model roll period. The model was forced to roll, and time for 5 and 10 periods was measured.

The survivability tests were performed in DMI's towing tank which has a length of 240 m, width of 12m and depth of 5.4 m. In one end the tank is equipped with a powerful wavemaker which is controllable to generate any physically realistic wave spectrum with maximum wave height up to approximately 0.9m in model scale. The wavemaker hydraulics are controllable from the towing carriage using digital data generated by a PC. The opposite end of the tank has a wave-absorbing beach.

Each test is started with the model placed in the tank approximately 20m from and beam onto the wavemaker with the damage side facing it. The model is allowed to cross flood. Part of the ballast is shifted such that an adequate initial heel is achieved. This angle is checked

prior to each run with an automatic digital level gauge which reads to 0.1° accuracy.

A reference 'zero' reading is taken on all sensors when the model is at rest, and thereafter the wavemaker is started. When, after a few seconds, the waves reach the location of the model, the data recording and video recording is started.

The model is allowed to drift freely in beam seas, followed by the carriage such that it stays in approximately the same position relative to the moving wave gauge. A soft line connected to each end of the model at the water line prevents the model from drifting into the tank wall and limits the maximum yaw to 10° - 15°.

The test continues for more than 850 seconds model time, which corresponds to more than 1 hour in full-scale. If the model had 'capsized' within this period it would have been rescued by safety lines at one end mounted on the model, and at the other end by a lifting arrangement on the carriage. The lines of low weight and low bending moment are slack during the measurements and they do not affect the behaviour of the model. Immediately after each test the model is slightly lifted and turned with the damage side up, which prevents more water from flooding on to the Ro-Ro deck. In this way, the water amount which floods on the Ro-Ro deck during the entire test run can be isolated and determined after it is pumped out from the Ro-Ro deck.

After completion of each test, the model is towed back to the starting position, any remaining small water quantities are dried from the deck and any small quantity leaked into and trapped inside closed compartments is pumped out.

Figures 7.1 and 7.2 show two sequences from the survivability tests.

8. MODEL TEST RESULTS

8.1 SURVIVAL TESTS OF PHASE I

In both damage cases, the model had no heel in the equilibrium condition. None of the tests resulted in final heel towards the damage. Very insignificant mean heel angles of up to about 0.1° away from the damage were measured during the respective tests. They were caused by wave forces acting on the side of the model, rather than by water accumulation on the intact side of the Ro-Ro deck. Therefore, an initial 1° heel towards the damaged side as prescribed by the 'Model Test Method' in Appendix to SOLAS/CONF. 3/46, Annex, was not imposed during these tests.

The survival criteria as defined in this Appendix was fully satisfied and there is no doubt that the model survived both tests with a very comfortable margin of safety.

8.2 SURVIVAL TESTS OF PHASE II

Based on the results of Phase I, it was attempted to defined the limit of survivability by a gradual reduction of

Fig. 7.1 General View of the Model During the Survivability Tests

Fig. 7.2 The Model Hit by a 4m High Wave

Run No	Target Sign. Wave ht. (m)	Displ. (m³)	KG (m)	GM$_{int}$ (m)	GM$_{dam}$ (m)	Damage Position	Vol. of Fl. Water at Init. Cond.	Perme-ability	Dam. Freeb. (m)	Initial Heel Angle (deg)	Mean Heel to Intact Side?	Sign. Wave ht. (m)	Water on Deck (t)
201	4.0	design	6.517	5.158	4.36	Mid	399.6	95%	1.48	0.0	Y	3.97	-
202	4.0	design	6.517	5.158	4.52	Aft	742.1	85%	2.06	0.0	Y	4.07	-
301	4.0	+25.6%	7.380	3.990	3.08	Mid	508.4	100%	1.06	0.0	Y	4.11	64.0
302	4.0	+25.6%	7.380	3.990	3.12	Aft	1257.0	100%	0.99	0.0	Y	4.08	30.0
421	3.2	+25.6%	7.570	3.800	2.48	Mid	869.7	100%	0.67	0.0	Y	3.31	32.0
422	3.2	+25.6%	7.570	3.800	2.51	Mid	867.5	100%	0.53	1.0	N	3.32	29.6
411	3.5	+25.6%	7.570	3.800	2.48	Mid	869.7	100%	0.67	0.0	Y	3.63	60.0
412	3.5	+25.6%	7.570	3.800	2.51	Mid	867.5	100%	0.53	1.0	N	3.72	28.0
401	4.0	+25.6%	7.570	3.800	2.48	Mid	869.7	100%	0.67	0.0	Y	4.39	128.0
402	4.0	+25.6%	7.570	3.800	2.51	Mid	867.5	100%	0.53	1.0	N	4.44	80.8
403	4.0	+25.6%	7.690	3.680	2.36	Mid	869.7	100%	0.67	0.0	Y	4.56	146.4
404	4.0	+25.6%	7.690	3.680	2.39	Mid	867.5	100%	0.53	1.0	N	4.76	48.0
461	2.0	+25.6%	7.690	3.680	2.39	Mid	867.5	100%	0.53	1.0	N	2.07	52.0
501	4.0	+31.1%	7.820	3.490	2.28	Mid	907.4	100%	0.58	0.0	Y	4.54	148.0
502	4.0	+31.1%	7.820	3.490	2.19	Mid	907.6	100%	0.44	1.0	N	4.56	62.4
503	4.0	+31.1%	7.820	3.490	1.70	Mid	910.7	100%	0.14	3.0	N	4.51	48.0
504	4.0	+31.1%	7.820	3.490	1.65	Mid	927.0	100%	-0.16	5.0	N	4.50	71.2
601	4.0	+31.1%	7.820	3.490	1.68	Mid	1184.0	100%	0.34	0.0	Y	4.47	188.0

TABLE 8.1 Summary of Test Results

damage stability of the model by reducing freeboard and increasing the height of the centre of gravity, KG. At freeboards tested in Phase II, the Ro-Ro deck no longer remained dry. During the tests, where the model had no heel in the equilibrium condition, the flooded water had a predisposition to stay on the intact side of the Ro-Ro deck which increased the mean heel angles of the model up to several degrees away from the damage. In the continuation of the majority of these tests, and in accordance with the above referred 'Model Test Method', initial heel angles of not less than 1° were imposed towards the damaged side of the model.

The model never capsized, and the survival criteria as defined in the Appendix to SOLAS/ CONF. 3/46, Annex, namely:

- a stationary heel to the damaged side of less than 20°;

- the roll angle not exceeding 30° in more than 20% of the roll cycles,

were fully satisfied in all the tests performed during Phase II of the investigation.

8.3 SUMMARY OF THE SURVIVAL TESTS

Table 8.1 presents a summary of the Survival Tests of Phase I and II.

9. DISCUSSION OF RESULTS

The present model for investigating damage stability characteristics is probably the first representing a modern fast (HSC) mono-hull Ro-Ro ferry. However, a number of Ro-Ro ferries which do not have to meet the MSC.36(63) HSC-code but with a similar arrangement of Ro-Ro deck and a similar range of stability parameters, have been modeltested at DMI.

The Ro-Ro deck of 'Superseacat' is an open deck. The small side casings in the aft part of the Ro-Ro deck in the damage conditions as tested, did not provide any reserve buoyancy. In the case of midship damage, due to the rise of the Ro-Ro deck in the aft-ship, water never reached the positions of the side casings. In the case of aft-ship damage, the starboard casing was damaged and, as, to some extent, it reduced the passage of water through the damage opening, it only had a limited importance for results of the tests.

For two 'Non-HSC' Ro-Ro ferry models, which were tested during intensive research programmes, very clear survivability limits were determined; both of them in the case of midship damage and with arrangements on the Ro-Ro deck without or with very limited reserve buoyancy. In external dimensions, they represented conventional Ro-Ro ferries, about 130m long.

Ship I with an open Ro-Ro deck was tested in significant wave heights of 2.5m and 5.0m, at a damaged freeboard 0.6m ship scale. The survivability points in terms of 'just

survival GM_{int}' were in the range of 1.1m to 1.5m depending on the wave height. In terms of the 'just survival GM_{dam}' the corresponding values were between 0.8m and 1.2m.

The same ship with narrow side casings of limited side buoyancy was tested in the same waves and at the same freeboard. The measured 'just survival GM' were in the 3.0m to 3.5m range.

Ship II with an open Ro-Ro deck was tested in significant wave heights of 3.0m and 5.0m, at damaged freeboards between 0.5m and 1.5m ship scale. At the 1.5m freeboard the model survived the 3.0m waves, while it capsized in all other combinations of freeboards and significant wave heights at GM_{int} of about 4.1m.

According to hydrostatic damage stability calculations, Ship I which was of an older design and in conditions as tested, was not a SOLAS 90 ship. Ship II, in combination with GM values as reported above, satisfied the SOLAS 90 stability requirements only at the highest damaged freeboard (1.5m).

In the case of 'Superseacat', most of the tested conditions exceeded the displacement of the existing design, while damage GM and damaged freeboard were considerably less than the 'Superseacat' design. As the Test Results in Table 8.1 show, the minimum GM_{dam} applied during the tests was 1.65m and the minimum damage freeboard was 0.34 m. At forced initial heel angles, the figures were 1.65m and -0.16m (negative freeboard), respectively. All are in the region of respective values valid for the two conventional ferries mentioned above which capsized frequently.

Considering all tests involving the midship damage in tests with no initial heel angle, the stability of the damaged model was consequently reduced, as testing proceeded. As shown in Fig. 10.1, at no initial heel conditions and constant significant wave height, the damaged freeboard is the most decisive parameter for the amount of water collected on the Ro-Ro deck.

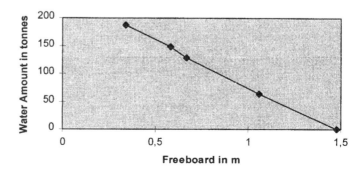

Fig. 9.1 Water Amount on Ro-Ro Deck in 4m Waves and at 0 Initial Heel Angle - as Function of Damaged Freeboard.

According to the results of Runs 421, 411 and 401, the amount of water measured on the Ro-Ro deck depends strongly on the significant wave height. This trend would be most pronounced in waves of a constant peak period length. However, this trend is less clear in waves of a constant wave steepness, as the high waves would than become long and therefore less dangerous. This observation is demonstrated by results of Runs 422, 412 and 402 or by Runs 404 and 461, where an initial heel angle was applied.

In general, the amount of water collected on the Ro-Ro deck during the tests without the initial angle of roll is higher than it is when an initial angle of roll is applied. This can be explained by the fact that in the absence of any form for obstruction, as on 'open' Ro-Ro, the water from the wave crests is unhindered in crossing over the centre line, thus raising the damaged side of the model more and more from the surrounding 'sea' water and stabilising the situation. Thus the model is very unlikely to capsize to the intact side, as the buoyancy to the intact side is preserved. The fact that the mean heel during such tests is towards the lee side and away from the damage, reduces the water ability to leave the Ro-Ro deck and results in a steady increasing amount of water on the Ro-Ro deck. As the resulting mean heel angle towards the lee side during such tests is quite small, and if the tests are not stopped after about 60 min. ship scale, this process would probably continue until the model would sink rather than capsize.

The water amount collected on the Ro-Ro deck during the tests with an initial heel angle towards the damage, in general, is smaller. As water on the Ro-Ro deck is a factor of decisive importance in the capsize process of Ro-Ro ferries, this fact, to some extent offsets the corresponding reduction of restoring moment (GZ) and probably is the reason why the model did not capsize during the respective tests.

In continuation of the present model test results, damage stability calculations were made using the NAPA-programme with starting points in all initial conditions, damage cases and wave heights used during the tests. The results are presented in respect to the SOLAS - 90 formulation and in respect to the methods prescribed by the Specific Stability Requirements for Ro-Ro Passenger Ships', which, depending on the significant wave height, includes effects of 'additional' water on the Ro-Ro deck.

Table 9.1 summarises the most important results of these calculations.

TABLE 9.1 Results of Damage Stability Calculations

Run Nos.	Water on Deck (t)	Initial Heel Angle (deg)	Range of Pos. Stab. (deg)	Max. of GZ-Curve (m)	Area of Pos. Stab. (m rad)	Range of Pos. Stab. (deg)	Max. of GZ-Curve (m)	Area of Pos. Stab. (m rad)
	Measured val.		Dam. Stab. - SOLAS 90 - Req.			Regional 'Water on Deck' - Req.		
201	-	0.0	>40.0	1.170	0.379	38.7	1.051	0.349
301	64.0	0.0	>40.0	0.707	0.243	31.9	0.489	0.161
401	128.0	0.0	>40.0	0.524	0.179	12.7	0.066	0.009
402	80.8	1.0	39.0	0.481	0.159	0	< 0	0
403	146.4	0.0	>40.0	0.487	0.166	8.7	0.033	0.003
404	48.0	1.0	39.0	0.449	0.148	0	< 0	0
501	148.0	0.0	38.2	0.421	0.142	6.8	0.024	0.002
502	62.4	1.0	35.5	0.376	0.122	0	< 0	0
503	48.0	3.0	31.1	0.303	0.090	0	< 0	0
504	71.2	5.0	27.3	0.249	0.069	0	< 0	0
601	188.0	0.0	39.0	0.361	0.117	12.8	0.066	0.009
Note: Area of pos. stability is calculated for heel angles up to 27°, as for SOLAS-90								

As a MSC.36(63) HSC-code ship, 'Superseacat' satisfies the requirements of SOLAS - 90 formulation, even in the worst investigated combination of initial condition and damage case without any problems. Much more demanding, the 'Regional Agreements', in combination with the smallest damaged freeboard and the lowest values of GM, would not be met by the calculation method. Calculations made with the same requirements, but applied to cases with positive initial heel angles, show no equilibrium in the upright condition at all. That means, that according to these calculations, the ship in this damage condition and with water amount corresponding to the 'regional requirements' would capsize immediately, even in calm water. As discussed previously in this report, the model survived in all these damaged conditions for more than 60 min. of testing (ship scale) in 4m high waves, with a very comfortable margin of safety.

10. CONCLUSION

Damage stability tests were performed in DMI's towing tank with a model of the fast mono-hull passenger Ro-Ro ferry 'Superseacat', which was designed and built in scale 1:20.0, resulting in a 4.5m long model.

The model was built with all essential features up to the passenger deck, although this deck was not included.

Based on damage stability calculations provided by the Client, concerning the ferry 'as is', the model was loaded in design condition and prepared for testing in the following two damage cases:

(a) The most critical damage with regard to the prescribed 'amidships' damage in terms of the lowest freeboard. This damage was identified as being centred at fr. 86.

(b) The most critical damage in terms of area under the residual stability curve up to the angle of maximum GZ. This damage was identified as being centred at fr.32.

Both damages are two-compartment damages which resulted in symmetric flooding.

In Phase I of this investigation, the model was loaded in the intact condition to the loading draughts specified by the Client, and subjected to an inclining test for verification of the intact GM and to a roll test for verification of the radii of gyration of the intact ship. Survivability tests with the model damaged at both damage locations were performed in this loading condition. Survivability tests of Phase II concentrated on loading conditions and damage cases beyond the limits of the existing design. The majority of the tests were performed in irregular waves exceeding 4m significant wave height.

The damaged model was checked with regard to sinkage, trim and heel to verify its compliance with the calculated target values.

The results of all individual survivability tests are presented as plots of time series and as tables of time domain constants of all recorded quantities. Time series are available in digital format for further analysis, if desired.

During the entire test programme, the model of the fast Ro-Ro ferry - 'Superseacat' never capsized. The length of each individual test corresponded to just over 60 min. in ship time scale. As this model was tested in loading and damage conditions well beyond the limits of the present design (regarding decisive parameters for survivability of damaged Ro-Ro ferries), the observed result shows 'Superseacat' to be extremely safe with respect to damage stability. Based on model test results, her survivability is considerably better than indicated by static calculations as prescribed by the 'Regional Agreement on Specific Stability Requirement', which refers to Ro-Ro passenger ferries for which MSC.36(63) HSC-code do not apply.

11. ACKNOWLEDGEMENTS

The present investigation of the stability of the fast Ro-Ro passenger ferry "Superseacat" was commissioned by the Fincantieri C.N.I. Yard in Genoa as a private venture. The kind permission of Mr. Luigi Grossi from Fincantieri to allow DMI to publish the results from this investigation in an international forum is much appreciated.

The intentions of this paper are essentially informative, but where views are expressed, they are the opinions of the author only.

12. REFERENCES

1 PUCILL, K F and VELSCHOU, S: Paper No.7, 'Ro-Ro Passenger Ferries Safety Studies - Model Test of Typical Ferry', Danish Maritime Institute, International Symposium on the Safety of Ro-Ro Passenger Ships, The Royal Institution of Naval Architects and UK Department of Transport, London 26 & 27 April 1990.

2 VELSCHOU, S and SCHINDLER, M: Session 13, 'Ro-Ro Passenger Ferry Damage Stability', Danish Maritime Institute, RoRo 94, The 12th International Conference on Marine Transport Using Roll-on/Roll-off Methods, Gothenburg 26 - 28 April 1994.

3 VELSCHOU, S and SCHINDLER, M: Paper No.5, 'Ro-Ro Passenger Ferry Damage Stability Studies - A Continuation of Model Tests of Typical Ferry', Danish Maritime Institute, Symposium on Ro-Ro Ship's Survivability, Phase 2 of the UK Department of Transport Sponsored Research, The Royal Institution of Naval Architects, London 25 November 1994.

4 DAMSGAARD, A and SCHINDLER, M : Paper No.3. 'Model Tests for Determining Water Ingress and Accumulation', by Danish Maritime Institute, International Seminar - The Safety of Passenger Ro-Ro Vessels Presenting the Results of the Northwest European Research & Development Project, The Royal Institution of Naval Architects, London 7 June 1996.

PAPER NO.2.

COMPARISON OF TYPICAL DAMAGED STABILITY CHARACTERISTICS OF CATAMARAN AND FAST MONOHULL TYPES

by J C Lewthwaite, Independent Maritime Assessment Associates Ltd, UK

Paper presented at the

International Symposium & Seminar

THE SAFETY OF HIGH SPEED CRAFT

6 - 7 FEBRUARY 1997 LONDON

COMPARISON OF TYPICAL DAMAGED STABILITY CHARACTERISTICS OF CATAMARAN AND FAST MONOHULL TYPES

J C Lewthwaite

Independent Maritime Assessment Associates Ltd

SUMMARY

The HSC Code requires designers of fast craft to consider the possibility of sustaining longitudinal hull damage up to about 10% of the vessel's length. In view of the increasing operational speed of commercial fast ferries, the possibility of sustaining more extensive side or bottom damage would appear to be rather likely, particularly following a glancing type impact.

This paper reviews the typical damaged stability characteristics of both fast monohulls and catamarans, assuming multi-compartment damage and subsequent flooding. Particular consideration is given to category B craft, for which a higher disabled capability is required. Calculations for a range of displacements and vertical centres of gravities are presented for several variations in the hullform of each type of vessel. Comparisons are made with a view to proposing revised criteria for the High Speed Craft Rules.

AUTHOR'S BIOGRAPHY

Mr John Lewthwaite is a Chartered Naval Architect with over 35 years experience in the design of high speed craft. He has worked in both the Industry and in research establishments. He holds a Master's Degree in Ship Science and is a Member of the RINA. In 1990 he helped to form IMAA Ltd, and is now its Managing Director.

1. INTRODUCTION

Over the past ten years or so an increasing number of fast craft of various designs have come into service in European waters." In recognizing the need for regulation of such craft the IMO issued a Code of Safety governing the design and operation of fast craft in January 1996. This is generally referred to as the HSC Code.

Two basically different types of fast ferries appear to be gaining acceptance in the market. These are based on either slender chined monohulls or semi-swath round bilged catamarans. Current versions of these craft are between 75 and 125 metres long and carry both passengers and cars with a payloads of between 150 and 500 tonnes.

The buoyancy, stability and subdivision requirements of such vessels are addressed in Chapter 2 of the HSC code, and this covers both the intact and damaged conditions. Damaged lengths are expressed as a function of the underwater watertight envelope of the hull, L. The assumed extent of damage of L is similar to that adopted by SOLAS II-1/8 for conventional ships. In general terms this requires consideration of side or bottom damage over a proportion of L (about 10%) anywhere on the periphery of the craft.

The Code also recognizes that in the case of the category B craft which carry more than 450 passengers, an increase in the length of bottom damage should be assumed. An increase of 50% is to be applied in the case of damage in the forward half of the craft.

Recent craft operational incidents have suggested that these damaged limits are likely to be exceeded. In practice, damaged lengths in excess of 0.5L have been incurred, fortunately without sinking or loss of life. The question therefore remains as to whether the current HSC Code requirements are satisfactory or should be revised.

In order to help clarify this subject, the damaged stability characteristics of the two types of fast craft referred to earlier have been examined. Hullforms representing a 100m long slender chined monohull and a 80m long semi-swath round bilged catamaran have been developed. It should be stressed that these were intended as examples of present-day design and are not based on any particular craft.

2. DESCRIPTION

2.1 HULLFORM EXAMPLES

The parent forms of the fast monohull and catamaran are shown in Figures 1(a) and (b). Both craft were designed to carry the same payload and have the same initial displacement of 1000t. They also have the same initial freeboard. The monohull has an overall length of 100m and maximum beam of 15m. The catamaran has an overall length of 80m and maximum beam of 20m; that is, with a similar planform area.

The monohull has a chined form with a midship deadrise angle of 20°. The bulkhead deck is set initially at 5.5m above the base-line giving 3.5m freeboard at the design draught of 2.0m.

The catamaran has a reduced waterplane area along its waterline. The bulkhead deck is set initially 6.5m above the baseline giving 3.5m freeboard at its design draught of 3.0m. The tunnel height is 2.5m which is considered adequate for operation in typical UK-European waters.

2.2   HSC CODE REQUIREMENTS

(a)   Intact Stability

The intact stability requirements are mainly concerned with the heel righting moment curve. Slightly different criteria are applied for monohulls as compared to catamarans, but in general both require a stated minimum area (A) under the righting moment curve up to a heel angle of around 30°, and a maximum righting lever (GZ) at an angle not less than 15° for monohulls and 10° for catamarans. In addition, monohulls are required to have an initial metacentric height of at least 0.15m.

These criteria are examined in rather more detail following calculations for the two craft type examples.

(b)   Longitudinal Damage

The longitudinal extent of damage to be applied to all types of high speed craft is as follows:

With respect to side damage, the length shall be 0.1L or 3m+0.3L or 11m, whichever is the least. The transverse extent is to be 0.2B or 0.05L or 5m, whichever is the least. (Note that B is the greatest width on or below the waterline). The vertical extent is to be the full depth of the hull.

With respect to bottom damage, the length is the same as above, plus 50% for category B craft in the forward 0.5L. The transverse extent is the full width or 7m whichever is the least. The vertical extent is 0.02B or 0.5m, whichever is the least.

In the case of the two above craft examples these limits translate to the following damage dimensions:

Craft type		Monohull (L = 90m)	Catamaran (L = 80m)
Side damage	{ Long.	5.7m (0.07L)	5.4m (0.07L)
	{ Trans.	2.8m (0.20B)	4.0m (0.20B)
	{ Vert.	5.5m (0.39B)	6.5m (0.33B)
Bottom damage (in ford. 0.5L)	{ Long.	8.6m (0.10L)	8.1m (0.10L)
	{ Trans.	7.0m (0.50B)	7.0m (0.35B)
	{ Vert.	0.3m (0.02B)	0.4m (0.02B)

It will be noted that the longitudinal side damage is in all cases equal to or less than 10% of L.

(c)   Stability following Damage

In general following damage and after flooding has ceased, the waterline should be 300mm below any opening through which further flooding could occur. For conventional ships this level is usually taken as the line of bulkhead deck and the 300mm level is referred to as the margin line. Since details of openings have not been itemised on the above craft examples, it is assumed that in the limiting damaged condition the "conventional" margin line should not become immersed. A further requirement is that the craft should not heel more than 10° in any direction, and it must be ensured that evacuation routes are accessible.

The residual stability requirements are slightly different for monohulls and catamarans, and relate to minimum righting levers (GZ values) and minimum areas (A) under the stability curves. These aspects are addressed in more detail later.

3.   CALCULATIONS

3.1   MONOHULL CASE

(a)   Intact Stability

The intact stability curves for the parent monohull at 1000t displacement, initially in level trim are shown in Figure 2(a). These relate the righting lever GZ to the angle of heel θ. A range of vertical CG heights (usually expressed as initial metacentric height GM values) has been covered. The vertical CG of the parent form is assumed to be on the bulkhead deck; that is, 5.5m above the baseline. The initial GM value is 6.2m.

Figure 2(a) also shows how the freeboard reduces as the vessel heels. The margin line set 300mm below the bulkhead deck, becomes immersed at an angle of heel of 28°. Over the whole range of VCG heights the areas under the stability curves are well in excess of that stipulated by the HSC Code Regulations which requires a minimum of 0.055m-rad up to an angle of 30° heel. The vessel is therefore more than adequately stable.

The effect of variation in displacement on the intact stability of the parent form at the baseline vertical CG height is shown in Figure 2(b). Little difference in stability is seen over the weight range.

The effect of variation in overall hull beam on the intact stability at 1000t displacement and the baseline vertical CG height is shown in Figure 2(c). As might be expected, beam makes an important contribution to the stability of the vessel.

(b)   Watertight Configuration

In slender monohulls it is not usual to fit a double bottom due to constraints in the machinery arrangements. Therefore only side damage extending vertically to the bulkhead deck was considered, this of course being a more demanding condition. Longitudinal watertight bulkheads at B/5 could be fitted, but these will require some form of cross-connection to reduce subsequent heeling. Transverse bulkheads will allow symmetrical flooding and this is the main type of condition examined with respect to damaged length.

(c)   Limiting Damaged Lengths

The monohull was subjected to increasing amounts of longitudinal side damage with resultant flooding over an equivalent two-compartment length. In the forward part of the hull a flooded permeability of 95% was assumed. In aft compartments containing machinery a value of 85% was assumed. The cases were based on a longitudinal CG giving an initial level trim condition with the vessel intact.

The lengths of the flooded compartments which cause the margin line to become immersed at either the bow or stern, are shown in Figure 3. The effect of changing the VCG height had a negligible effect on the limiting damaged length. Variations in displacement and in changing the beam of the parent hullform are included. In all cases the flooded lengths can be seen to be well in excess of the HSC Code requirements (8.6m forward or 5.7m aft).

Examples of the residual stability of the damaged hull-forms are shown in Figure 4. The baseline case with the VCG at 5.5m retains adequate stability with either bow or stern damage. The more severe condition arises with stern damage, but even with the VCG raised to 6.5m the residual righting lever and area under the stability curve (up to $\theta = 27^{\circ}$) are adequate allowing for the effects of passenger movement and wind heeling moments.

The residual stability of the monohull with its beam reduced to 13m and the displacement increased to 1200t, is the other example shown in Figure 4. For this extreme design the stability with stern damage is marginal with a VCG height of 5.5m. The residual righting lever is 0.10m and the area under the stability curve up to 27° is 0.015m-rad. These values just meet the requirements of Regulation II-1/8 of the SOLAS Convention.

3.2   CATAMARAN CASE

(a)   Intact Stability

The intact stability curves for the parent catamaran at 1000t displacement, initially in level trim are shown in Figure 5(a). The VCG height of the parent form was 6.5m above the baseline and additional calculations have been made over the range of between 5.5 and 7.5m. The initial GM value at 6.5m VCG was 18.2m.

Figure 5(a) also shows how the freeboard reduces as the vessel heels. The margin line becomes immersed at an angle of heel of 18°. At this point the area under the stability curve of the 6.5m VCG baseline is 1.08m-rad. The HSC Code Regulations require a minimum area of 0.09m-rad in this case. The Figure shows that the vessel is still very stable with the VCG raised to 7.5m.

The effect of variation in displacement on the intact stability of the parent form at the baseline vertical CG height is shown in Figure 5(b). Little difference in stability is seen over the weight range.

The effect of variation in overall hull beam on the intact

stability at 1000t displacement and the baseline vertical CG height is shown in Figure 5(c).

(b)   Watertight Configuration

Catamarans are not usually fitted with double bottoms, although this is now recommended by some authorities. Only side damage to one hull extending vertically to the bulkhead deck is considered in this study. This is clearly a very demanding condition since the vessel will both trim and heel following damage. The centre part of the cross-deck structure (with a width of 13m on the parent form) was assumed to be watertight.

(c)   Limiting Damaged Lengths

The catamaran was subjected to increasing amounts of longitudinal side damage to one hull in both forward and subsequently in aft compartments. A flooded permeability of 95% was assumed forward and 85% aft. The cases were based on a longitudinal CG giving an initial level trim condition with the vessel intact.

The lengths of the flooded compartments which cause the margin line to become immersed at either the bow or stern, are shown in Figure 6, together with the final angle of heel. The effect of changing the VCG height only had a small effect on the limiting damaged length.

Variations in displacement and in changing the beam of the parent hullform are also shown in Figure 6. In all cases the flooded lengths can be seen to be well in excess of the HSC Code requirements (8.1m forward or 5.4m aft).

Examples of the residual stability of the damaged hullforms are shown in Figure 7. The baseline case retains more than adequate stability over the VCG range, with either bow or stern damage. There is a requirement for a minimum area under the curves of 0.028m-rad up to an angle where downflooding is likely to occur. Although this angle is not defined in these generalised designs it is likely to be at least 15°. Even with the VCG raised to 7.5m the area under the stability curve is well in excess of this limit including allowance for the effects of passenger movement and wind heeling.

The residual stability of the catamaran with its beam reduced to 18m and the displacement increased to 1200t, is the other example shown in Figure 7. For this extreme design the vessel retains adequate residual stability in all the damaged conditions, but with reduced margins compared to the parent form.

4.   DISCUSSION OF RESULTS

4.1   INTACT STABILITY

It is clear from examination of Figures 2 and 5, that both craft examples exhibit adequate intact stability. For the parent forms the relevant areas under the stability curve are approximately ten times those required by the HSC Code. This degree of safety suggests that the area requirements in the Code might be rather low compared with those typical of current craft designs, even with somewhat extreme VCG heights.

Although it is clearly possible to conceive hullforms which may exhibit low intact stability, it is suggested that these should not be encouraged by unrealistic minimal safety requirements.

4.2 DAMAGED LENGTHS

The damaged lengths which have resulted in the immersion of the margin line on the two craft examples, are summarised in Figures 3 and 6. The catamaran is shown to be slightly more sensitive to increases in displacement than the monohull. This is mainly due to the narrow waterline width of the sidehulls which results in a reduced heave stiffness. The tolerable damaged lengths of the parent forms of the two craft at their design displacements of 1000t, are as follows:

	Monohull	Catamaran
Forward damage	0.47L	0.30L
Aft damage	0.20L	0.24L

These values are considerably in excess of those specified by the HSC Code requirements. Even the extremes in design at reduced overall beam and increased displacement, have tolerable damaged lengths in the aft hull of about twice those required. These extreme designs have residual stabilities which are in general sufficient.

It would therefore appear that the damaged length requirements in the Code could be approximately doubled. These would then cater for the more extreme designs which still maintain an adequate margin of safety.

4.3 OTHER FACTORS INFLUENCING STABILITY

(a) Effect of Variation in the Height of the Margin Line

The results of this study are clearly dependent upon the selected height of the margin line for the two design examples. These are believed to be in realistic positions and typical of present day trends in design.

If the freeboards are reduced the tolerable damaged lengths will clearly become less but the residual stabilities for extremes in design will become marginal. Hence any major reductions in free-board are likely to fail to meet the HSC Code damaged stability requirements.

(b) Consideration of "Water on Deck"

The IMO has recently considered changes to SOLAS Regulations, in order to consider the possibility of water accumulating on the bulkhead deck. International

agreement on this subject has not been obtained, but a draft method of assessing such a condition was agreed at the November 1995 IMO Conference (Resolution 14). On a regional basis European Nations have adopted this rule under the Stockholm Agreement and in the UK the Marine Safety Agency have proposed to apply this to high speed craft.

In its original full implementation the amount of "water on deck" was a function of the damaged freeboard. None was assumed if the residual freeboard was greater than 2m and upto 0.5m equivalent water depth over the whole deck was assumed as the waterline progressively approached the margin line.

The tolerable damaged lengths shown in Figures 3 and 6 for the two forms of craft, have been determined by the trimmed condition which causes the margin lines at the bow or stern just to become immersed. In these cases therefore the equivalent of 0.5m of "water on deck" should be applied to the residual stability curves. The lever caused by this accumulation of water has been approximately calculated and appended to the example cases shown for the monohull in Figure 4 and the catamaran in Figure 7.

It can be seen that in the case of the monohull the effect of this quantity of "water on deck" greatly exceeds the available residual stability. In the case of the catamaran this "water on deck" condition can be tolerated by the parent form with an overall beam of 20m, but not by the reduced beam case.

The effect of introducing such a regulation may therefore have a significant influence on craft design particularly for monohulls. The method most likely to be used to cope with such a demand will be to increase the freeboard height and hence with a raised margin line to reduce the depth of "water on deck".

5. CONCLUSIONS AND RECOMMENDATIONS

This study has reviewed the stability of two typical types of fast craft based on (a) a slender chined monohull and (b) a semi-swath round bilged catamaran. Although these forms have very different hull shapes the study has concluded that both are well adapted to the requirements of the HSC Code, and in their parent forms both fully comply with the current stability and sub-division requirements.

The examples are simplified versions of real craft and some of the more detailed requirements, based for example on the location of downflooding openings, have not been fully assessed. However, certain trends in the application of the Code have been found. These may be summarised as follows:

(a) With regards to intact stability, the relevant areas under the GZ curves for both types of vessel are well in excess of the requirements, even allowing for quite wide variations in VCG heights. This perhaps suggests that the required areas should be increased in order to encourage such trends in design. An increase of at least twice the present values is suggested.

(b) Tolerable damaged lengths on both types of vessel under the most severe flooding conditions were noticeably greater than those required by the Code. In general the Code values appear to have been transferred from conventional ship Regulations, with an additional 50% allowance for forward damage to larger craft. However, recent incidents suggest that much longer damaged lengths are likely to occur in practice.

(c) Since the typical vessels considered more than adequately met the damaged length criteria, consideration should be given to increasing this requirement in order to maintain good design practice and safety margins. It is suggested that the current damaged length requirements should be doubled.

(d) The introduction of SOLAS "water on deck" type requirements to the HSC Code is likely to have a significant influence on the required freeboard height of high speed vessels, particularly monohull types. A more detailed study of the implication of this regulation on craft design is recommended.

(a) Fast Monohull (Parent form)

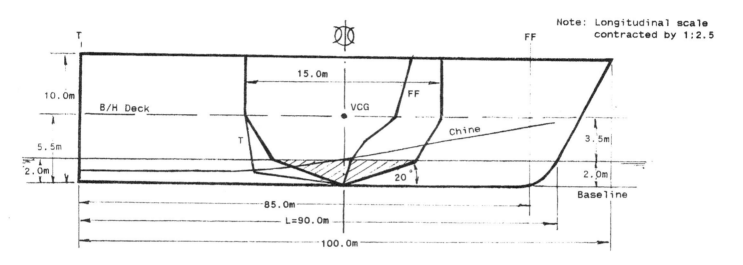

(b) Catamaran (Parent form)

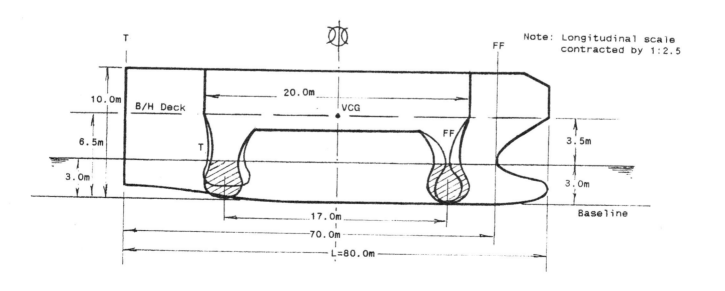

Fig. 1 Details of Parent Hullforms

5

(a) Parent form at 1000t

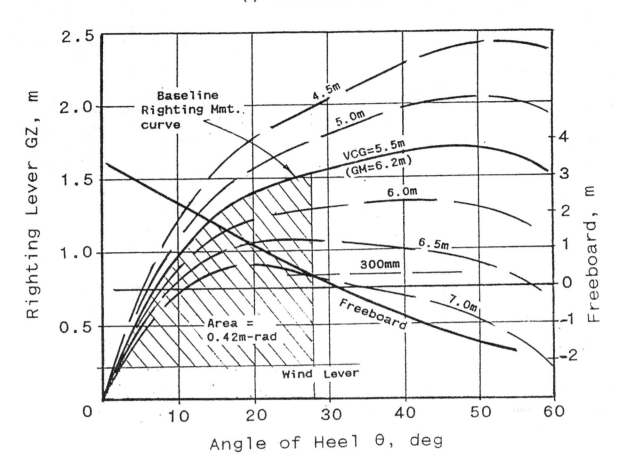

(b) Variation in Displacement
(at VCG=5.5m)

(c) Variation in Overall Beam
(VCG=5.5m & Disp.=1000t)

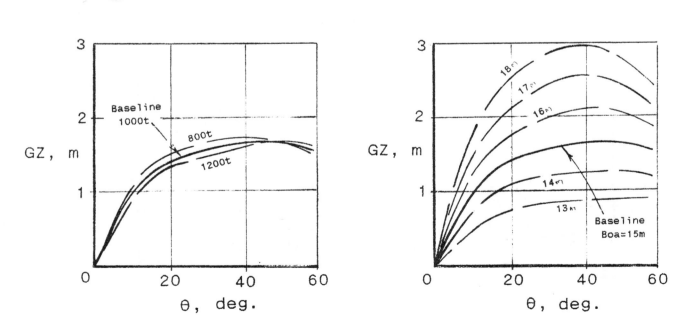

Fig. 2 Intact Stability of the Monohull

FLOODED COMPARTMENT LENGTHS WHICH CAUSE IMMERSION OF THE MARGIN LINE
AT EITHER THE BOW (DAMAGED FORWARD) OR STERN (DAMAGED AFT)

Note: All cases symmetrical flooded with no resultant heeling

(a) Damaged Forward Hull

(Aft of the fore-foot)

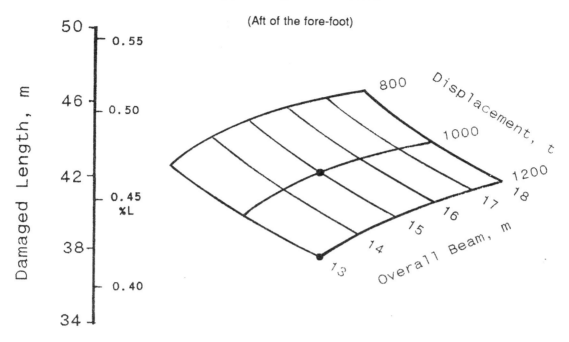

(b) Damaged Aft Hull

(Forward of the transom)

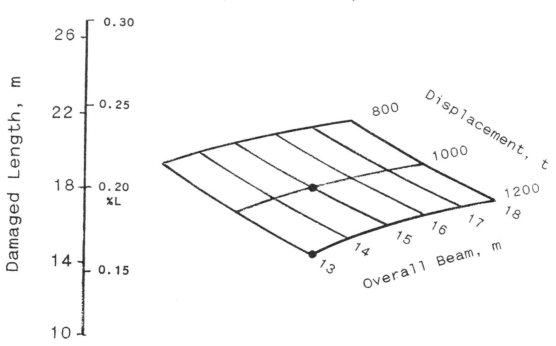

Fig. 3 Limiting Damaged Lengths of the Monohull

EXAMPLES COVERING BASELINE AND MINIMUM BEAM CASES

(a) Damaged Forward Hull

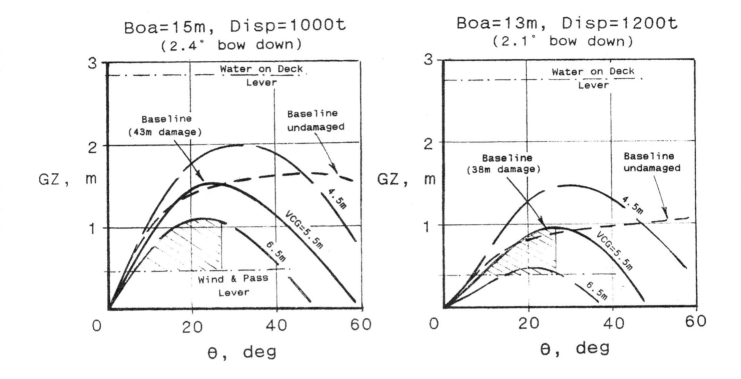

(b) Damaged Aft Hull

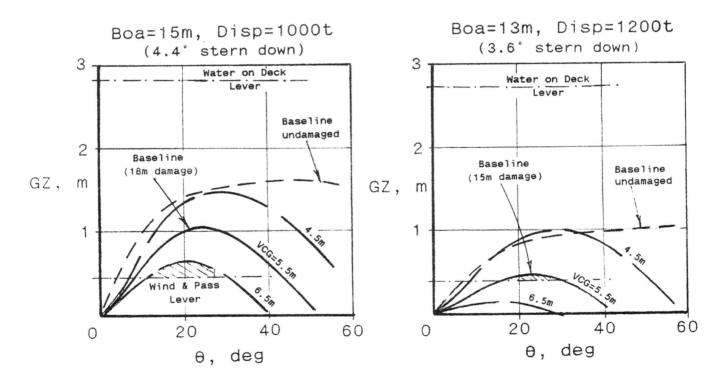

Fig. 4 Residual Stability of the Damaged Monohull

(a) Parent form at 1000t

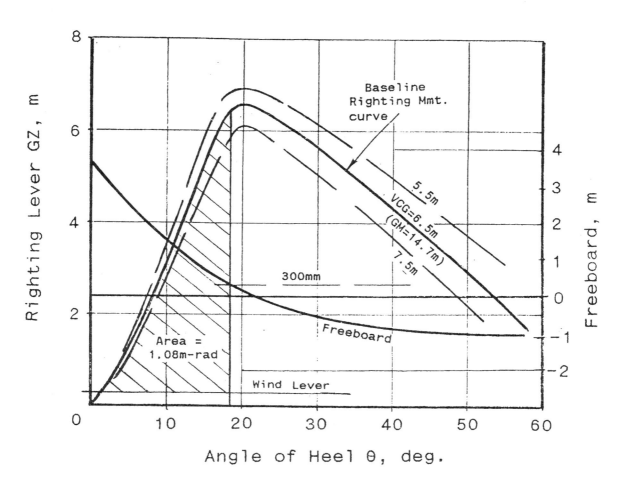

Angle of Heel θ, deg.

(b) Variation in Displacement
(at VCG=6.5m)

(c) Variation in Overall Beam
(VCG=6.5m & Disp.=1000t)

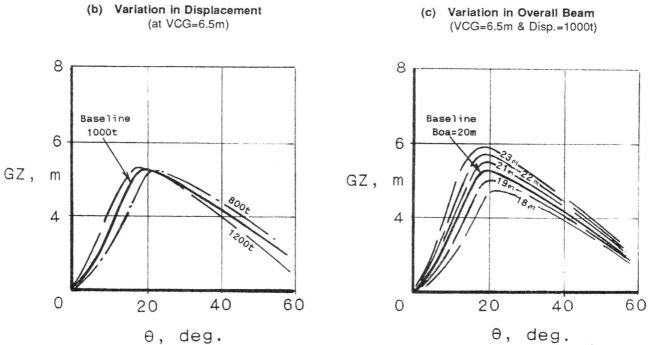

Fig. 5 Intact Stability of the Catamaran

FLOODED COMPARTMENT LENGTHS WHICH CAUSE IMMERSION OF THE MARGIN LINE AT EITHER THE BOW (DAMAGED FORWARD) OR STERN (DAMAGED AFT)

Note: All cases asymmetrically flooded (one hull damaged) with subsequent heeling

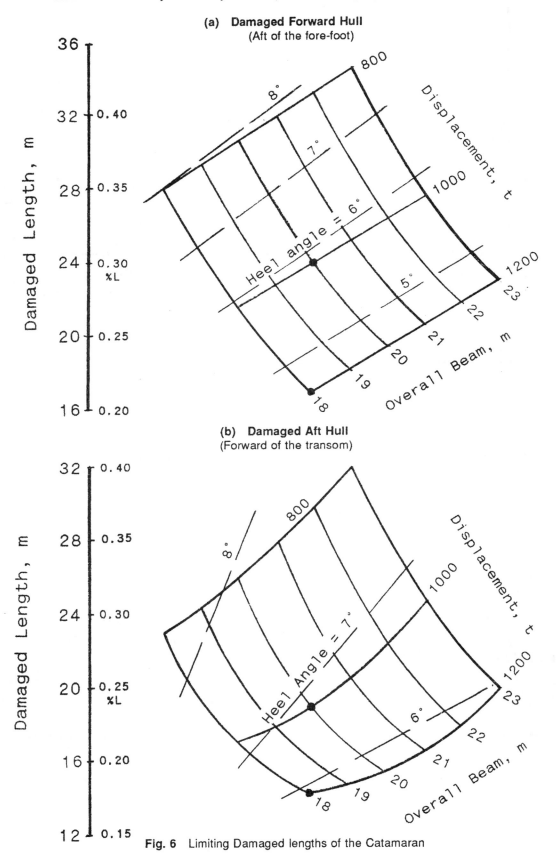

(a) Damaged Forward Hull
(Aft of the fore-foot)

(b) Damaged Aft Hull
(Forward of the transom)

Fig. 6 Limiting Damaged lengths of the Catamaran

10

EXAMPLES COVERING BASELINE AND MINIMUM BEAM CASES

(a) Damaged Forward Hull

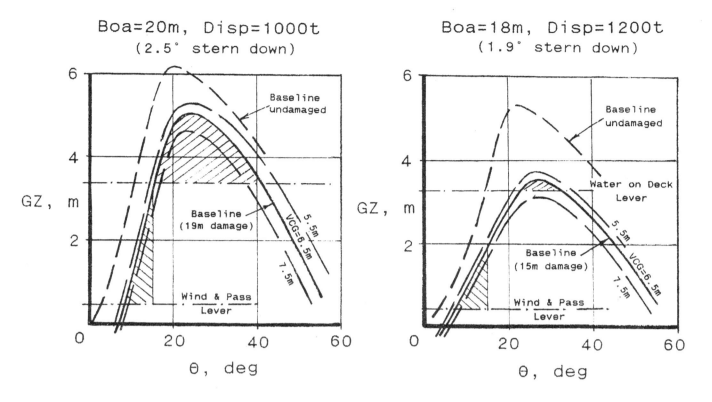

(b) Damaged Aft Hull

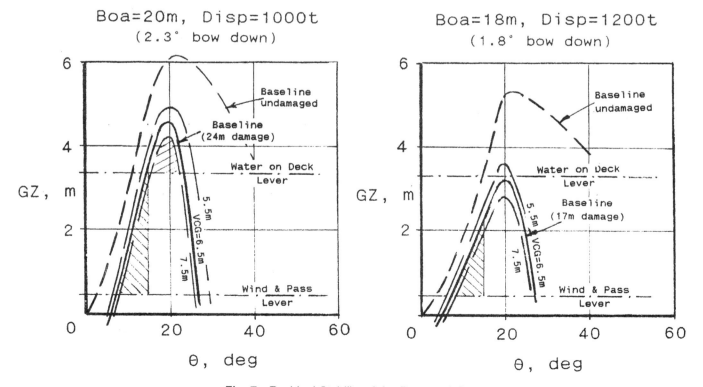

Fig. 7 Residual Stability of the Damaged Catamaran

PAPER NO.3.

DYNAMIC STABILITY OF PLANING SHIPS

by S L Toxopeus and J A Keuning, Delft University of Technology, and
J P Hooft, MARIN, Wageningen, The Netherlands

Paper presented at the

International Symposium & Seminar

THE SAFETY OF HIGH SPEED CRAFT

6 - 7 FEBRUARY 1997 LONDON

DYNAMIC STABILITY OF PLANING SHIPS

S L Toxopeus, Delft University of Technology, The Netherlands
J A Keuning, Delft University of Technology, The Netherlands
J P Hooft, MARIN, Wageningen, The Netherlands

SUMMARY

At present, most of the dynamic research on planing ships has been directed towards analysing the ship's motions in either the 3-DOF (Degrees Of Freedom) mode in the longitudinal vertical plane or in the 3-DOF or 4-DOF mode in the lateral vertical plane.

For this reason Delft University of Technology and MARIN have started the set-up of describing the dynamic behaviour of planing ships in a 6-DOF mathematical model. This research program consisted first of all in developing a 6-DOF computer simulation program in the time domain. Such a simulation program is to be used to predict the response of these type of vessels to disturbances during high speed sailing.

For describing the behaviour of planing ships in still water static tests have been executed with two planing hull forms in the towing tank of Delft University of Technology. The test program consisted of measuring three force- and three moment components as a function of the pitch, rise (draught), roll, drift and speed of the model.

At a next stage a model test program is anticipated to determine the added mass and damping components of these two hull forms and also the rudder forces. In the meantime the program is in operation while using empirically estimated values for these quantities.

In this paper the set-up of the mathematical model will be presented. Also a discussion will be given about the use of these static contributions in a time domain simulation to model the behaviour of the ship.

AUTHORS' BIOGRAPHIES

Mr S L Toxopeus graduated from the Delft University of Technology in 1996. He is currently employed as project manager at the Maritime Research Institute of the Netherlands in Wageningen.

Dr J A Keuning graduated from the Delft University of Technology in 1977 and obtained his doctorate at Delft University of Technology in 1994. He is employed as a lecturer at the Ship Hydromechanics Department of Delft University of Technology, his main subject being the dynamics of advanced naval vehicles, including sailing yachts.

Dr J P Hooft graduated from the Delft University of Technology in 1962 and obtained his doctorate at Delft University of Technology in 1970. He has been employed at MARIN since 1962. He is currently senior project manager involved in developing mathematical models for simulating the behaviour of various kinds of marine structures.

1. INTRODUCTION

The motions of planing craft have been the subject of many research projects during the last few decades. The dynamic research was largely directed towards analysing the motions of the ship in either the longitudinal vertical plane for three degrees of freedom, see e.g. [13], [19], or in the four-DOF mode in the lateral vertical plane or horizontal plane [9], [14]. Reviewing the literature about dynamic stability of high speed craft, it appears that a mathematical model with six degrees of freedom does not exist.

At present it is thought that incorporating all six degrees of freedom into the mathematical models becomes increasingly important. Instabilities have been reported in both longitudinal and lateral directions with motions ranging from rapid loss of running trim, progressive heeling, broaching or a sudden combined roll-yaw motion, possibly resulting in crew injury or craft loss (Refs. 14, 20 and 21). Most instabilities are suspected to originate from coupling between the six degrees of motions. For example, large bow-down trim angles will most likely result in transverse instability: yaw motions. For reliable prediction of the dynamic stability and manoeuvrability of planing craft, all six degrees of freedom have to be accounted for.

For describing the behaviour of planing ships in still water, static captive model tests have been executed with two planing hull forms in the towing tank at Delft University of Technology, see Reference [17]. The test program consisted of measuring three force and three moment components as a function of the pitch, rise (draught), roll, drift and speed of the models. At a future stage a model test program is anticipated to determine the added mass and damping forces of these planing hull forms and also the rudder and propeller forces acting on the models. At present, the computer program is in operation while using empirically estimated values for these quantities.

In this paper, the set-up of the preliminary non-linear mathematical model for six degrees of freedom based on the data obtained from the model experiments will be described. This mathematical model has been incorporated in a time-domain computer simulation program in order to predict the dynamic stability and manoeuvrability of a planing ship, see Reference [16]. The results of some simulations performed will be included and discussed. Also, recommendations will be made for further study, to increase the accuracy of the mathematical model.

2. COORDINATE SYSTEM

The coordinate systems used in this study are cartesian coordinate systems. One coordinate system is the ship-fixed coordinate system, with the x-axis pointing forward perpendicular to the baseline of the ship and the z-axis downward. The y-axis is pointed to starboard. The origin is at the intersection of frame 0 and the baseline of the model.

The x-y-plane of the earth-fixed coordinate system coincides with the undisturbed water surface, the z-axis is pointed downward.

Rotations in both coordinate systems are positive if clockwise, looking in positive direction. The roll angle ϕ, the pitch angle θ and the yaw angle ψ are rotations around the ship-fixed x, y and z axis respectively. The drift angle is used to define the non-dimensional lateral velocity component:

$$\beta = \psi - \arctan\left(\frac{v_e}{u_e}\right)$$

with u being the longitudinal velocity component.

3. MODEL TESTS

3.1 MODEL PARTICULARS

The models used for this study are Model 233 and Model 277 of Delft University of Technology. Model 277 is based on the Clement and Blount [1] 62 series with a deadrise of 25 degrees. Keuning [6] performed seakeeping tests with this model. Model 233 is used by Keuning et al [8] during experiments with models with warped bottoms. The main particulars are stated in the table below:

	Symbol	Model 233	Model 277
Type		Deadrise 25°	Twisted bottom
Length	L	1.50m	1.50m
Max. beam at chine	B_{max}	0.367m	0.367m
Projected area	A_P	0.450m²	0.4589m²
Centre of planing area forward of ord 0	C_{AP}	48.8%L	48.8%L
Length/Beam ratio	L/B	4.09	4.09
Mass model incl. transducer	m	9.45kg	6.67kg
Longitudinal centre of reference	$LCOR$	0.726m	0.726m
Vertical centre of reference	$VCOR$	0.080m	0.080m

In Figure 1 the body plans of both models are included

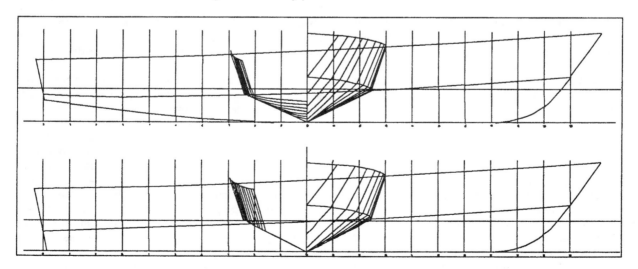

Figure 1 Body plans of Model 233 (above) and Model 277 (below)

3.2 TEST PROGRAM

In the present study some static captive tests have been performed with both models during which the forces and moments in the six degrees of freedom were measured. These tests will only provide a limited amount of information about the hydrodynamics of planing ships. Therefore in further studies additional tests will be performed to determine the remaining hydrodynamic characteristics.

The following variables have been tested:

Speed U:

the speed has great influence on the position of the ship relative to the free water surface. A change in speed will result in a change of trim and rise. The model was tested at the speeds of: $U_1 = 2.0ms^{-1}$, $U_2 = 3.0ms^{-1}$ and $U_3 = 4.0ms^{-1}$.

Pitch θ:

For planing ships, the pitch varies due to speed variations and has great effect on the lift and drag and on the dynamic stability. A combination of low pitch angle and roll or drift can result in large yaw moments. The model was tested at the pitch angles of: $\theta_1 = -2^o$, $\theta_2 = 3^o$ and $\theta_3 = 5^o$.

Drift β:

To study the effect of drift, the model was tested at three drift angles of: $\beta_1 = 0^o$, $\beta_2 = 5^o$ and $\beta_3 = 10^o$.

Roll ϕ:

Also the influence of the roll angle has been determined as it affects the transverse and course stability of the planing ship. The model was tested at four roll angles of: $\phi_1 = 0^o$, $\phi_2 = 5^o$, $\phi_3 = 10^o$ and $\phi_4 = -5^o$. The negative roll angle was only tested with Model 277, to study the effect of symmetry.

Rise of COR z:

The rise of the centre of reference z has great influence on the behaviour of planing ships. When the ship accelerates from zero to full speed, first the ship sinks more into the water, while at higher speed the lift force pushes the ship out of the water. Assuming the design draughts of both models were $T = 0.080m$, a negative rise of $z = -5mm$ and a positive rise of $15mm$ were chosen, corresponding to draughts of $T = 0.085mm$ and $T = 0.065mm$ respectively.

The ranges of the variables were chosen after examining previous results of model experiments with Model 233 [8] and Model 277 [6].

Some combinations of the variables were skipped during the experiments due to expected problems with spray. The total number of test runs was 304.

3.3 EXPERIMENTAL SET-UP

Two six-component transducers were fixed into the models, evenly spaced around the centre of reference. Adding the components of the transducers, three forces and three moments about the centre of reference could be found.

The measurement of the forces was divided in two parts: a velocity independent part at speed $U = 0ms^{-1}$ and a velocity dependent part, obtained by measuring the change in forces due to the towing speed. Adding the two components yields the total force acting on the hull during the run.

The forces and moments acting on the hull in the centre of reference COR as a function of speed, drift, trim, roll and rise have been published in Reference [17]. The forces and moments acting in any arbitrary centre of gravity CG are found after transforming the values from the COR to the CG.

4. MATHEMATICAL MODEL

4.1 FORCES AND MOMENTS BASED ON EXPERIMENTAL DATA

Using the data obtained from the model experiments in tabular form in the computer program poses two difficulties. First, interpolating in a five dimensional parameter space is rather complex, especially since certain combinations of variables were not used during the experiments. Secondly, because of the six degrees of freedom, the amount of memory needed during the simulation would be rather high. It was therefore decided to describe the data by mathematical formulations derived from regression analysis.

The hydrodynamic forces acting on the hull comprise of linear as well as non-linear components. The basic structure of the analysis of the mathematical model of the hydrodynamic forces is described in full detail in Reference [16].

It must be noted that the mathematical model found in this study is only valid to describe the forces and moments acting on the two ship models, Model 233 and Model 277, because the coefficients in the mathematical descriptions are not presented in non-dimensional form. In further studies, the scale effects should be examined to be able to predict stability and manoeuvring characteristics for full-sized planing ships.

4.2 DAMPING FORCES

It was desired to run the computer simulation program without having determined the damping of most of the motion components. Therefore use has been made of some rough values of the damping coefficients in the roll and pitch motions.

In future studies additional tests will be conducted to determine the damping of planing hulls at a higher accuracy. In this aspect it is thought that only roll and pitch decay tests will already provide more information about the damping factors.

For the present research, the damping coefficients in the x, y and z direction are supposed to be incorporated in the mathematical model. It is also assumed that the couple terms are comparatively small and can therefore be neglected. The remaining damping coefficients $K(p)$, $M(q)$ and $N(r)$ remain to be determined in more detail, especially as a dependency on the speed.

4.2(a) Roll damping

For planing ships with deadrise and hard chines, damping of roll motion is relatively high, because of the immersion of the planing area at roll angles. Therefore the non-dimensional damping factor κ_ϕ defined as:

$$\kappa_\phi=\frac{\nu}{\omega}=\frac{b}{2\sqrt{(I_{xx}+M_{pp})\cdot c}}$$

is assumed to have a relatively large value. Using the following equation yields the damping coefficient b, when κ_ϕ and the time-dependent I_{xx}, M_{pp} and c are known, see also Rutgersson and Ottosson [14]:

$$b=2\cdot\kappa_\phi\sqrt{(I_{xx}+M_{pp})\cdot c}$$

The spring coefficient c is taken from the mathematical model of the roll moment and depends on the position and speed of the ship, while the added mass coefficient M_{pp} is determined below.

In the present study, κ_ϕ has been varied in the simulation program in order to ascertain the influence of the roll damping coefficient. From experimental observations with free running ships sailing a straight course at high speed at an initially non-zero roll angle, it was found that the decay of the roll would occur during a limited number of oscillations until a stable situation is reached. The value of κ_ϕ should therefore be chosen such that also during the simulation the number of oscillations is found to be small (approximately one or two). It is expected that κ_ϕ is speed dependent and may therefore vary in time as a consequence of the change of speed.

The damping moment for roll is now: $K_{damp}=K_p\cdot p=-b\cdot p$

4.2(b) Pitch damping

In this study, the pitch damping will be modelled similar to the roll damping. The following equation is used for determining the time-dependent pitch damping:

$$b=2\cdot\kappa_\theta\sqrt{(I_{yy}+M_{qq})\cdot c}$$

The damping moment for pitch is now: $M_{damp}=M_q\cdot q=-b\cdot q$

Similar to the formulation of K_p, the damping coefficient M_{uq} is thought to be implemented in M_q through the speed dependency in κ_θ.

4.2(c) Yaw damping

Inoue [4] and Hooft [2] give an empirical expression for the damping coefficient of the yaw motion. Based on these expressions the following equation is used in the simulation program:

$$N_{ur}=-\frac{\pi}{2}\rho L^2 T^2(0.25+0.039\frac{B}{T}-0.56\frac{B}{L})\cdot(1+0.3\frac{L\tan\theta}{T})$$

where B and T are the time-dependent maximum beam and draught of the ship. In this study, it is assumed that the non-linear damping term $N_{r|r|}$ is small compared to N_{ur} and can therefore be neglected.

The damping moment for yaw is now: $N_{damp}=N_{ur}\cdot u\cdot r$

4.3   PROPELLER FORCES

Various methods exist to predict the thrust of the propeller as a function of the propeller rate of turning and the ship's longitudinal speed. Also approximations exist to take into account the effect of the lateral motions of the propeller. Often, however, the exact dimensions of the propeller are not yet determined in the initial design stage.

Therefore a simplified description of the propeller effect is used in the simulation program which is assumed to be acceptable when the propeller RPM are not affected by the motions of the ship. It should be noted that these formulae assume that the axis of the propeller shaft is parallel to the ship-fixed x-axis.

For this study one determines the propeller thrust X_{prop} from:

$$X_{prop}=\rho D_p^4 K_T n^2$$

in which D_p is the diameter of the propeller and n the number of revolutions per second. The thrust coefficient K_T is described by:

$$K_T=K_{T0}+K_{T1}\cdot J+K_{T2}\cdot J^2+K_{T3}\cdot J^3$$

in which the advance ratio J is defined by: $J=\dfrac{u_p\cdot(1-w_p)}{n\cdot D_p}$

where u_p is the propeller inflow velocity and w_p is the propeller wake fraction. The coefficients K_{Ti} have to be determined otherwise and are required as input to the simulation program.

Using the distances between the propeller and CG, y_{prop}-y_g and z_{prop}-z_g, the pitch and yaw moment induced by the propeller thrust are calculated with:

$$M_{prop}=(z_{prop}-z_G)\cdot X_{prop}$$
$$N_{prop}=-(y_{prop}-y_G)\cdot X_{prop}$$

4

The current formulae do not take the propeller torque into account to induce a roll moment.

4.4   RUDDER FORCES

The formulation of the rudder forces is based on Inoue [5] and Hooft [2], [3]. The rough approximations are suitable for the preliminary design process, when the actual rudder dimensions are not determined in detail. It is assumed that the velocities around the rudder are high and that flow separation does not occur. This last assumption should be re-evaluated in future studies to increase the accuracy of the prediction of the rudder forces. For this preliminary study, added mass and damping of the rudders are neglected. To increase the accuracy, these factors are to be included in future studies.

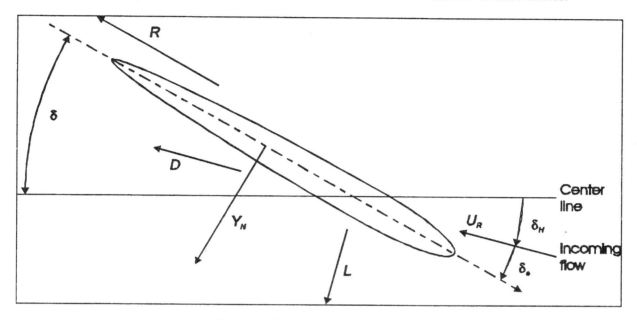

Figure 2 Forces acting on the rudder

To determine the forces on the rudder, as defined in Figure 2, the local effective rudder inflow velocity and the apparent angle of incidence have to be calculated.

The local rudder inflow velocity for a rudder with average height h_r, average chord length c_r, lateral rudder area A_r and effective aspect ratio A_e, is approximated by:

$$u_r = u \cdot (1-w_p) + C_{Du} \cdot \Delta u_p$$
$$v_r = C_{db} \cdot (v\cos\phi_F + w\sin\phi_F) - C_{dr}\sqrt{x_r^2 + y_r^2}\, r + C_{dr}\sqrt{x_r^2 + z_r^2}\, q$$
$$U_{rud} = \sqrt{u_r^2 + v_r^2}$$

where

$C_{Du} = \quad 0.7\dfrac{D_p}{h_r}$ [3] or $0.9\dfrac{D_p}{h_r}$ [2] effectiveness of velocity increment

$\Delta u_p = \quad \sqrt{u_p^2 + \dfrac{8 \cdot X_{prop}}{\rho\pi D_p^2}} - u_p$ velocity increment

$C_{db} \quad \approx 0.7$ flow straightening factor

$C_{dr} \quad \approx 1.0$

$\phi_f \qquad$ angle between rudder and vertical plane

$x_r, y_r, z_r \quad$ position of rudder relative to CG

The effective angle of incidence of the flow to the rudder follows from: $\delta_e = \delta - \delta_H$ where $\delta_H = \arctan\dfrac{v_r}{u_r}$.

The lateral rudder force can now be determined, using the above equations, with:

$$L = \frac{1}{2}\rho A_r C_{L\delta} U_{rud}^2 \sin\delta_e$$

where

$C_{L\delta} \quad \approx \dfrac{6.13 \cdot A_e}{A_e + 2.25}$ [2] rudder lift coefficient

The lift induced drag in the direction of the rudder inflow is described by:

$$D = \frac{1}{2}\rho A_r C_{Di} U_{rud}^2 \sin^2\delta_e$$

where

$C_{Di} = \dfrac{C_{L\delta}^2}{\pi A_e}$ rudder lift induced drag coefficient

The friction resistance of the rudder due to the friction drag of the rudder is formulated as:

$$R=\frac{1}{2}\rho S_{wr}C_{TR}\left(U_{rud}\cos\delta_e\right)^2$$

where

S_{wr} $\approx 2\cdot A_r$ rudder wetted area

C_{TR} ≈ 0.017 [3] high-lift rudder friction coefficient

≈ 0.007 [3] NACA profile friction coefficient

The normal force on the rudder due to the lateral drag coefficient $C_N \approx 1.8$ is:

$$Y_N=\frac{1}{2}\rho A_r C_N U_{rud}\sin\delta_e\,|U_{rud}\sin\delta_e|$$

Due to these rudder forces, one finds the following descriptions for the rudder induced forces on the ship:

$$X_{rud}=-R\cos\delta-D\cos\delta_H-Y_N\sin\delta-L\sin\delta_H$$
$$Y_{rud}=(-R\sin\delta-D\sin\delta_H+Y_N\cos\delta+(1+a_h)L\cos\delta_H)\cdot\cos\phi_F$$
$$Z_{rud}=(-R\sin\delta-D\sin\delta_H+Y_N\cos\delta+(1+a_h)L\cos\delta_H)\cdot\sin\phi_F$$
$$K_{rud}=-Y_{rud}\cdot z_r+Z_{rud}\cdot y_r$$
$$M_{rud}=X_{rud}\cdot z_r+Z_{rud}\cdot x_r$$
$$N_{rud}=-X_{rud}\cdot y_r+\left(\left(Y_N\cos\delta-R\sin\delta-D\sin\delta_H\right)\cdot x_r+(x_r+a_h\cdot x_h)L\cos\delta_H\right)\cos\phi_F$$

where

a_h $\approx 0.672\cdot C_B-0.153$ [2]

increase of rudder efficiency due to induced force on ship's hull

x_h $\approx 0.9\cdot x_r$ distance of induced hull force to centre of gravity

4.5 TOTAL EXCITATION FORCES

In this preliminary study, the forces and moments dealt with in the previous sections are supposed to be sufficient to predict the forces and moments acting on the tested planing hull forms sailing in calm water. To predict the behaviour of a vessel in all weather and sea conditions, descriptions to model the influence of waves, wind and current on the ship have to be incorporated.

It is generally known that the wave forces have a large influence on the behaviour of the ship, but the influence of wind can also be large. A strong side wind can induce large roll angles, changing the hydrodynamic forces and moments considerably. Strong wind gusts can result in coupled roll-yaw motions, possibly resulting in broaching or capsizing.

The total excitation forces and moments about the centre of reference in ship-fixed directions are found by adding all force components:

$$\Sigma F=F_{exc}=F_{grav}+F_{hull}+F_{damp}+F_{prop}+F_{rud}$$

This equation is used for calculating the accelerations of the ship.

4.6 ADDED MASS

4.6(a) Considerations

In this section, the description of the added mass of the planing ship models will be formulated based on descriptions from strip theory. The symbol used for the added mass of a strip at position x in direction i for an acceleration in direction k is:

$$m_{ik}(x) \quad \text{with} \quad i,k = 1\ldots6 \quad \text{or} \quad x,y,z,\phi,\theta,\psi$$

In Reference [10], Papanikolaou formulated the added mass per unit length for sway, heave and roll of a floating cylinder using potential theory. It can be shown that:

$$m_{ik}(x)=m_{ki}(x)$$

and on grounds of symmetry:

$$m_{ik}(x)=0 \quad \text{for } i+k \text{ odd}$$

With these considerations, the added mass matrix for a strip at position x looks like:

$$\begin{bmatrix} m_{xx} & 0 & m_{xz} & 0 & m_{x\theta} & 0 \\ 0 & m_{yy} & 0 & m_{y\phi} & 0 & m_{y\psi} \\ m_{xz} & 0 & m_{zz} & 0 & m_{z\theta} & 0 \\ 0 & m_{y\phi} & 0 & m_{\phi\phi} & 0 & m_{\phi\psi} \\ m_{x\theta} & 0 & m_{z\theta} & 0 & m_{\theta\theta} & 0 \\ 0 & m_{y\psi} & 0 & m_{\phi\psi} & 0 & m_{\psi\psi} \end{bmatrix}$$

In most reports, the added mass of a section with half beam b is taken proportional to the mass of a semi-circle with radius b and specific mass ρ: $m_{ij}=\frac{1}{2}\pi b^2\rho\cdot f_1(\beta,T,\ldots)$.

When the chines of the ship are not immersed, the draught T of the ship is a measure for the half beam b, therefore one can also write: $m_{ij}=\frac{1}{2}\pi T^2\rho\cdot f_2(\beta,T,\ldots)$.

This factor can also be seen in the formulations for the added mass in this paper.

4.6(b) Added mass for x-direction

Because the values of m_{xz} and $m_{x\theta}$ are presumably small compared to m_{xx}, these added masses are taken to be zero in the present study. In future studies, these components can be assigned non-zero values if desired to increase accuracy.

For this study, the total added mass M_{xx} can be approximated by

$$M_{xx}=\frac{\pi\rho T_{max}^2 B_{max}}{2}\cdot C_{mx}$$

where C_{mx} is taken as: $C_{mx} = 0.8$. The parameters T_{max} and B_{max} are the time-dependent instantaneous maximum draught and breadth at the still water line of the ship.

4.6(c) Added mass for y-direction

Papanikolaou gives in his report tables to determine the added mass in y-direction for variable excitation frequencies and breadth to draught ratios. In the present study, the values for $\omega = 0\ s^{-1}$ should be used, because the equations of motions are solved for a quasi-static state of the ship.

Diagram 4 from [10] gives the non-dimensional added mass coefficient m_{yy}' of a section as a function of the beam to draught ratio. The values in this figure for zero oscillation frequency will be approximated in this study using the following function:

$$m_{yy}' = m_{yy0} + m_{yy1}\left(\frac{B}{T}\right) + m_{yy2}\left(\frac{B}{T}\right)^2 + m_{yy3}\left(\frac{B}{T}\right)^3$$

The coefficients m_{yyi} are determined by performing regression analysis. This results in the following coefficients:

$$m_{yy0} = 1.0274 \quad m_{yy1} = -0.1947 \quad m_{yy2} = 0.0358 \quad m_{yy3} = -0.0023$$

Care should be taken using this formula for high $\left(\frac{B}{T}\right)$ values (greater than approximately 5). Because of the regression model, extrapolating will yield unrealistic results.

The added mass in y-direction per unit length for a section with draught T can now be derived with:

$$m_{yy} = \frac{\pi\rho\,T^2}{2}\cdot m_{yy}'$$

When m_{yy} is known, the following added masses can be calculated:

$$M_{yy} = \int_L m_{yy}\ dx \quad M_{y\psi} = M_{\psi y} = \int_L m_{yy}\cdot x\ dx \quad M_{\psi\psi} = \int_L m_{yy}\cdot x^2\ dx$$

Papanikolaou also gave a relation between the added masses $m_{y\phi}$ and m_{yy} by plotting the virtual arm $h_{y\phi} = \dfrac{m_{y\phi}}{m_{yy}\cdot T}$. These values will be approximated using $m_{y\phi} = m_{yy}\cdot T\cdot h_{y\phi}$ and

$$h_{y\phi} = h_{y\phi0} + h_{y\phi1}\left(\frac{B}{T}\right) + h_{y\phi2}\left(\frac{B}{T}\right)^2 + h_{y\phi3}\left(\frac{B}{T}\right)^3$$

Performing regression analysis yields the following coefficients for the virtual arm:

$$h_{y\phi0} = 0.4472 \quad h_{y\phi1} = -0.0218 \quad h_{y\phi2} = -0.1349 \quad h_{y\phi3} = -0.0007$$

The added mass $M_{y\phi}$ can be calculated with:

$$M_{y\phi} = \int_L m_{y\phi}\ dx.$$

4.6(d) Added mass for z-direction

The added mass for an acceleration in z-direction is described by Payne [11] and Quadvlieg [13]. Both reports give the following description for the added mass per unit length for a section with deadrise angle β and draught T as:

$$m_{zz} = \frac{\pi\rho\,T^2}{2\cdot\tan^2\beta}\cdot f(\beta)$$

The function $f(\beta)$ gives the quotient of the added mass for a prism and the added mass for a flat plate. According to Payne, $f(\beta)$, with β in radians, is given by $f(\beta) = 1 - \dfrac{\beta}{\pi}$ while Quadvlieg gives: $f(\beta) = 1 - \dfrac{2\cdot\beta}{\pi}$. For zero deadrise, a flat plate, both deadrise functions yield the same value, i.e. $f(0) = 1$. However, for a deadrise of $\dfrac{\pi}{2}$, the function by Payne gives $f(\dfrac{\pi}{2}) = \dfrac{1}{2}$, while the function of Quadvlieg results in $f(\dfrac{\pi}{2}) = 0$.

In this study, it is decided to use the description by Quadvlieg in the simulation program. Further study should examine the added mass in more detail to determine which formulation yields more realistic results. Recent work by Payne [12] gives suggestions on improvements in the determination of the added mass.

This added mass per unit length m_{zz} can now be used to calculate the following added masses:

$$M_{zz} = \int_L m_{zz}\ dx \quad M_{z\theta} = M_{\theta z} = \int_L m_{zz}\cdot x\ dx \quad M_{\theta\theta} = \int_L m_{zz}\cdot x^2\ dx$$

4.6(e) Added mass for φ-direction

The hydrodynamic mass in φ-direction, depending on the beam to draught ratio and the oscillation frequency is given in Diagram 7 of the report by Papanikolaou [10]. Again, the values for zero oscillating frequency should be used. Similar to m_{yy}', these values will be approximated in this study using the following function:

$$m_{\phi\phi}' = m_{\phi\phi0} + m_{\phi\phi1}\left(\frac{B}{T}\right) + m_{\phi\phi2}\left(\frac{B}{T}\right)^2 + m_{\phi\phi3}\left(\frac{B}{T}\right)^3$$

The coefficients $m_{\phi\phi i}$ are determined by regression analysis, resulting in:

$$m_{\phi\phi0} = 1.5119 \quad m_{\phi\phi1} = -1.7190 \quad m_{\phi\phi2} = 0.5524 \quad m_{\phi\phi3} = -0.0317$$

Note again that extrapolation will probably result in unrealistic values. The added mass in φ-direction per unit length for a section with draught T can now be calculated with:

$$m_{\phi\phi} = \frac{\pi \rho \, T^4 \frac{B}{T}}{4} \cdot m'_{\phi\phi}$$

Using $m_{\phi\phi}$, the added mass for roll is found by:

$$M_{\phi\phi} = \int_L m_{\phi\phi} \, dx.$$

4.7 EQUATIONS OF MOTIONS

To calculate the ship-fixed accelerations $\vec{a}$ of the planing ship, the equations of motions are derived from Newton's second law: $M^{-1} \cdot \Sigma\vec{F} = \vec{a}$:

$$M^{-1} \cdot \begin{bmatrix} X & - & m(qw-rv) & & \\ Y & - & m(ru-pw) & & \\ Z & - & m(pv-qu) & & \\ K & + & (I_{yy}-I_{zz})qr & + & I_{xz}pq \\ M & + & (I_{zz}-I_{xx})pr & - & I_{xz}(p^2-r^2) \\ N & + & (I_{xx}-I_{yy})pq & - & I_{xz}qr \end{bmatrix} = \begin{bmatrix} \dot{u} \\ \dot{v} \\ \dot{w} \\ \dot{p} \\ \dot{q} \\ \dot{r} \end{bmatrix}$$

in which the mass matrix M is:

$$M = \begin{bmatrix} m+M_{xx} & 0 & 0 & 0 & 0 & 0 \\ 0 & m+M_{yy} & 0 & M_{y\phi} & 0 & M_{y\psi} \\ 0 & 0 & m+M_{zz} & 0 & M_{z\theta} & 0 \\ 0 & M_{y\phi} & 0 & I_{xx}+M_{\phi\phi} & 0 & -I_{xz}+M_{\phi\psi} \\ 0 & 0 & M_{z\theta} & 0 & I_{yy}+M_{\theta\theta} & 0 \\ 0 & M_{y\psi} & 0 & -I_{xz}+M_{\phi\psi} & 0 & I_{zz}+M_{\psi\psi} \end{bmatrix}$$

Solving the above equation at each time step will give the accelerations. Integration of these accelerations provides the velocities u, v, w, p, q and r, which determine the excitation forces $\Sigma\vec{F}$ at the next time step.

Transforming the velocities from the ship-fixed coordinate system to the earth-fixed system and subsequently integrating these earth-fixed velocities will provide the position of the ship in the earth-fixed system.

5. SIMULATIONS

In this section, the simulations performed during the study are described. The simulations were done to ascertain whether the program is working properly to evaluate the results of the computations. First the set-up of the test program is discussed, after which the results of the simulation are given and discussed. Details about the computer program can be found in Reference [18].

5.1 TEST PROGRAM

The test program consists of various types of simulation runs. The following types can be defined:

1. Change in model set-up, e.g. change of mass or position of CG.

2. Change in initial position or velocity, e.g. change of rise or speed.

3. Change in hydrodynamic coefficients, i.e. damping factors and deviation from equilibrium position.

4. Change in manoeuvring mode, e.g. turning circle test and zig-zag test.

The first type is used to determine the trends in the results due to changes in the input. The outcome of some changes can be predicted using general theory or publications about this subject.

The second type is used to determine the ability of the ship to return to its equilibrium position, irrespective of the initial deviation from this equilibrium.

The third type is used for stability criteria, concerning the values of these coefficients.

The fourth type is used to determine the manoeuvrability of the planing ship and the behaviour of the ship during these manoeuvres. Combining the third and fourth types can yield more strict limits than those found using the simulations from type three.

Before starting the test program, a few runs were done with both ship models to determine the values of the damping factors κ_ϕ and κ_θ. A value of $\kappa_\theta = 0.6$ was found to be satisfactorily for both Model 233 and Model 277. The value of κ_ϕ was for Model 233: $\kappa_\phi = 0.6$ and for Model 277: $\kappa_\phi = 0.55$. It appears that Model 277 is less sensitive to roll velocities than Model 233. This will be examined in more detail further on in this paper.

The first run for both models is derived from model experiments performed by Keuning [8], (Model 232-A is Model 233 in this study), and [7], (Model 188 is Model 277 in this study). The following conditions were selected:

	Weight	U	θ_{exp}	θ_{sim}	Rise z_{exp}	Rise z_{sim}
Model 233	164 N	2.3 ms-1	3.7°	3.7°	-4.5 mm	-3.1 mm
Model 277	159.9 N	2.4 ms-1	2.3°	1.5°	-5.3 mm	-3.9 mm

8

It appears that the mathematical model describes the state of Model 233 rather satisfactorily. For Model 277, the similarity between the test result and the simulation result is less clear. The difference may be caused by differences between the model test set-up and the mathematical model. Such differences exist for example in the set-up of the propulsion and the modelling of the rudder forces.

5.2 SIMULATION RESULTS

In this section the results of some simulation runs will be presented. For the set of runs where the model set-up was changed, the results stated in Table 1 were found.

TABLE 1 Results of first set of simulations

Run ID	Description	Expected behaviour	Simulation result
R233-12	Shift LCG aft	Increase θ	$\theta = 3.72° \rightarrow \theta = 4.30°$
R233-13	Shift LCG forward	Decrease θ	$\theta = 3.72° \rightarrow \theta = 3.22°$
R233-14	Decrease GM	Increase θ	$\theta = 3.72° \rightarrow \theta = 3.73°$
R233-15	Increase GM	Decrease θ	$\theta = 3.72° \rightarrow \theta = 3.71°$
R233-16	Decrease mass	Decrease draught	$T = 0.088m \rightarrow T = 0.082m$
R233-17	Increase mass	Increase draught	$T = 0.088m \rightarrow T = 0.093m$
R277-12	Shift LCG aft	Increase θ	$\theta = 1.49° \rightarrow \theta = 2.02°$
R277-13	Shift LCG forward	Decrease θ	$\theta = 1.49° \rightarrow \theta = 1.02°$
R277-14	Decrease GM	Increase θ	$\theta = 1.49° \rightarrow \theta = 1.50°$
R277-15	Increase GM	Decrease θ	$\theta = 1.49° \rightarrow \theta = 1.49°$
R277-16	Decrease mass	Decrease draught	$T = 0.085m \rightarrow T = 0.079m$
R277-17	Increase mass	Increase draught	$T = 0.085m \rightarrow z = 0.090m$

For all simulations, it appears that the behaviour of the computer program to changes in model set-up is consistent with theory or experience. Also, both ship models respond similarly to the changes in model set-up. However, although the damping factor κ_θ is larger for Model 233 than for Model 277, the oscillations around the equilibrium after the initial disturbance are more pronounced for Model 233.

In the graphs taken from the results of runs R233-13 and R277-13, see Figure 3, the difference in oscillation amplitude and duration can be seen. This can be explained by examining the mathematical model for the pitch moment M, see Reference [15] for more details. The spring term to calculate the damping moment is much larger for Model 277 than for Model 233. For Model 277, any pitch angular velocity will be damped stronger in comparison to Model 233. Because the damping is still unknown it is not possible to draw any conclusions on the difference in behaviour between the to hull forms.

Table 2 was constructed after simulation of the runs, with deviations from the initial equilibrium state. At the end of each simulation, the state of the ship model was returned to the equilibrium state, i.e. sailing at straight course and constant speed. It can therefore be concluded that for the used input the state of the planing vessel is stable. From runs R233-24 and R277-24, it also appears that the vessel is course stable.

In Figure 4 the results of the vertical position of the centre of gravity during runs R233-23 and R277-23 are presented in graphical form. Clearly, the oscillations due to the zero initial vertical (ship-fixed) velocity are larger for Model 233 than for Model 277. However, the vertical velocity in the equilibrium state is also much higher for Model 233 than for Model 277. Examining the results, it is seen that the vertical oscillations are a result of the combined heave-pitch system.

In Table 3, the results of the third set of runs are listed. It is clearly seen that decreasing the damping factors largely affects the stability of the ship. The limit values of the damping factors κ_ϕ and κ_θ below which the behaviour of the ship becomes unstable are probably as follows:

Model 233: $0.15 < \kappa_\phi < 0.30$, $0.15 < \kappa_\theta < 0.30$
Model 277: $0.1375 < \kappa_\phi < 0.275$, $\kappa_\theta < 0.15$

In future studies, the limits for the damping factors can be determined more accurately.

As an example of the behaviour of the model at low damping factors, the results of runs R233-34 and R233-36 are included in Figure 6. The unstable behaviour when the damping factor for roll is decreased is clearly visible in the increasing oscillation amplitudes of the roll angle and the increasing immersion.

TABLE 2 Results of second set of simulations

Run ID	Initial deviation	Simulation result
R233-21	Decrease of speed	$u_{t=0} = 1.285\ ms^{-1} \rightarrow u_{t=\infty} = 2.285\ ms^{-1}$
R233-22	Increase of speed	$u_{t=0} = 3.285\ ms^{-1} \rightarrow u_{t=\infty} = 2.285\ ms^{-1}$
R233-23	Zero vertical speed	$w_{t=0} = 0.000\ ms^{-1} \rightarrow w_{t=\infty} = 0.149\ ms^{-1}$
R233-24	Initial drift $\beta = -5^{\circ}$	$v_{t=0} = 0.200\ ms^{-1} \rightarrow v_{t=\infty} = 0.000\ ms^{-1}$
R233-25	Draught $T - 5\ mm$	$T_{t=0} = 0.0827\ m \rightarrow T_{t=\infty} = 0.0877\ m$
R233-26	Draught $T + 5\ mm$	$T_{t=0} = 0.0927\ m \rightarrow T_{t=\infty} = 0.0877\ m$
R277-21	Decrease of speed	$u_{t=0} = 1.370\ ms^{-1} \rightarrow u_{t=\infty} = 2.370\ ms^{-1}$
R277-22	Increase of speed	$u_{t=0} = 3.370\ ms^{-1} \rightarrow u_{t=\infty} = 2.370\ ms^{-1}$
R277-23	Zero vertical speed	$w_{t=0} = 0.000\ ms^{-1} \rightarrow w_{t=\infty} = 0.062\ ms^{-1}$
R277-24	Initial drift $\beta = -5^{\circ}$	$v_{t=0} = 0.207\ ms^{-1} \rightarrow v_{t=\infty} = 0.000\ ms^{-1}$
R277-25	Draught $T - 5\ mm$	$T_{t=0} = 0.0796\ m \rightarrow T_{t=\infty} = 0.0846\ m$
R277-26	Draught $T + 5\ mm$	$T_{t=0} = 0.0896\ m \rightarrow T_{t=\infty} = 0.0846\ m$

TABLE 3 Results of third set of simulations

Run ID	Description	Simulation result
R233-31	Zero pitch angle, $\kappa_\theta = 0.60$	Decreasing oscillations
R233-32	$\kappa_\theta = 0.5\ \kappa_{\theta,0} = 0.30$	Decreasing oscillations
R233-33	$\kappa_\theta = 0.25\ \kappa_{\theta,0} = 0.15$	Increasing oscillations
R233-34	Initial roll angle $\phi = 5^{\circ}$, $\kappa_\phi = 0.60$	Decreasing oscillations
R233-35	$\kappa_\phi = 0.5\ \kappa_{\phi,0} = 0.30$	Decreasing oscillations
R233-36	$\kappa_\phi = 0.25\ \kappa_{\phi,0} = 0.15$	Increasing oscillations
R233-37	Roll angle 5°, zero pitch	Decreasing oscillations
R233-38	$\kappa_\phi = 0.5\ \kappa_{\phi,0}$, $\kappa_\theta = 0.5\ \kappa_{\theta,0}$	Decreasing oscillations
R277-31	Zero pitch angle, $\kappa_\theta = 0.60$	Decreasing oscillations
R277-32	$\kappa_\theta = 0.5\ \kappa_{\theta,0} = 0.30$	Decreasing oscillations
R277-33	$\kappa_\theta = 0.25\ \kappa_{\theta,0} = 0.15$	Decreasing oscillations
R277-34	Initial roll angle $\phi = 5^{\circ}$, $\kappa_\phi = 0.55$	Decreasing oscillations
R277-35	$\kappa_\phi = 0.5\ \kappa_{\phi,0} = 0.275$	Decreasing oscillations
R277-36	$\kappa_\phi = 0.25\ \kappa_{\phi,0} = 0.1375$	Increasing oscillations
R277-37	Roll angle 5°, zero pitch	Decreasing oscillations
R277-38	$\kappa_\phi = 0.5\ \kappa_{\phi,0}$, $\kappa_\theta = 0.5\ \kappa_{\theta,0}$	Decreasing oscillations

TABLE 4 Results of turning circle tests

Run ID	Tactical Diameter	Advance	Transfer	Approach Speed	Speed Loss	Damping Roll	Pitch
	m	m	m	ms^{-1}	%	κ_ϕ	κ_θ
R233-41	11.37	13.50	5.77	2.29	7.6	0.60	0.60
R233-42	11.25	13.62	5.76	2.29	8.5	0.30	0.30
R277-41	12.68	14.45	6.47	2.37	7.1	0.55	0.60
R277-42	12.95	14.66	6.62	2.37	7.3	0.27	0.30
233: Difference	-1.1%	+0.9%	-0.2%	-	+12%	+50%	-50%
277: Difference	+2.1%	+1.5%	+2.3%	-	+2.8%	+50%	-50%
R233-TT	11.37	13.50	5.77	2.29	7.6	0.60	0.60
R277-TT	12.78	14.31	6.48	2.28	7.0	0.55	0.60
Difference	+12.4%	+6.0%	+12.3%	-0.4%	-9.2%	-8.3%	+0%

The simulation results of the turning circle tests for both ship models are summarized in Table 4. The first run of each ship model is with the original damping factor values and with a rudder angle of 35° to starboard. During the second run, the damping factors were divided by two. It should be noted that, except for runs R233-TT and R277-TT, the approach speed of both models is not exactly the same (difference approximately 3.5%), therefore the results are not similar. In these runs, a small influence of the damping factors on the manoeuvring characteristics is seen.

Runs R233-TT and R277-TT were performed to illustrate the difference in manoeuvrability between both ship models. The mass, position of centre of gravity and the approach speed were identical for both ships. In Table 4 and Figure 7 the results of the simulations are included. During the simulations, speed losses of approximately 8% were found, while in reality the speed loss during close turning of planing ships can reach values of 70% or even higher. Implementing rotational velocity dependent hydrodynamic coefficients such as X_{vr} in the mathematical model in the future should increase the accuracy of the simulation program considerably.

TABLE 5   Results of 20/20 zig-zag tests

Run Id	Damping		First overshoot	Second overshoot
	Roll	Pitch	Angle	Angle
R233-43	0.60	0.6	27.3	31.5
R233-44	0.30	0.3	28.9	34.3
R277-43	0.55	0.6	26.5	30.4
R277-44	0.275	0.3	27.1	31.2
233: Difference	-50%	-50%	+5.9%	+8.9%
277: Difference	-50%	-50%	+2.3%	+2.6%

The results from the 20/20 zig-zag tests are stated in Table 5. In this table it is seen that for this manoeuvre Model 233 reacts stronger to changes in the damping factors than Model 277. It appears that decreasing the damping results in an increase of the overshoot angles. In Figure 8 the time samples of both the rudder and yaw angles during run R277-43 are included. Note that a starboard rudder angle has a positive sign in this figure.

6.   CONCLUSION

In this paper, a time-domain computer simulation program to predict the dynamic stability and manoeuvrability of planing ships in still water for six degrees of freedom is described. The formulations used in the program were based on experimental data and additional empirical coefficients taken from literature.

Simulation runs have been performed to ascertain whether the program is working properly and to evaluate the calculation results. Some of these results are discussed in this paper.

Examining the simulations, it is seen that changes in the input of the program resulted in the expected changes in the output. Changing the damping factors appears to have great influence of the behaviour of the ships. Further study should emphasize in determining the dynamic coefficients in the mathematical model more accurately. In general it is concluded that the results from this computer simulation program can be used in the early design stage to predict the stability and manoeuvrability of the planing ship.

7.   ACKNOWLEDGEMENTS

The authors wish to express their gratitude to the Maritime Research Institute the Netherlands in Wageningen for supporting this research.

Also thanks to Prof. Dr. Ir. J A Pinkster at Delft University of Technology for his support and guidance during this project. The authors also wish to thank the members of the Ship Hydromechanics Laboratory for their help during preparation and performing of the model experiments.

8.   REFERENCES

1.   CLEMENT, E P and BLOUNT, D L: 'Resistance tests of a systematic series of planing hull forms'. SNAME Transactions, Vol. 71, 1963.

2.   HOOFT, J P: Computer simulation of the ship's manoeuvrability, Part 1 & 2. Maritime Research Institute the Netherlands.

3.   HOOFT, J P and NIENHUIS, U: 'The prediction of the ship's manoeuvrability in the design stage'. SNAME Annual Meeting, November 1994.

4.   INOUE, S, HIRANO, M, and KIJIMA, K: 'Hydrodynamic derivatives on ship manoeuvring'. International Shipbuilding Progress, Vol. 28, No. 321, pp. 112-125, 1981.

5.   INOUE, S, HIRANO, M, KIJIMA, K, and TAKASHINA, J: 'A practical calculation method of ship maneuvering motion'. International Shipbuilding Progress, Vol. 28, No. 325, pp. 207-222, 1981.

6.   KEUNING, J A: Invloed van de Deadrise op het zeegangsgedrag van planerende schepen. Report 794-O Delft University of Technology, June 1988.

7.   KEUNING, J A and GERRITSMA, J: 'Resistance tests of a series of planing hull forms with 25 degrees deadrise angle'. International Shipbuilding Progress, Vol. 29, No. 337, pp. 222-249, 1982.

8. KEUNING, J A, GERRITSMA, J, and VAN TERWISGA, P F: Resistance tests of a series planing hull forms with 30 degrees deadrise angle, and a calculation model based on this and similar series. Report 959, Delft University of Technology, December 1992.

9. LEWANDOWSKI, E M: 'Trajectory predictions for high speed planing craft'. International Shipbuilding Progress, Vol. 41, No. 426, pp. 137-148, 1994.

10. PAPANIKOLAOU, A: 'Hydrodynamische Koeffizienten für die linearen Schwingungen von schwimmenden Zylindern'. Schiffstechnik, Vol. 27, No. 3, pp. 127-166, 1980.

11. PAYNE, P R: 'The vertical impact of a wedge on a fluid'. Ocean Engineering, Vol. 8, No. 4, pp. 421-436, 1981.

12. PAYNE, P R: 'Recent developments in 'added-mass' planing theory'. Ocean Engineering, Vol. 21, No. 3, pp. 257-309, 1994.

13. QUADVLIEG, F F H A: Non linear motions of planing ships. Report 920-S, Delft University of Technology, March 1992.

14. RUTGERSSON, O and OTTOSSON, P: 'Model tests and computer simulations - an effective combination for investigation of broaching phenomena'. SNAME Annual Meeting, New York, N.Y., November 1987.

15. TOXOPEUS, S L: A time domain simulation program for manoeuvring of planing ships. Delft University of Technology, September 1996.

16. TOXOPEUS, S L: Mathematical model of the behaviour of planing ships. Delft University of Technology, August 1996.

17. TOXOPEUS, S L: Model experiments on dynamic stability of planing ships. Delft University of Technology, June 1996.

18. TOXOPEUS, S L: VesSim User's Manual. Maritime Research Institute the Netherlands, to be published.

19. ZARNICK, E E: A nonlinear mathematical model of motions of a planing boat in regular waves. Report DTNSRDC-78/032, David W. Taylor Naval Ship Research and Development Center, March 1978.

20. COHEN, S H, BLOUNT, D L: 'Research Plan for the investigation of Dynamic Instability of small High-Speed Craft', SNAME Transactions, Vol. 94, 1986, pp 197-214.

21. BLOUNT, D L and CODEGA, L T: 'Dynamic Stability of Planing Boats', Marine Technology, Vol. 29, No. 1, January 1992, pp 4-12.

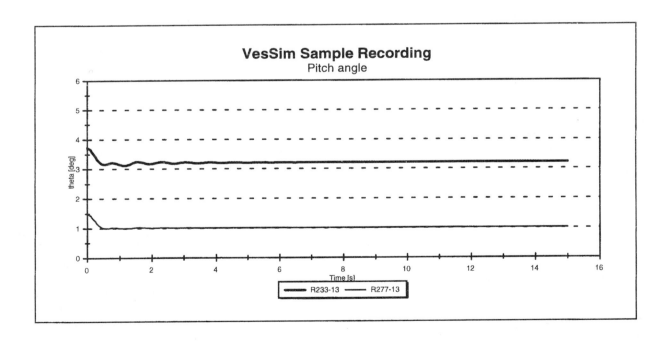

Fig. 3 Results of simulation, runs R233-13 and R277-13

NOMENCLATURE

Symbol	Description	Unit
C_B	Design block coefficient	-
GM	Metacentric height	m
K	Ship-fixed moment in longitudinal direction	Nm
L	Length between perpendiculars	m
LCG	Longitudinal position centre of gravity	m
$LCOR$	Longitudinal position centre of reference	m
M	Ship-fixed moment in lateral direction	Nm
N	Ship-fixed moment in vertical direction	Nm
p	Rate of turning around x-axis	$rads^{-1}$
q	Rate of turning around y-axis	$rads^{-1}$
r	Rate of turning around z-axis	$rads^{-1}$
T	Draught of the model at centre of reference	m
u	Ship's longitudinal velocity	ms^{-1}
u_e	Ship's longitudinal velocity, earth-fixed	ms^{-1}
U	Towing speed	ms^{-1}
v	Ship's lateral velocity	ms^{-1}
v_e	Ship's lateral velocity, earth-fixed	ms^{-1}
VCG	Vertical position centre of gravity	m
$VCOR$	Vertical position centre of reference	m
w	Ship's vertical velocity	ms^{-1}
X	Ship-fixed force in longitudinal direction	N
x_e	x-position of centre of gravity, earth-fixed	m
x_G	x-position of centre of gravity, ship-fixed	m
x_R	x-position of centre of reference, ship-fixed	m
Y	Ship-fixed force in transversal direction	N
y_e	y-position of centre of gravity, earth-fixed	m
y_G	y-position of centre of gravity, ship-fixed	m
y_R	y-position of centre of reference, ship-fixed	m
z	Rise of centre of reference, coordinate along z-axis	m
Z	Ship-fixed force in vertical direction	N
z_e	z-position of centre of gravity, earth-fixed	m
z_G	z-position of centre of gravity, ship-fixed	m
z_R	z-position of centre of reference, ship-fixed	m
β	Drift angle, twist around earth-fixed z-axis or deadrise angle	deg
θ	Trim angle, twist around ship-fixed y-axis	deg
ϕ	Roll angle, twist around ship-fixed x-axis	deg
ψ	Yaw angle	deg
δ	Rudder angle, positive to port	rad
δ_d	Desired rudder angle	rad
κ_ϕ	Damping factor for roll damping	-
κ_θ	Damping factor for pitch damping	-

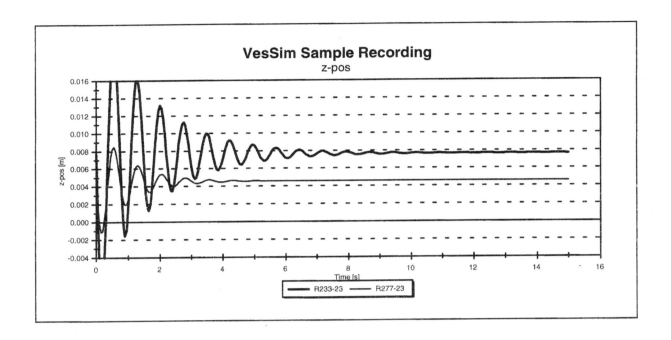

Fig. 4 Results of simulation, runs R233-23 and R277-23

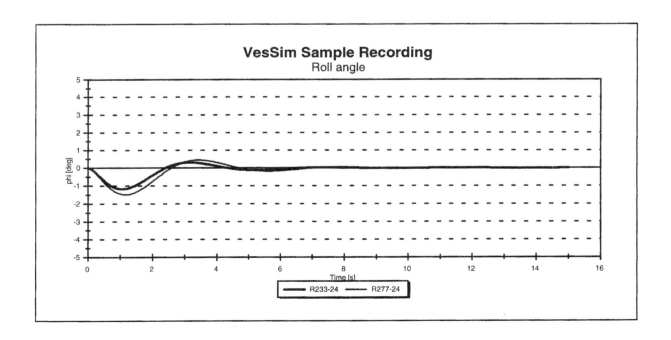

Fig. 5 Results of simulation, runs R233-24 and R277-24

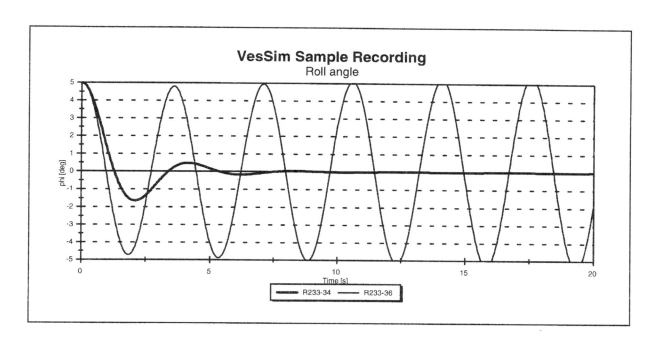

Fig. 6 Results of simulation, runs R233-34 and R233-36

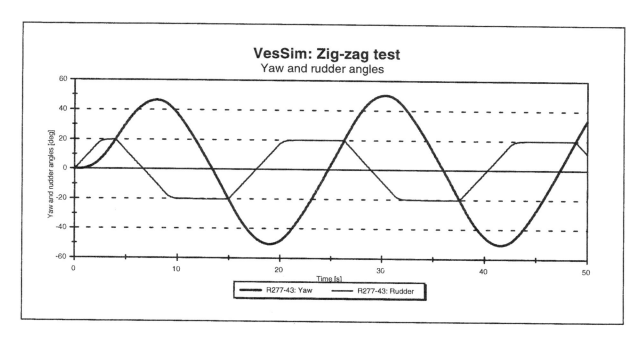

Fig. 8 Results of simulation, run R277-43

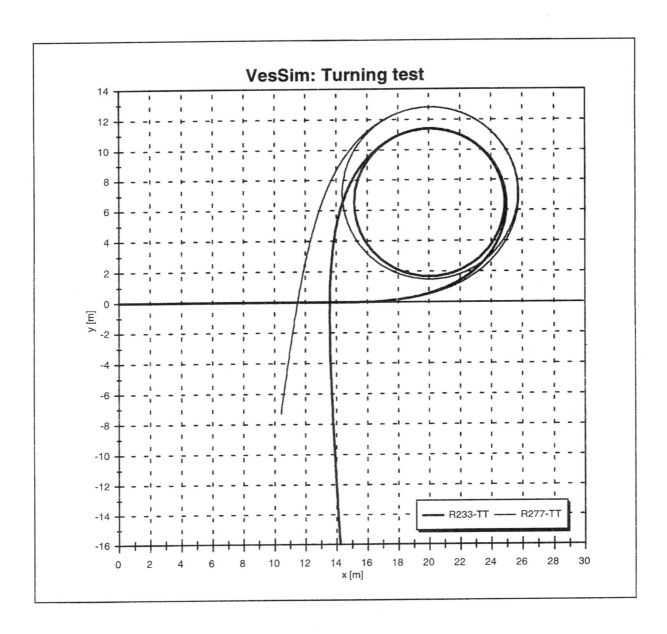

Fig. 7 Results of simulation, runs R233-TT and R277-TT

DESIGN LIMITATIONS: OPERATING LIMITATIONS
THE SAFETY OF HIGH SPEED CRAFT

by M Simpson and R Bryce, Hart, Fenton & Co Ltd, UK

Paper presented at the

International Symposium & Seminar

THE SAFETY OF HIGH SPEED CRAFT

6 - 7 FEBRUARY 1997 LONDON

DESIGN LIMITATIONS: OPERATING LIMITATIONS
THE SAFETY OF HIGH SPEED CRAFT

Michael Simpson and Robert Bryce
Hart, Fenton & Co Ltd

SUMMARY

It was hoped that with the implementation of the IMO Code of Safety for High Speed Craft at the beginning of 1996 a simpler regulatory environment would exist.

Even with the inadequacies of the new Code it is an improvement on the previous state of affairs. However when working with the Code, Classification Society Rules and other IMO standards a plethora of variations in criteria emerges.

The paper will address some of these issues and view these criteria against the various operating limitations which are applied to these craft. These topics will be considered with reference to the comfort of the passenger, or end user.

AUTHORS' BIOGRAPHIES

Mr Michael Simpson joined Hart Fenton in 1978 after working for two years at Smith's Dock Teeside. A Chartered Engineer, qualifying at Sunderland Polytechnic, he has been involved in a variety of vessel types, during his nineteen years with HF, and in recent years has had close involvement with the company's High Speed Craft activities. Mr Simpson also attends the High Speed Craft Operators' Association meetings.

After training and working as a Shipwright in Sydney, Mr Robert Bryce joined Incat Designs as a draughtsman. In 1989 he moved to the U.K. and joined Aluminium Shipbuilders as Technical Co-ordinator for the construction of the wavepiercer "Condor 9". In 1991 he joined Hart Fenton as a designer and more recently has worked in Project Management on HSC projects. He is presently working towards Chartered Engineer accreditation and CEDR mediator accreditation.

1.   INTRODUCTION

It is interesting to note that the HSC Code[1] applies to craft operating on International routes. This allows a wide range of National differences in surveying and approving HSC. T he end effect of this is that craft constructed to operate in certain countries could not be sold outside of those same jurisdictions, a financial impediment for an owner and operator.

The basis for approval to operate HSC and restricted service ferries, for example, has always been permitted by the trade off between scantling reductions and limitations of operation. The approval was given via the DSC Code[2] or Class Rules. So the imposition of operating restrictions is not a new practice. This point and the basis for operating restrictions appears to have been forgotten in some circles.

2.   WHAT ARE THE LIMITATIONS

The limitations come in a variety of essential forms com-

prising of time, distance, wave height and acceleration components.

All the criteria are brought together to enable the issuance of the Safety Certificate and the Permit to Operate which are required to define the Operating parameters of each HSC.

To give an overview of the range of criteria which needs to be assessed by the designers and operators of HSC we have compiled two tables, ref Table 1. and Table 2. In this simplified form the range of criteria which needs to be met is made apparent.

The picture the tables present should not be considered as a criticism of the scope of criteria which need to be considered, rather the aim is to highlight some of the inconsistencies and also to bring to mind the range of issues which need to be addressed.

Within the HSC Code[1] the time and distance elements combine with passenger numbers to define the Category of the craft.

From Tables 1 and 2, it is immediately apparent that there is a spread of criteria with a time element being very common. For the purpose of the table comparison the time element covers issues such as route times and lengths of surveys. Time and acceleration composites can be found in seat testing criteria, for example.

One of the most obvious time constraints is that which relates to the relationship between Structural Fire Protection and passenger evacuation.

Acceleration criteria has a broad spread of application in the HSC Code[1] as well as Classification Society Rules. In the latter these criteria establish the structural scantlings and the parameters of the design as well as the operating limitations.

The basis for approval of HSC has always been to limit or restrict the operating parameters of a craft. With the growth in the size and cost of these vessels the commercial imperative requires an ever greater maximization of revenue earning time. This commercial demand needs to be clearly understood to enable the correct assessment of the restricting criteria to be made.

With the drive towards larger craft operating longer and more exposed routes it is essential that the industry improves it's understanding of the loads imposed upon the structures of HSC across the broad range of operating conditions. Real time accelerations and loads have to be compared and validated against the computer analysis and design criteria we are presently using.

A design limit yet to be applied to High Speed Craft, but soon to be, is the application of the Stockholm agreement.

The Stockholm agreement provides for the ability of the vessel to withstand an amount of water on deck, based on that which is accumulated from the vessel being in waves of 4.0m significant wave height. The agreement recognised that these were exceptional in some short sea routes and provided reductions based on geographical location.

Therefore, once applicable to HSC, the owners will be required to demonstrate by model testing that their vessel is able to withstand the amount of water accumulated on deck, in waves of the significant height applicable to their operating area, as defined by the agreement, or by applying the standard 500mm water on deck calculation.

3. APPLYING THE REGULATIONS.

The design and operating limitations imposed upon HSC come from two primary sources. These are the IMO HSC Code[1] and the Classification[3][4][5][6] in which the craft is placed.

The HSC Code empowers the Flag State Administration with the authority for issuance of the High-Speed Craft Safety Certificate and the Permit to Operate, after consulting with the Port State. The Flag State Administration being the authority in which the craft is registered and entitled to fly the flag of that State whilst the Port State is any State in which the craft operates from. These survey authorities are no different from those for conventional shipping.

In respect of the issuing of the Permit to Operate the Port State has the right to inspect the vessel and its documentation. The wording of the Code thereafter is ambiguous in that it states ".. if there are deficiencies the Permit to Operate ceases to be valid,...." but it does not state who invalidates the Certificate.

Further, the Code also requires the Port State Authorities to give assistance to the Administration to conduct surveys and if applicable should ensure that the vessel does not operate until safe.

The organisations who act on behalf of Flag State Administrations have in instances approved schemes, systems and equipments and issued Certificates of Approval whereupon Port State Authorities have found errors and omissions or disagreed on interpretation.

These problems have the effect of diminishing the standing and confidence in these organisations.

In practice, the Port State Authorities in many circumstances require conditions, in some instances other than those specified by the Permit to Operate, and generally withhold approval for the vessel to trade until their particular interpretation of the Code is accepted and any technical modifications which they require are implemented onboard the craft.

These problems manifest themselves, most graphically and in particular, when existing larger size car and passenger craft, constructed prior to 1996, change routes and a Port State. The Code does not give guidance on enforcing compliance upon existing craft, retrospectively. Some Port State Authorities accept the problems in applying the Code retrospectively and seek gradual improvements, where practicable, to the existing craft. Other Authorities act differently. It is this inconsistency in approach which causes severe frustration to the Operator who seeks to comply with Port State requirements, especially when authorities at either end of the route are requesting incompatible requirements.

On the basis of tonnage on register the main Classification Societies which have the greatest coverage of HSC are Det Norske Veritas, Lloyd's Register of Shipping, UNITAS comprising of Germanischer Lloyd, Bureau Veritas and Registro Italiano Navale as well as the China Classification Society. These Societies are members of IACS but this membership does not ensure consistency.

4. INCONSISTENCIES IN LIMITS AND APPLICATION

Classification societies, in their rules for High Speed Light Craft, generally have used the acceleration value at the longitudinal centre of gravity as the predominate figure in being the basis for sizing the scantlings. This value is normally associated with a significant wave height and it is from this that the operation limit of the craft is derived and recorded in the Class certification.

Some Classification Societies provide for the certification to allow the craft to proceed to sea in higher significant wave heights, but with a reduced operating speed, thus maintaining the acceleration levels to the same value as operating at full speed in waves of a lower significant wave height.

Other Classification Societies do not provide for a similar envelope and merely confirm that the vessel is not allowed to operate above the significant wave height associated with the crafts full operating speed. Naturally this is a greater restriction on the operator.

What is worth noting is that Classification Societies reserve the right to have an accelerometer fitted at the LCG, but this option is not regularly applied.

DNV in their rules also apply a service area restriction, based on the Load Lines rules zones, areas and seasonal periods, and restricting the craft's maximum distance from a harbour or safe anchorage. This service area restriction is reflected in the scantlings of the craft. This service restriction based on distance seems in contradiction to the HSC Code where the Code allows for the craft to be no more than four hours from a place of refuge, which based on a 40 knot vessel, which is a common speed, allows the craft to be 160 nautical miles from refuge. A common DNV classification for car carrying HSC is R1 where the distance from a safe refuge in summer would be 300 nautical miles.

Recently we have seen operational limitations come from an unexpected quarter. The proposed amendments (now agreed) to IMO resolution A 689 (17) described in LSR 26/20 provided for Marine Escape Systems (MES) to undergo a performance test, whereby it requires a full deployment of the system in a wind of Beaufort Force 6 and in association with a 3 metre significant wave height and shown to be operable both in windward and lee conditions. This is not an operational restriction upon the craft, solely a performance test of the MES.

However, what has transpired is that craft with MES that are unable to comply with these heavy weather requirements, have had a significant wave height restriction imposed upon them by Port States. This has been an arbitrary figure. In some cases these restrictions have been as low as 2.0 metres significant wave height, this means the craft has been operating at 57% of its true, and proven capability. In this particular case the sister vessels operating into other Port States operated without this particular restriction.

We believe due to a lack of (or limited) experience in the operation of High Speed Craft some Port States have been unable to allow Permits to Operate to be issued which allow the operator to make full use of the significant wave height capabilities as envisaged by the Classification society structural approval. This rather arbitrary capping of the significant wave height capability has caused some distress to owners and detracted from their significant investment.

5. PROBLEMS AND SOLUTIONS - IN DAILY PRACTICE

As stated above in 3., a significant number of problems relating to the HSC Code stem from it's retrospective implementation to existing craft and variations in interpretation by different Survey Authorities.

The availability of significant wave height information is very fragmented and may not be readily available on a demand basis to the base port/craft. Therefore decisions about significant wave height and the ability of the craft to sail or continue on route are made by the master in conjunction with the forecast information provided by a meteorological service for the period of the vessel's journey.

This situation becomes significantly more difficult in longer sector voyages i.e those of more than two hours duration. The situation is further complicated when the vessel has a significant course change round a headland or when conditions at the port restrict or impede the ability of the craft to manoeuvre and berth.

It seems in-appropriate to expect the master to evaluate the significant wave height, from a fast moving craft, to an accuracy of 0.1 metre, which is the level of accuracy required to establish whether the craft remains within its operational envelope or not, (see table 3). Those involved in the regulating, specifying and building of these craft should recognise the need to assist the master and navigator in making these judgements.

Having recognised the need to assist, it soon becomes obvious that significant wave height is not the parameter that should be measured. Heading of the craft, wave period, displacement, speed, trim are all parameters which are effecting the overall response of the vessel to the sea. What needs to be measured is the response of the vessel and the most simple way to do that is by means of the vertical acceleration at the LCG. This will not be the ultimate answer but with a graphical trend display of the acceleration level, the master will have discreet information about the current situation and its trend. Based on this information he can make decisions on course, speed or even to return to port.

With craft fitted with this type of display, Port States may be inclined to relax their arbitrary significant wave height restrictions, in the knowledge that the master is provided with an instrument to assist him in making a series of complex decisions, in the protection of the passengers and craft.

To ensure that the display of any acceleration trends are valid for the craft the location of accelerometers used for gathering this data needs to be considered. Structural scantlings are derived from accelerations at the LCG. Whilst this may be appropriate for structural design the governance of passenger comfort levels from the same location is not so clear.

In general the LCG of a monohull is approximately two thirds aft whilst for catamarans and multihulls the LCG tends to be further forward. Obviously this is dependant upon hull forms and locations of machinery and other large masses. Accelerations at the forward end of passenger accommodations, which on most HSC tend to be a reasonable distance forward of the LCG, will be higher than those experienced at the LCG. In a bow quartering wave heading for catamarans the forward outboard seating locations will experience the worst accelerations onboard the craft.

Historically most attention and discussion has been given to the vertical components of motion however, the horizontal components also have a contributing effect. In Annex 8 of the HSC Code[1] definition of operating levels requires assessment of the maximum horizontal accelerations for reference to Annex 3 to establish the safety level for the craft.

The level of horizontal accelerations is important but so too are the directions they act in. The longitudinal component is most extreme in a collision, and on this point we refer to Ch.4.4, Accommodation Design, and the calculations contained within. The range of answers which these calculations provide is most onerous for smaller craft. The assumptions on which these calculations are made need to be re-assessed to ensure that the range of calculated accelerations is appropriate.

The roll characteristics or transverse accelerations vary greatly for the different types of HSC and it is appropriate that attention is given to it. Many passengers are disconcerted when they first travel on a wavepiercing catamaran, for example, as these craft tend to have faster roll periods coupled with a tendency to yaw in a bow quarter direction, hence the higher accelerations in the forward outboard passenger locations, when compared with conventional RoRo ferries.

The motion characteristics vary for each type of craft therefore it is important to consider the location of motion sensors used for assessing passenger comfort to ensure that the position of maximum discomfort is assessed, rather than the best.

To render meteorological forecasts into a useable format in an environment of acceleration governed operating restrictions, analysis of craft motions could be performed. This analysis would indicate the anticipated acceleration levels to be experienced on the route for a range of conditions. These analyses would be performed and submitted to Flag and Port State authorities to enable the Safety Certificate and Permit to Operate to be issued.

Once the craft entered service recordings would be made during operation allowing the analysis to be compared with real time acceleration levels. In this way Flag and Port State authorities would be able to specify the Operating Restrictions with a more appropriate benchmark.

In a similar manner the structural responses of the craft could be monitored by the Classification Society.

6. OPERATIONAL DILEMMAS

Contained within the Operating Manual of each craft are the Operating Restrictions with which approval by the Classification Society is given. As noted above some Societies issue Operating Restrictions in the form of a graph or table, see Table 3, of wave height against speed, As the sea state increases the operating speed decreases. Whilst others give a cutoff point and leave it to the operators discretion as to the speed of the vessel in the seaway, up to that limit.

In the first case the result is that in borderline operating conditions the speed reductions increase the time spent at sea, which could exceed the time restriction placed upon a Category A craft, and because the time is increased the incidence of motion sickness amongst passengers will increase.

For example a 40m craft operating a forty nautical mile route, comprising sheltered and exposed conditions, at forty knots could have its time at sea more than doubled as the wave height increases towards its operating limit if its Class imposes graduated operating restrictions up to its limiting wave height.

For passengers the net effect would be a greater exposure to the risk of an increased incidence of motion sickness with 2% to 5% categories being reached, based purely on time criteria, with the greater incidence bands being rapidly approached.

The criteria or sea state limitation is based upon a significant wave height and it is clear that the period of the wave spectrum has an importance in the excitation of craft motions. For certain types of HSC very short sea states can be handled effectively whilst for most craft a wave length of 1.25 times the craft length will prove the most onerous with the accelerations reducing, as the wavelength increases.

Variations in sea conditions on the route, from changes in direction of prevailing weather patterns to confused seas at the mouths of rivers due to changes in seasonal river flows or tidal changes, all are aspects which can limit the effectiveness of significant wave height criteria as being the governing factor for the limitation to operation of the craft.

Further, significant wave height is a statistical statement of recorded wave height over an extended period of time. As we have discussed above, the crew are presented with a considerable difficulty in assessing sea states from fast moving craft and this difficulty is compounded with increased elevation of control positions as the craft gain in size.

The levels of motion or accelerations of craft varies with the relative attributes of the hull form and how the particular craft contours the sea surface. As a consequence it is the course and the craft's heading to the predominant wave direction that govern the accelerations, which will be exacerbated in a confused seaway. It is therefore apparent that it is important for the craft to be steered for the conditions to reduce motions and minimise passenger discomfort. The experienced crew will not suffer at the same level or manner as the general public and the reliance upon the autopilot to steer the vessel, does not assist and in some cases hinders.

The results of excessive craft motion and the consequential motion sickness cannot be under estimated. The effects on the business of the operator can be manifold, immediate with the passengers who have experienced the uncomfortable journey who are unlikely to be repeat customers, and delayed as the news of the experience is shared with other members of the public.

These same problems will be experienced by an operator of HSC cargo craft as excessive motions will lead to cargo damage thence insurance claims and the loss of the customer's good will and custom.

7.   CONCLUSION

The retrospective application of the Code needs to be clarified and addressed because it is obvious that some of the older craft can not comply with the most recent requirements.

At present there are a host of conflicting and inconsistent requirements placed upon high speed craft presently under construction. This requires a closer unification of the HSC Code and a range of the Classification Societies' requirements.

There is a need for a better method of evaluating the ability of the craft to operate in a range of weather conditions. This could be readily achieved by using the monitored accelerations of the craft, which would be presented in real time and time history or trend displays for the crew. This would allow for both structural and passenger comfort criteria to be taken into consideration without the arbitrary imposition of wave height limitation.

Further advantages of this method of describing the Operating limits of a craft is that it encourages good design and safe operation. It should also provide more assurance for the Flag and Port State Authorities.

In essence it should provide assurance to all parties who have a vested interest in the safe functioning of these craft.

Our personal view is, that at the time of writing this paper in November 1996, that some practical ways forward for dealing with the present challenges are within the reach of industry.

REFERENCES

1.   International Code of Safety for High-Speed Craft (HSC Code) Resolution MSC.36(63).

2.   IMO, Code of Safety for Dynamically Supported Craft, Resolution A.373(X).

3.   Lloyd's Register of Shipping, Rules and Regulations for the Construction and Classification of Steel Ships, 1996; pp 165-166, para. 3534 to 3541.

4.   Det Norske Veritas - Rules for the High Speed and Light Craft, January 1993.

5.   Resistro Italiano Navale: Rules for the Classification and Construction of High Speed Craft, January 1995.

6.   Lloyd's Register: Special Service Craft Rules.

TABLE 1 Criteria for Compliance to the Chapters of the HSC Code

Ref.	Description	Time	Dist	Wave	Acc.	V	Other
1.2	General Req.		X				
1.3	Application	X					
1.4	Definitions			X		X	X
1.5	Surveys	X					
1.8	Certification	X		X			
Ch.2	Stability						X
Ch.3	Structures	X			X		
Ch.4	Accommodation & Escape	X			X		X
Ch.5	Direct. Control	X					X
Ch.6	Anchoring etc						X
Ch.7	Fire Safety	X					X
Ch.8	LSA	X					X
Ch.9	Machinery	X					X
Ch.10	Aux. Machinery	X					X
Ch.11	Cont/Alarm/Safe						X
Ch.12	Electrical	X					X
Ch.13	Nav. Equip.		X			X	X
Ch.14	Radio	X					X
Ch.15	Op. Comp. Layout						X
Ch.16	Stab. Sys.						
Ch.17	Handling, Control & Performance						
Ch.18	Op. Requirements						
Ch.19	Inspection & Maintenance						

TABLE 2 - Criteria for Compliance to the Annexes of the HSC Code

Ref.	Description	Time	Dist	Wave	Acc.	V	Other
Anx. 1	Safety Cert.		X				X
Anx. 2	Permit to Op.		X				X
Anx. 3	Probability	X					
Anx. 4	FMEA	X					
Anx. 5	Ice Accretion						X
Anx. 6	Hydrofoil Intact Stability						X
Anx. 7	Multihull Stab.						X
Anx. 8	Compliance Criteria.				X	X	
Anx. 9	Testing of Seats	X			X		
Anx. 10	Liferafts						X

TABLE 3 Class Operating Restriction, a typical range for a large car carrying craft

Sign. Wave Height (m)	Maximum Speed (knots)
0.0-1.5	40
1.5-2.5	35
2.5-4.0	30
4.0-5.0	25
above 5.0	seek shelter at slow speed

PAPER NO.5.

CATAMARANS: THE SAFEST WAY TO TRAVEL BY SEA?

by N A Armstrong, Australian Shipbuilders Association, Australia

Paper presented at the

International Symposium & Seminar

THE SAFETY OF HIGH SPEED CRAFT

6 - 7 FEBRUARY 1997 LONDON

CATAMARANS: THE SAFEST WAY TO TRAVEL BY SEA?

N A Armstrong, BSc, CEng, MRINA
Australian Shipbuilders Association

SUMMARY

This paper will consider the history of large aluminium catamarans, with respect to their safety.

Problems with the application of the IMO High Speed Craft Code are suggested; and a dissertation of some recent accidents to Australian built catamarans is also included.

It is argued that catamarans of this type are inherently safer than the equivalent monohulls or conventional vessels, and are now being legislated against to such an extent that they have to meet a greater equivalent level of safety than conventional vessels.

AUTHOR'S BIOGRAPHY

Mr Tony Armstrong is currently involved in full-time research at the University of New South Wales on the subject of 'The form factor of high-speed craft', leading to a PhD. He is involved with the Australian Maritime Engineering Co-operative Research Centre as a Program Manager, and has a part-time position as Co-ordinator of the Technical Committee of the Australian Shipbuilders Association. He was the Director of Design at International Catamaran Designs Pty. Ltd. during 1989-1995 when the first large high-speed vessels were designed and built. Some time prior to this he was a Surveyor of Ships with the Hong Kong Government.

1. INTRODUCTION

The idea that catamarans could be involved in the international transport of passengers and vehicles was unthinkable a mere nine years ago. High-speed craft were limited to a few hydrofoils and hovercraft, which (with one notable exception) were small craft carrying up to two hundred passengers on short journeys. The one exception was the SRN4 hovercraft of Hoverspeed, and it is noteworthy that two of these craft are still in regular operation some twenty six years after first starting the English Channel run, and remain the fastest craft.

The "Owner" of the SRN4 at that time was Sir James Sherwood of Sea Containers, and it was largely his vision that led to the development of the large high-speed catamaran to those that we have today. The SRN4 was expensive to operate and limited in its capability; on the other hand the small 30 metre catamarans that Sea Containers were operating to the Isle of Wight were simple and inexpensive to operate. It was fortune that led to Sir James Sherwood coming together with Robert Clifford and Phil Hercus, because Robert Clifford was convinced that his company, Incat Tasmania, could build anything in aluminium as long as it was a catamaran, and Phil Hercus believed that he could design anything in aluminium, as long as it was a catamaran.

The technical issues involved in the design of the first high-speed car-carrying aluminium catamaran passenger ferry were quite large but not insolvable. However each time the problems were progressively solved, so it was decided to increase the capability of the craft, and so the size of the craft increased from an initial 61 metre length, to 66 metres, to 71 metres, and finally to the 74 metre length of the first craft. This progression inevitably delayed the completion of the first craft, and there were many occasions where the design had to be altered because the shipyard had already built a particular piece of structure based on a previous plan.

From a design viewpoint there were two major issues to be resolved:

- Structural Design;

- Safety of Passengers and Crew.

Neither of these issues were adequately addressed in Legislation, Rules or Regulations current at that time. The principal structural design rules in use at the time were the High Speed Light Craft Rules of Det Norske Veritas (DnV), and many vessels had been successfully completed to these rules. However they were limited to vessels having a length of up to 50 metres, and the proposed craft was to be some 50% longer than this limit. How the structure was designed and subsequently refined over a series of vessels is a fascinating story that is outside the scope of this paper, but it should be told one day.

The safety issues were to prove to be as difficult to resolve as the structural issues. To understand this, it is necessary to go back a decade.

By the mid-1970's, a number of small high-speed craft had proved that they were a viable method of transporting passengers over short distances. The safety certification in common use at that time for such craft was issued under SOLAS, and utilized the clause that permitted "ships of a novel nature" to be allowed exemptions. IMO quickly recognized that this was unsatisfactory and could lead to a wide variety of safety standards on such craft. Consequently IMO produced the Code of Safety for Dynamically Supported Craft (The DSC Code), adopted in

1977, and so-called because all high-speed craft at that time relied on some mechanism to (partly) support their weight and hence achieve high speed. These were typically hydrofoils or hovercraft.

The preamble to the DSC Code makes for very interesting reading. It stresses that the Code has been prepared in order that Research and Development may be facilitated and accepted internationally, and makes the point strongly that the traditional methods of regulating passenger ships for safety are not be accepted as being the only methods of achieving an appropriate level of safety. It then introduces the concept of an "equivalent level of safety" to that embodied in SOLAS.

It can also be noted in the Preamble to the Code that the largest vessels conceived at that time had a capacity of 300 passengers, and that a limit of 450 passengers was therefore included in the Code to allow an arbitrary 50% increase above current technology.

The designers of the first large catamaran in 1988/89 consequently decided to stay within the maximum limit of the DSC Code of 450 passengers, and to have the finished craft certified as a SOLAS vessel, with exemptions granted under the DSC Code. One major difficulty that arose during the design and build period was that it was not known where the vessel was to be registered, nor where it was to trade, and therefore it was not possible to discuss safety issues with any particular Administration. This was particularly important because the DSC Code is a very brief document, and leaves much "to the satisfaction of the Administration".

Sea Containers appeared to be happy with the idea that the vessel would be completed to a standard of safety as interpreted by the shipyard, and then re-examined as necessary once the Flag was agreed. The first vessel was finally registered in the Bahamas, successfully certified, and delivered for operation between the UK and France. There were immediate problems. The Bahamian, UK and French authorities all had their different interpretations of the DSC Code, and the UK and French Administration wanted to impose their own regulations on the craft not included in the DSC Code. It took a considerable amount of additional work and modification for the vessel to be allowed to operate.

The first craft, Hoverspeed Great Britain, was thrust into the public's attention in 1990 by successfully winning the Blue Riband of the Atlantic, the Hales Trophy, for the fastest crossing of the Atlantic by a passenger vessel.

She was followed by four sister ships, all having a similar outward appearance, but underneath all the lessons being learnt from the previous craft were being applied, particularly in the area of structural design and in the application of the safety philosophy.

By 1991, it was evident that these types of craft were viable, and that their numbers would dramatically increase with time. Again IMO showed remarkable initiative by starting a review process of the DSC Code so that the new generation of craft could be more easily certified, and

the result was the International Code of Safety for High-Speed Craft (The HSC Code) which came into effect on 1 January 1996.

The HSC Code is a more substantial document than the old DSC Code (216 pages compared to 80 pages), and it attempts to detail many of the safety requirements that had previously been left up to "the satisfaction of the Administration". It also differs from the DSC Code in one very important matter. It provides its own mechanism for certification, and it is no longer necessary to certify the craft under SOLAS, with exemptions granted using the Code. SOLAS has been modified, to include a new chapter which acknowledges that High-Speed Craft have their own certification requirements under the HSC Code.

2.   SOME PROBLEMS ASSOCIATED WITH THE APPLICATION OF THE HSC CODE

There are two major shipyards in Australia currently building large aluminium car-carrying passenger ferries, and about five shipyards building passenger-only ferries at any given time. In addition there are a number of specialized designers and associated industries.

Almost all of the problems that are experienced by Australian shipyards relate to the one problem of interpretation of the HSC Code, or the interpretation of other IMO regulations.

Recognizing this fact, IMO has started the process of a review of the HSC Code.

These problems of interpretation are greatly compounded by three factors:

2.1   Many vessels are built for operation within the national boundaries and are not certified for international voyages under the HSC Code. Invariably the national authority does not have specific rules for such high-speed craft, and therefore uses the national certification process and uses the HSC Code for guidance. In doing so, this usually ignores that the HSC Code is a document that has to be used in its entirety, and it is not possible to take one chapter out of context with another.

For example, the Code requires that as part of the safety philosophy... "The management of the company operating the craft exercises strict control over its operation and maintenance by a quality management system". This is frequently ignored by National Certification.

2.2   There are several vested interests. There are many Operators and Owners of conventional vessels who do not like the competition that high-speed craft represent. Worst of all is the type of nationalism that has been experienced where the Administration of one country has made ridiculous demands on the safety aspects of a vessel to be operated within that country, but built in Australia, apparently in order to hinder progress on the craft whilst another vessel is built within the country. That later vessel is then granted exemptions that the foreign-built vessel could not get.

In this same category it is possible to list many surveyors who pine for the traditional methods of SOLAS and the known interpretations of the rules, rather than to have to put their name on a document or certificate that shows that they have made a decision. It is not suggested that Surveyors take risks, rather it is suggested that they attempt to understand and apply the entire philosophy of the HSC Code instead of just applying a list of what can and cannot be done even if it is out-of-context.

2.3 A lack of knowledge of the existence of the HSC Code within IMO process. The HSC Code is a recent document and there has been insufficient time for it to be absorbed by all parties involved with the process of the writing of rules and regulations.

New-building vessels built to the HSC Code have to comply with many other regulations, and these other regulations have been, and are being, written without consideration of the requirements of high-speed craft, indeed in many cases they are being written in apparent total ignorance of the HSC Code.

A typical example might be MARPOL, which requires that all vessels carry an oily water separator, even though the vessel might be on a voyage of only a few minutes, has an unmanned engine room, and pumps any bilge water to a holding tank before pumping ashore at the end of the day's work. Many high-speed vessels are presently carrying oily water separators which are not used and probably never will be. This regulation was written with only traditional SOLAS vessels in mind.

Another example is those documents that are referenced in the HSC Code but which have been written without consideration for catamarans. The Code for the Testing of Lifesaving Appliances is a typical example, specifying the procedure for the testing of Marine Evacuation Systems as if they were fitted to monohulls, and making no allowance for the behaviour of catamarans.

A further example refers to a new source of Rules and Regulations outside those of IMO, coming from the Regional Agreement of the European Region and set up following the loss of the "Estonia". These requirements have many aspects, but the damage stability requirements have been derived entirely from research on conventional monohulls. Whilst it is not yet clear that these new regulations will be applied to catamarans, it appears that lacking any other information the rules will be so applied, and this is nonsensical, because the damage behaviour of a catamaran is entirely different to that of a monohull.

Finally, one of the most emotive areas involving passenger safety involves that of fire. There is no question that on a conventional ship there is a fire risk that has to be managed, and the current regulations appear to do this adequately. However there is a substantial penalty to pay if the same approach is applied to a high-speed vessel, involving additional weight and the consequent reduction on ship speed. The requirements for the fitting of structural fire protection to aluminium structures has been allowed to get out-of-hand, because

of a lack of knowledge of those demanding such requirements, and the consideration that fast ferries are similar to a high-speed conventional vessel. There are many cases where structural fire protection has had to be fitted to void spaces adjacent to the outside of the ship where there is nothing to protect, not even essential structure for the safety of the vessel, and where there is an almost zero risk of fire. The consequences of such action are an appreciable loss of speed of the vessel, or a reduction in the cargo-carrying deadweight.

High-speed vessels are not conventional vessels having a high speed. They are bound by regulations that disallow sleeping cabins, and do not allow cooking facilities having a heat source. The passenger spaces are always large open spaces and it is incomprehensible to consider any fire originating outside the engine room that is not in the immediate vicinity of a large number of eyes and noses, and can be detected immediately, (unless it is a deliberate act of sabotage). This low risk is borne out by the very low numbers of high-speed passenger craft that have experienced a fire.

3. SOME ACCIDENTS ON AUSTRALIAN-BUILT CATAMARANS

The catamaran high-speed ferry represents an interesting solution to the problems of designing for safety. Some of the advantages of catamarans over monohulls are listed in Reference 1, however the principal advantage is that the catamaran is inherently safe, whereas the monohull can be considered inherently unsafe.

As an example, the freeboard to the main deck on a Ro-Ro monohull is frequently the minimum allowed, say 50 mm. In case of any accidental breach of the hull watertight integrity, then there will be water on the deck, leading to very large stability problems. The catamaran on the other hand has a main deck well above the waterline, having a freeboard of many metres, and any accidental breach of the watertight integrity will only result in a heel or trim of the craft, with little change in the stability characteristics and no water on the main deck.

The catamaran represents a stable platform for the launching of liferafts. When disabled, both monohull and catamaran high-speed craft will most likely lie perpendicular to the waves. The monohull will roll, and this can be out-of-sequence with the incoming waves if there is resonance. Consequently the relative motions of the liferaft and the vessel can be very large. A catamaran on the other hand rolls very little, and in beam seas one hull will tend to go up-and-down as the waves come in, resulting in generally harmonious motion between the liferaft and the hull on one side.

The catamaran has two hulls compared to the single hull of the monohull, and this leads to an inherent redundancy of machinery and systems. If one engine room is disabled through fire or flooding, then it is extremely unlikely that the engine room on the other side will be affected, and propulsion power, electrical power and any mechanical pumps can continue in operation as required.

Furthermore because of the requirements of two widely separated engine rooms it is normal for the pipework and the electrical systems connected to those engine rooms to be widely separated outside of the engine room, again providing a large degree of redundancy.

Some of these features have been illustrated by incidents involving Australian-built ships. The following examples are a personal interpretation of events, and for the official report on these incidents it is necessary to refer to the official Board of Inquiries.

Fire aboard Reef Link II

On the morning of 5 July 1987, a recently commissioned 30 metre passenger catamaran, Reef Link II, left Townsville for a scheduled trip to the outer Barrier Reef. This craft was built to local (State) rules, but the DSC Code had been used for guidance. The operator of the craft was aware that there was a fuel leakage in a cracked fuel return line in the void space forward of the engine room, and was in the habit of using a portable pump to shift the spilt fuel to oil drums on the aft deck. No attempt had been made to repair the leakage because this would require the vessel to be out of service.

The portable transfer pump used to empty the oil had a faulty seal and leaked a considerable amount of fuel into the engine room. At the same time, the fuel filters were being serviced, and the fuel priming pump was left running. The result was a considerable amount of fuel left in the bilge of the engine room as the vessel went into service. As the vessel accelerated and adopted a bow-up attitude, the fuel oil in the bilge flowed to the after end of the engine room where it came into contact with the main engine flywheel and was sprayed outwards. Directly above this spray were the hot main engine turbochargers, which ignited the spray of fuel. This in turn appears to have melted the electrical cabling in the vicinity, and the resultant short circuit appears to have started an electrical fire in the switchboard room in the superstructure aft of the passenger compartment.

To compound the problem, the clutch connecting the fire-fighting pump to the engine on one side had been removed for service and not re-installed, thereby placing reliance on the one remaining pump on the other side.

In any case, the crew appears to have done little to fight the fire. A crew member alerted the Master who went aft to investigate. The engine room smothering system was not manually operated, but the main engines were shut down. This was unfortunate because there was now no power for the remaining fire pump. (Later it was determined that the ship's valves were not set in a position to provide water for fire-fighting, rather they were left in the "bilge-pumping" position).

It appears that little effort if any was made to fight the fire. The engine smothering system did eventually operate automatically and extinguish the engine room fire, but by then the fire in the accommodation was well alight. This set off an automatic radio alarm ashore, which brought the normal ship's engineer (who had been ashore) racing to the scene in a high-speed vessel.

All the passengers were evacuated to the liferafts and to other vessels nearby, and no-one was injured.

It should be made clear that this vessel was built before the current regulations came into effect. Accommodation outfit materials were combustible, and the electrical power supply did not have the necessary devices to shut itself down automatically. What is important is that the crew and operators of that vessel were untrained in the use of the fire-fighting equipment, and furthermore there was very little if any Total Quality Management in place, highlighted by a regime that allowed fuel to remain in the bilge. It can be argued that the cause of this accident lay ashore.

This was a case where only a part of the safety philosophy had been put into place and not the entire requirement. The fact that the vessel was a catamaran helped in that the fire was to one side, and the vessel could be evacuated on the opposite side fairly easily. If an attempt had been made to extinguish the fire, then the fire pump on the port side was still fully active even though the other engine room was out of action.

The grounding of Condor 11

On the 9th October 1994, the latest car-carrying aluminium 78 metre wavepiercer "Condor 11" was undergoing shipyard trials in the Derwent River estuary in Hobart. It had been a long day, and many small things had gone wrong. Night had fallen and everyone was tired. The Master was also the Shipyard Owner, and he is a very experienced navigator who knew the waters extremely well, and has extremely good boat-handling skills.

As with many trials procedures, it was common practice to pass through two known positions for the purposes of timing the passage and thence deduce the vessel speed. At the northern end of the run was a small rocky outcrop known as Black Jack Rock, which had a small beacon on it. It was this beacon that served as a timing mark. (There may also have been some speed advantage in passing close to the mark, as the water was more shallow here.) It was common to pass very close to the mark, possibly as close as five to ten metres, and on this particular night the Master misjudged the distance. Because several people in the wheelhouse were actually looking at the mark for timing purposes, there was time for a brief exclamation before the ship hit the rocks at about 38½ knots.

From examination of the damage afterwards, it is surmised that the vessel struck the rock with one hull first, and this lifted the vessel upwards and slewed it around. The craft would have had a certain degree of dynamic trim by the stern, as well as having a rise of keel, and this keel inclination would have also helped to provide an upwards motion to the vessel. The vessel came down again, and it appears that this is when most damage may have occurred.

The main engines and generators continued to run and were manually closed down. It was very quickly obvious that the boat was stuck on the rocks and was not floating, and therefore the safest procedure was to remain on board. There were a few injuries of a moderate nature (a broken leg, bruises etc) caused by the rapid deceleration. The crew slept onboard overnight until the vessel could be evacuated in daylight. The subsequent salvage of the vessel is another story that can be told elsewhere, with the vessel sustaining possibly as much damage in being removed from the rocks as it did getting on to them. The vessel is now successfully trading in Denmark.

The extent of the damage was large, encompassing the bottom metre of the vessel from the forward perpendicular through to the engine room bulkhead on both sides. (The starboard side engine room plating was pierced in one place with a small hole). In general terms the bottom frames were tripped back and the plating pushed up.

There are many "ifs" to be considered in this experience. If the vessel had been a conventional vessel of steel it would have decelerated at a much greater rate and the injuries could be expected to have been much greater. It is possible that a conventional vessel might not have gone on to the top of the rock in such a spectacular fashion and might have sunk. Certainly the vessel appears to have saved itself by being so lightweight and strong. However if the vessel had not stopped then it might have continued over the rock and floated on the other side. From an analysis of the damage it is unlikely that the vessel would have sunk in this scenario, although there would have been a considerable trim by the bow. It is unlikely that a monohull would have floated with a similar extent of damage.

When the vessel was eventually pulled free of the rock, the air vents were sealed and the vessel towed back to the shipyard on the air pressure in the hulls. This has led to the argument that the air vents should be normally closed so that the vessel can float on the air pressure in the case of such damage, because the air vents are not required to prevent corrosion where the hull is of aluminium. However such arrangements may make it difficult to allow for regular inspections of the hull voids because of foul air.

This incident illustrates how immensely strong these vessels are. The hull structure remained intact, although the bottom metre was somewhat re-arranged. The overall geometry of the vessel was not altered, because there is a large amount of structural redundancy.

It is probable that this was an accident where the vessel (and passengers) were saved because the vessel was constructed from aluminium rather than from steel.

There has been a previous occurrence of a small aluminium passenger catamaran striking a reef at speed, hurdling the reef and continuing on the other side without breaching the watertight integrity of the shell plating.

It would appear to be prudent, from considering this experience, to design large high-speed vessels with a double bottom forward of the engine room. This has been done with the Seajet, designed in Australia and now in operation in Denmark, and also with the new ferries under construction in Canada for BC Ferries, also an Australian design. There is however a size below which it is impractical to fit a double bottom, and there is of course a substantial weight penalty to pay and a loss of speed. It is also unfortunate that this double bottom structure is at a position where it contributes very little, if anything at all, to the global strength of the vessel, being located very close to the neutral axis.

A collision between two high-speed ferries

This incident occurred in the Pearl River estuary when a high-speed catamaran ferry approached from abeam and then passed behind the stern of a large container carrier. Unfortunately another high-speed catamaran ferry was approaching from the other side of the container vessel and it also passed astern. The two high-speed ferries collided in a classic "T-bone" fashion.

One vessel remained embedded in the other and no attempt was made to remove them whilst the passengers were evacuated. When the vessels were separated the vessel with the damaged bow floated close to the normal waterline, and was found to be damaged back to the collision bulkhead. The other vessel was substantially damaged with penetration completely through one hull approximately to the centre of he vessel. Unfortunately on this vessel a few passengers were seated on the side of the collision and were killed. After separation, this vessel floated, although the foredeck was under water and there was a substantial heel and trim.

This example illustrates the immense strength of the narrow hulls of aluminium catamarans. The most frequently asked question about the high-speed of these types of ferries is what happens when they hit a partly-submerged steel container? Ignoring the question as to whether there is in reality such a thing as a partly-submerged container (usually they would either sink or float), then the answer would appear to be that the vessel would rise up above the container, pushing it down, and would slash the container open. The craft hull would sustain superficial damage, but it is considered unlikely that the watertight integrity would be breached.

4. THE AUSTRALIAN SHIPBUILDERS AND THE AUSTRALIAN MARITIME SAFETY AUTHORITY (AMSA)

The Australian Shipbuilders recognize that safety is the prime factor in the design and construction of high-speed vessels. Having built more of these types of craft than any other country, there exists a wealth of experience of the problems that can be encountered, particularly with the wide variation of interpretation of the rules.

The various shipbuilders have also seen a wide variation of interpretation of the regulation by different Administrations. In one particular case, the Flag State of

Vessel A accepted a particular type of cabin lining, which had the required low flame spread characteristics. For another ship of almost identical size and capability, building at a different shipyard, the Flag State for Vessel B would not accept the same material. Both ships were eventually completed and went into service.

Now the interesting thing is that Vessel A (with the unacceptable lining) is in operation between the two countries represented by Flag States A & B, and is carrying the nationals of Flag State B, who deemed the material to be unacceptable. The conclusion is that Flag State B does not really care about the safety of its nationals, rather it just wants to get the paperwork right. The difference in cost between the two vessels to change the cabin linings was about Aus$ 1.3 million, representing some expensive paperwork, and some considerable frustration by the shipyards.

The Australian Maritime Safety Authority (AMSA) is the national body representing Australia at IMO. There are no high-speed craft certified with AMSA (although there have been), and it is unlikely that there will ever be very many certified craft, because of the distance of Australia from other countries. AMSA therefore might be expected to have little interest in these types of craft.

This in fact has not been the case, and AMSA has taken an active role in the production of the HSC Code, and is expected to take a similar role in its review. This acknowledges the importance of the high-speed craft building industry to Australia, and represents an attempt by Government to support the industry as much as possible. AMSA maintain a close liaison with the Shipbuilders so that their problems are understood, and it is anticipated that by this means useful feedback can be provided to IMO with the aim of improving the HSC Code.

5.   RESEARCH INTO REGULATORY PROBLEMS

There is a considerable amount of research being carried out into proposed new regulations, and none of this is known to involve catamarans.

An example of the research that has been carried out is that of the amount of water that may accumulate on the vehicle deck of a RoRo. The Regulations issued by the Regional Agreement on RoRo Ferry Safety require 0.5 metres of water on the vehicle deck in the damaged condition. This figure was arrived at after model testing and numerical studies on a wide variety of monohull shapes in beam seas when damaged.

The catamaran behaves entirely differently in a beam sea to a monohull. It does not roll like a monohull, rather the individual hulls move vertically with the passing waves.

Consequently the research that found that 0.5 metre of water might typically accumulate on the vehicle deck of a monohull has no bearing on the amount of water that might accumulate on the deck of a catamaran, and the application of this regulation to catamarans is not only unnecessarily onerous to catamarans but practically meaningless. It represents the application of a greater level of safety for catamarans, rather than applying an equivalent level of safety.

There needs to be more research carried out on catamarans and their behaviour, rather than apply conventional monohull results, and similarly there needs to be an awareness that high-speed catamarans are increasing in numbers and safety issues cannot be thought of in terms of conventional monohulls terms.

6.   CONCLUSION

Many Australian Shipbuilders and Designers are of the opinion that catamarans are the safest way to travel by sea. Not only do catamarans have inherent safety features such as very high damage stability character-istics, and a large degree of redundancy by the very nature of having two hulls, but they are being asked to meet considerably higher standards than conventional vessels and even other types of high-speed craft.

This situation has been brought about by the IMO process where individual topics (outside the HSC Code) are discussed and new regulations written in different sub-committees, and very few of these sub-committees have any experience of the characteristics or behaviour of catamaran high-speed ferries. Lacking this information, the regulations become more and more restrictive, and end up as imitations of SOLAS philosophies instead of acknowledging that an equivalent level of safety can be achieved by alternative means. The philosophy of the HSC Code needs to be disseminated amongst all those who attend IMO if we want to embrace better and safer methods of travelling by sea.

7.   ACKNOWLEDGMENTS

The opinions expressed are entirely those of the Author, and do not necessarily represent those of the Australian Shipbuilders Association nor its individual members.

8.   REFERENCES

1.   ARMSTRONG, N A: 'Safety Aspects of Catamaran Fast Ferries', Cruise & Ferry Conference, 1991.

PAPER NO.6.

DESIGNING A SPECIAL PURPOSE SWATH TO THE HSC CODE

by N F Warren, FBM Marine Ltd, and
G Rudgely, DGSS, UK

Paper presented at the

International Symposium & Seminar

THE SAFETY OF HIGH SPEED CRAFT

6 - 7 FEBRUARY 1997 LONDON

DESIGNING A SPECIAL PURPOSE SWATH TO THE HSC CODE

N F Warren, FBM Marine Ltd
G Rudgely, DGSS

SUMMARY

Despite having modest particulars (23m long, carrying 75 passengers at 15 knots) the SWATH Passenger Transfer Craft (PTC) now being built for the UK Ministry of Defence poses considerable design challenges in terms of the required safety level. The craft are designed to meet the new IMO Code of Safety with the extra requirement of Category B damage stability.

This paper discusses how this was achieved by a combination of double bottom and foam buoyancy, despite the inherent problems that a SWATH poses in this respect. SWATH designs have a higher freeboard than normal; the paper discusses how evacuation into liferafts is carried out in a novel but simple way. A powerful ballast system creates an extra dimension to the question of trim and heel after damage not normally found in fast ferries.

The reason for adopting the Code (rather than conventional MSA Class IIA requirements) despite the modest speed, is discussed, together with the reasoning for aluminium construction.

The craft must also satisfy MSA interpretation of the IMO Code, culminating in a passenger certificate for operation in the Plymouth area. In addition the MOD requirement was for a Safety Case to be built up for use throughout the life of the craft - again an unusual requirement in the world of commercial fast ferries. Apart from the fact that this is now MOD policy, these craft are required to lay alongside ships at sea and transfer passengers. This naturally creates a particular and unusual safety scenario and the design of a system to achieve safe transfers is discussed.

Aspects of the high speed Code from this design exercise, that could be improved, are also highlighted.

AUTHORS' BIOGRAPHIES

Mr Nigel Warren, BSc, CEng, MRINA, has been Chief Designer at FBM Marine for the last 10 years involved in the design and build of the Company's fast patrol boats and fast ferries. Prior to that he was with Hovermarine, Vosper International and Vosper Thornycroft, involved in the design of sidewall hovercraft, frigates and patrol boats. He started his career as an apprentice at J I Thornycroft having obtained his degree in Naval Architecture at the University of Newcastle-upon-Tyne. His interest has always been with the sea and ships.

Mr Gavin Rudgley, MSc, BEng, is currently with the Minor War Vessels, Auxiliaries and Boats Project within the Ministry of Defence Procurement Executive as the Assistant Constructor dealing with naval architecture matters with the additional role of the Project Safety Officer. He initially joined the Royal Corps of Naval Constructors in 1987 spending a year undertaking basic training with the Royal Navy. Following this training he spent four years at University College London reading Naval Architecture gaining his BEng and MSc. Further training with the Royal Navy followed culminating with a period of sea time on a frigate. His first appointment was with the Director of Naval Architecture in Bath with the cell responsible for naval architecture policy, environmental effects and procurement project support.

1. INTRODUCTION

Two small SWATH passenger craft are currently being built for the UK Ministry of Defence, with delivery late in 1997. The craft are being built to the IMO HSC Code, and MSA requirements which pose considerable design challenges because the craft is small, weight sensitive and a SWATH.

In addition to this a unique hydraulic passenger transfer brow system was required to allow transfer to take place at sea alongside small and large ships. A Safety Case study was also required.

2. VESSEL REQUIREMENTS

2.1 GENERAL REQUIREMENT

Flag Officer Staff Training (FOST) heads the training organisation of the Royal Navy (RN) that is responsible for sea training and the assessment of operational readiness of RN ships, Royal Fleet Auxiliary (RFA) ships and ships of other customer navies to enable ships to carry out their varied duties to full effect.

All operational ships will periodically be programmed for training with FOST to improve and undertake exercises to test their operational readiness. During these exercises, FOST training staff will embark to run specific tests and assess the subsequent performance. The major weekly exercise for these periods is known as the 'Thursday War'. For this exercise, all ships training with FOST take part and FOST training staff will be embarked in all ships at the start of the day and disembarked on completion of the exercise.

The requirement for new Passenger Transfer Craft (PTC) which are the subject of this paper originated in the decision made by the Ministry of Defence to close the Naval Base at Portland and to transfer the 'Thursday War' exercise to Plymouth. The transfer of FOST training staff to and from vessels taking part in the 'Thursday War' at Portland occurred within a large sheltered harbour with a short transit from the dockside. The distance from the dockside of the Naval Base at Plymouth though is some 5 to 7 miles from the area where passenger transfers occur. The passage will be mostly within the speed controlled area where the speed limit is 10knots and may be with or against the tide.

Other than the specific requirement to transfer passengers from ship to ship at sea (see following section), there are a number of other prime requirements raised by the FOST Staff that have affected the procurement:

- As stated above, the transit of the PTC to the Staddon Breakwater from Devonport Naval Base and returning with the FOST training staff is a journey of approximately half an hour. A high value is placed on the requirement that such extended transfers are undertaken comfortably to allow rest and relaxation when required. To this end, comfortable seating and limited cafe facilities are required.

- There is scope for FOST training staff to make use of the passage time with briefings for the forthcoming serials and debriefings on return. Time spent on passage writing sea training reports would release valuable office time for other administrative tasks. The design of the vessel addressed this requirement.

2.2 PERSONNEL TRANSFER REQUIREMENT

The locations around Plymouth where underway transfers take place are inside and outside the Staddon Breakwater. These areas will be subject to higher sea states than the equivalent location at Portland, although it is only intended to transit beyond the breakwater before undertaking transfer of personnel if favourable weather conditions prevail. Hence, because of the open sea conditions of operation, the Small Waterplane Area Twin Hull (SWATH) hullform was selected to give a stable platform during the transfer operation and good directional control when coming alongside the receiving vessel. The selection of the SWATH hull form followed a pre-qualification consultation period with industry during which monohull, catamaran and SWATH hullforms were compared.

The most frequent transfers will be to vessels small enough to safely navigate unescorted around the Plymouth breakwater. The receiving vessels will pass the breakwater by the eastern channel, turn on to a westerly course to conduct the transfer, which will predominantly be heading into the prevailing weather. The receiving vessels will then depart by the western entrance. This provides a one-way system in the Sound for operations involving the transfer of FOST personnel and is termed the "race track" (see Figure 1). This system of operation therefore defines the time available for transfer by the speed of the vessels and the length of the westward leg, and this results in a maximum allowable transfer time of 4 minutes.

The passenger transfer craft will converge on the receiving vessel and obtain a consistent alignment at the transfer point with the minimum number of holding lines. Transfers will take place with the receiving vessel and transfer craft maintaining a forward speed of up to 4 knots. The minimum speed of the transfer will be set by the commander of the receiving vessel as a result of the prevailing environmental and navigational conditions. Transfers will also be required to vessels at anchor.

For larger vessels, the use of an automatic transfer brow will not be possible due to the difference in freeboard. In such cases, a pilot ladder will be used for transfer.

Following on from these top level requirements, the Minor Warships, Auxiliaries and Boats Project derived a number of restrictions and technical requirements for the passenger transfer arrangements that had implications on the nature of the design and the inherent safety therein.

Firstly, it was identified that given the requirement for a rapid transfer, up to 30 personnel within 4 minutes, the only solution is to incorporate on the PTC, a semi-automatic passenger transfer brow, that would serve to bridge the gap between the PTC and the receiving vessel. The safety of such a system is naturally subject to close scrutiny during the design and build.

The resulting technical requirements relating to passenger transfer are discussed in turn:

- The semi-automatic brow should work in up to and including Sea State 3 wave conditions.

- The vast majority of staff who will undertake transfers at sea will be Naval personnel who are experienced, trained, briefed in transfer routines and physically fit.

- Arrangements are to be made to enable transfers to be made either to port or to starboard of the PTC, both options being available but only one used for any one transfer.

- The transfer departure point on the PTC is to be as near horizontal as possible to the transfer receiving point on the warships and auxiliaries to facilitate the use and design of the mechanical brow.

- When differential freeboard or motions of the vessels preclude the use of a mechanical brow, use will be made of a pilot ladder noting that the transfer arrangement is to be designed to maximise safety whilst minimising time of transfer.

- Experience has shown that only one transfer vessel can be alongside a warship or RFA at a time. Transfer also needs to be conducted with, typically, 4 knots of headway to provide necessary ship control against wind and tide.

- The receiving vessel may present hazards experienced during the transfer operation due to the nature of their design. These hazards may be of two types. Firstly, above water hazards such as significant flare and hazards more local to the transfer position on the receiving vessel. Typical local hazards would include such items as guard rails, sponsons, bollards, flight deck nets and so on, thus the requirement is such that the brow must not land on the deck of the receiving vessel. The transfer point on a typical receiving vessels is shown in Figure 2. Secondly, in addition to above water hazards, there are also underwater hazards to transfer vessels from receiving vessels (eg bilge keels).

- Critical to the safety of the transfer operation will be the minimisation of motions in the transfer craft and prompt and accurate response in terms of manoeuvring. This would include good directional control, rapid turning rate assisted by a twin propulsion line arrangement, rapid response to propulsion power demands and low sensitivity to wind.

- The PTC must have a clear and uncluttered deck area around the transfer point on the transfer craft. The layout is to ease the safe and orderly assembly and positioning of transferring personnel.

- The PTC bridge operational positions are to have a clear view of the transfer area, the aft quarters of the vessel and the deck edge on port and starboard sides.

The overall design and construction of the vessels must allow the operational requirements to be met in a safe and easily operated manner. Particular attention is to be paid to both the safety of personnel and the craft during embarkation of personnel, passage, manoeuvring close to another vessel and within confined waters, and transfer of personnel. The most onerous task will be the transfer of personnel at sea, the transfer system being designed to maximise safety whilst minimising time to transfer.

3. THE MINISTRY SAFETY REQUIREMENT

In the past, the Ministry of Defence has been exempted from legislation under Crown Immunity. Although exemptions have been granted, it is the policy of the Ministry of Defence that Health and Safety standards are at least as good as those required by statute and this is ensured by self regulation.

This policy, although extant, is changing emphasis. Procurement projects within the Ministry of Defence are increasingly encouraged to abide by the requirements of statute. In parallel to this, another change in policy is that associated with the provision of a Safety Case for all vessels. It is the combination or these two approaches that ensures that safety is dealt with in an adequate manner. These two aspects are discussed in the following paragraphs.

3.1 SELECTION OF STANDARDS

There are two key aspects of standards that principally affect the design and build of the PTC, these being certification to MSA and Classification Society approval. These are discussed in turn.

Prior to pre-qualification, the Ministry based the requirement for commercial standards on those perceived to be applicable to the predecessors of the PTC. This would have resulted in Department of Transport Class IIA or Class VII notation depending on the required operational area. Early design studies demonstrated that this selection potentially would lead to a displacement of the PTC of nearly 200 tonnes. A vessel of this size presents a possibility of the receiving vessel becoming structurally damaged should the speed of approach be too great. This is highlighted by the comparison of this displacement to the displacement of a Hunt Class Minehunter which is just under 700 tonnes.

During the pre-qualification phase, discussions also took place with the MSA on choosing appropriate certification. The choice, having ruled out traditional MSA Class IIA certification, fell between the MSA Code for Small Passenger Vessels used mostly for commercial pleasure or 'entertainment' craft and the HSC Code. The new code for Small Passenger Vessels has recently raised the level of safety of such vessels in the UK. Liferafts are now in evidence as a requirement for these craft while subdivision or buoyancy standards, and fire protection standards are also incorporated. However, there is no denying that the HSC Code represents a greater level of safety.

The decision to take the HSC Code route to certification raised a further problem in qualification of the vessel for the code itself. The HSC Code requires that a vessel's 'maximum design speed' is high enough in accordance with a prescribed formulae related to displacement to enable the vessel to be considered for certification to the HSC Code. The Ministry did not want, firstly, the penalty of excessively powerful and expensive machinery just to meet the letter of the code, and secondly, any exemptions at such an early stage. This has lead the shipbuilder to select aluminium as the hull material to reduce displacement.

The second aspect of standards that affect the design and build is the choice of Classification Society approval. At the same time that the Class IIA certification was considered, the preferred option for Classification Society approval was to Lloyd's Register with +100A1 LMC/CCS notation. This would have forced the selection of steel for the hull material, which was clearly not compatible with the requirement to reduce displacement to enable certification of the vessel to the HSC Code.

Having now eliminated traditional classification, it was then discovered that the preferred option, the Lloyd's Register Special Service Craft (SSC) Rules, would not be available for use at award of contract. Following negotiation with LR, a set of notation was chosen for the craft based on the Provisional Rules for the Classification of High Speed

Catamarans that enabled the draft SSC Rules, and now the extant rules, to be applied. This then enabled the selection of aluminium as the main hull material.

It can be concluded that the final combination selected, the HSC Code and the SSC Rules, is the most appropriate for this vessel.

3.2 THE SAFETY CASE

Prior to outlining the specific requirements of the Safety Case for the FOST PTC, it is appropriate to discuss the background leading up to the current safety policy within the Ministry of Defence.

The concept of a Safety Case relating to a specific product has come about not as a sudden revelation, but rather as a gradual emergence from past safety practices. At this time, Safety Cases are produced by the offshore oil industry for all platforms in UK sector of North Sea, and these are submitted to the Health and Safety Executive (HSE). Also, the Marine Safety Agency are currently developing a requirement for ships to provide a Formal Safety Assessment for certification. As stated above, the Ministry of Defence is responsible for self-regulation of its affairs in respect of the design, material state and operation of ships although it is implicit that the Ministry should operate a system which is no less effective than the civil system. The system that the Ministry has chosen to follow with regard to the application of Safety Cases is based on lessons learnt from industry.

To control and monitor the development of Safety Cases within the Ministry of Defence, a management structure with stated levels of delegation and terms of reference has been implemented. Overall, the Secretary of State for Defence holds responsibility for the safety of all vessels and associated equipment owned or operated by the MoD. This authority is then exercised through the Ship Safety Board (SSB) under the chairmanship of the Controller of the Navy. Below the SSB, the Project Managers through the senior line management are responsible for the management of safety within their project which requires the development of a Safety Case. The Project Managers are supported by the Ship Safety Management Office (SSMO) for safety policy and management and by specialist sections who provide technical advice. The subsequent delegation is shown in Figure 3.

It is important to point out that there are a number of definitions for the term 'Safety Case', even internally within the Ministry of Defence. No definition is incorrect and neither is there one correct definition. Safety Cases for vessels being supplied and operated by the Ministry of Defence vary in approach and level of detail. In recognition of this, the Safety Case that has been developed by the shipyard for the FOST PTC follows the particular requirements of the Minor War Vessels, Auxiliaries and Boats Project.

The Safety Case for the FOST PTC is defined as the collection of all documents relating to safety and this includes:

- Description of the Safety Management System - includes both that relating to the shipyard as the Contractor and that relating to the Ministry of Defence Project.

- Safety Analysis documents; Hazard Log, Action grid, meeting minutes.

- Certification.

- Design Description.

- Tests/inspection Reports.

- Emergency plans.

- Audits.

- Feedback.

- Other miscellaneous supporting documentation as required such as Failure Mode and Effects Analysis (FMEA) and Stability Information Booklet (SIB).

The 'Safety Analysis' is the cornerstone of the Safety Case. The aim of the analysis is to ensure that all significant hazards are identified and that the level of subsequent risk is 'As Low As Reasonably Practicable'. This principle, known as ALARP is included graphically as Figure 4. The Safety Analysis is the methodical examination of the design of the vessel consists of a number of stages:

Scope of work

- Identification by team brainstorming to identify all the potentially hazardous systems, zones or procedures associated with the vessel design and operation that require a HAZard and OPerability (HAZOP) Study to be carried out.

HAZOP Studies

- A HAZOP Study is carried out on all all systems, zones and operating procedures, identified in the scope of work, to identify and classify the hazards. This essentially is split into two activities; firstly, Hazard Identification, using a list of keywords to identify hazards, and secondly, Risk Assessment, qualitative classification by frequency and severity of all hazards identified. This second step determines whether the level of risk is sufficiently low to avoid any design changes, whether it is intolerable or whether it is within the ALARP region. See Figure 4.

Hazard Control

- Should the risk classification require, design or operating procedures must be changed to lower the level of risk in accordance with the ALARP principle.

Emergency Arrangements

- It will not be possible to remove all major hazards from the design. To this end, an emergency plan must be developed. For example, escape in the event of fire or flood.

4. CRAFT DESCRIPTION

In order to meet the vessel requirements a design was prepared as shown in the General Arrangement drawing, Fig. 5, and artist's impression, Fig. 6, and having the following particulars:

Overall length is 24m; breadth 11.1m; draft 2.25m. Displacement at this draft, which is the normal seagoing draft, is 97 tonnes. Construction is all welded aluminium alloy except for the nose cones of the lower hulls (of GRP - discussed later) and the fairing structure forward of the wheelhouse which is non-structural aluminium and made with adhesive joints. Twin fixed-pitch propellers are turned by twin Caterpillar 3408 diesels of 448kW each via a ZF reverse reduction gearbox. The inclined arrangement of shafting can be seen on the GA drawing. Shafting is entirely conventional without using articulated shafts; the gearbox is rigidly mounted, the engine flexibly. The engines are housed in the haunch area slightly offset inboard with a corresponding bulge on the inboard side of the haunch. Twin 34kW AC diesel generators are fitted, one in each engine room.

The design speed of 15.3 knots, at full power, meets the IMO High Speed Code requirements of $3.7 \nabla^{0.1667}$ m/sec. It may be appreciated that the power required for the majority of the vessel's journey (in the 10 knot speed limit) is a small fraction of the full power. Nevertheless the power and speed margin will be appreciated beyond the Plymouth breakwater and during occasional transits to another port, but most particularly when manoeuvring alongside.

No active motion control fins are fitted because at the crucial low speeds they would be ineffective. Instead, fixed fins were incorporated after conducting tests on a 1:10 scale model fitted with various fixed damping devices. The tests were carried out stopped, measuring damping rates and as a result large horizontal fixed fins are fitted aft (pointing inboard from the two tubular hulls) plus a full length bilge keel again on the inboard sides of the hulls. It would have been more effective to fit the bilge keels outboard but these would be a menace when coming alongside a ship at sea.

This is a small SWATH and to give an idea of the internal access space the struts are about 1m wide at the waterline and the raft (platform) is 900mm deep. The former is a compromise to achieve the required IMO stability standard and yet is minimised to achieve heave, roll and pitch periods which are as long as possible. The raft depth is sensibly the smallest that a man can work in to build the structure. In service the raft is virtually devoid of equipment and so requires little more access that once a year at the annual MSA and Lloyds inspections.

5. PASSENGER TRANSFER ARRANGEMENT

The IMO Code does not address the issue of passenger boarding - safe passage from craft to shore - let alone the problem of boarding onto another vessel at sea, anchored or underway. The MSA's reaction to the idea of transferring large numbers of passengers (rather than one pilot) from boats to a ship at sea was naturally enough rather negative since normally this would not be allowed. However the ameliorating factors are:

1) Only service personnel, who can be assumed to be physically fit, will transfer.

2) The operation will be closely controlled by the PTC crew.

3) Crew training is inherent in the HSC Code (page 152).

Naturally enough a lot of attention has been put in the Safety Case on the brow and transfer arrangements.

The design concept of the brow is shown in Figure 7. Since the brow is not allowed to land on the deck of the receiving ship, a scheme was devised for the end of the brow to 'stick' on the side of the ship just below the deck.

The concept is to lay the end of the brow against the ship's side just below the entrance way and keep it there by means of a feedback loop to the hydraulic circuits activating a vertical hydraulic cylinder under the brow. The feedback is accomplished by a rubber tyred wheel fitted to the end of the brow and pressed against the side of the ship. The wheel drives a rotary encoder. The feedback loop continuously attempts to obtain zero wheel rotation.

The end of the brow (i.e. the wheel) is pushed against the ship's side by another hydraulic cylinder. The design allows a constant force to be maintained while the telescopic end of the brow moves in and out as the PTC rolls alongside. Therefore roll, sway and heave are compensated by the two cylinders.

Surge is constrained as follows: The PTC lays alongside the ship with a long 'boat rope' bow line led from the foredeck of the PTC. The offside propeller is put slow astern. The objective is to keep the bow rope taut and the PTC pressed heavily against the ship. This minimises roll but, more importantly, obviates any surge.

Once the PTC is laid alongside in the right fore and aft position the brow operator will aim the end of the brow some distance below the boarding point and activate the telescopic section. This puts the wheel onto the ship's side where it rolls up and down. The operator will then activate the feedback loop and the wheel will stop. He will then be able to adjust the position of the wheel so that the brow is positioned a few inches below the level of the receiving deck. Brow control positions are fitted, one port, one starboard, adjacent to the brow.

Some 'what if' questions immediately came to mind with an arrangement like this:

- What happens if a hydraulic pipe bursts?;

- what happens if the PTC is caught by a very large wave?;

- what happens if the feed-back sensor fails?

These questions and many more are asked within the Safety Case, formally logged in the HAZOP Study and the ALARP principle applied. In this way the design of the hydraulic system was modified in many small ways to reduce the risk of failure or reduce the hazards of a failure. For instance it was decided to change to 24 volt DC supply for the control system rather than AC thus avoiding the situation where a generator failure could cause a failure of the brow. The question of what happens if the brow accidentally rolls up the ship side onto the deck, the telescopic part actively pushing inboard, was addressed by incorporating a hydraulic accumulator with enough energy to retract the telescopic part rapidly even if all hydraulic power has been lost.

Because of the novelty of the design a sequence of testing is being carried out at each stage of development. Firstly the telescopic mechanics of the brow itself, then a dynamic factory test of the whole brow and hydraulics. This test will simulate the movement of the PTC alongside in a seaway all at the right periods of motion. The brow will be able to be tested hydraulically and the feed-back loop wheel system checked to see if it reacts as intended. There is a compromise to be struck between over-rapid hydraulic reaction to keep the wheel at zero rotation (i.e. the end of the brow stationary on the frigate's side) and a 'dozy' reaction that allows a degree of permissible movement before reaction begins. Finally the whole system will be set to work and tested both on basin trials and then at sea alongside a barge with a representative shipside fitted.

The Safety Case HAZOP Study on the brow also included procedural aspects, such as should only one person at a time walk across the brow? And should a crew member act as traffic controller? And who should decide whether it was safe to use the transfer system - the master of the PTC or the Captain of the Frigate? Decisions of the HAZOP Study are being incorporated in the Operating Manual.

6. RESCUE BOAT

The HSC Code says that a rescue boat for retrieving persons from the water should be carried. If the vessel is less than 20m in length exemption may be granted, provided that an arrangement to enable retrieval of a helpless person from the water is fitted and the vessel is manoeuvrable enough to get alongside the person in the water.

Originally the design excluded a rescue boat on the above grounds and an efficient recovery gantry and hoist was

fitted. However if a man overboard incident occurs, it is likely to be while the PTC is tied alongside during transfer and thus the PTC would not be able to respond quickly. A reversion to a rescue boat was therefore made and endorsed by the Ministry.

On a general theme, two items of note here are quite onerous for small HSC craft. The first is that the requirement for a rescue boat is one of the new items in the Code compared to the old DSC Code. While a small (say 3m inflatable) rubber boat is itself may not seem too onerous in terms of weight and cost, at the end of the day the PTC is to carry a 4.5m long boat fitted with a 30HP electric start outboard weighing complete with fuel and equipment some 350kg. In addition the launching and retrieving arrangement must be capable of lifting the boat with its maximum number of persons onboard (6) with large factors of safety and static and dynamic proof loads. The mechanism must be able to launch without power i.e. a brake must be fitted. Thus the whole arrangement of boat and crane weighs some ¾ tonne - not an insignificant amount on a small craft. The reason in this instance for such a large boat is the MSA's referral to SOLAS regulations 47 and 48 and the view that only the larger boat capable of carrying a larger engine could tow a 50 man loaded liferaft at the required SOLAS 2 knots.

Other flag authorities would allow the smaller inflatable boat, 4 person, 3.5m with manual start, 9.9HP motor which is some half the weight and cost. Other flag authorities e.g. Hong Kong do not require a rescue boat at all, even for International voyages.

The second effect of adding a rescue boat is that the crew numbers of the PTC increased from 3 to 5 - the additional two crew being needed to launch and man the rescue boat during an evacuation.

In passing it is worth highlighting the fact that the Code is only mandatory for craft engaged on International voyages (Page 6 of Code). In the case of a craft on national voyages the local flag authority may or may not take the code to assess the safety level of a craft. If it chooses the Code then exemptions may be granted if local conditions of operation are special. The local flag authority is currently more potent than the Code.

7. STABILITY

The IMO Code is a stringent criteria both for intact and damage stability. Usually in multihull craft the problem in meeting the criteria comes from the angle of heel after flooding on one side. A SWATH, because of its geometry, is naturally even more prone to large angles of heel after damage on one side; it will also trim more for the same reason. (The GM_L is only about twice the value of GM_t; on a monohull it is some twenty or thirty times greater). The Ministry's requirements included of course the HSC Code stability criteria plus their own (somewhat less severe) but also asked for Category B craft extent of bottom damage which means that in the forward half of the craft the extent of bottom damage is increased by 50%.

The "Category B" is really intended for large craft on longer voyages carrying more than 450 passengers. The Ministry's extra requirement foreshadows the perceived need to increase the length of prescribed bottom damage in the wake of accidents such as that which happened to the St Malo fast catamaran (The St Malo ripped her bottom open on rocks and the damage extent was well in excess of the criteria in the Code).

Clearly some special features were required in the design of the PTC. The extent of subdivision is shown on the General Arrangement drawing. Conventional transverse bulkheads are set as closely together as the rules effectively allow (10%L). In addition it was found necessary to use fixed buoyancy and also buoyant air tanks. With fixed buoyancy several options were considered. Formed-in closed cell foam within aluminium void spaces was ruled out on the grounds that one could not inspect the interior of the structure during surveys. Besides there would be a risk of serious corrosion in the bilge areas where water would inevitably collect. Solid blocks of foam strapped in place were considered and rejected because the SWATH shape does not lend itself to this method due to restricted access. The permeability achievable with this method is remarkably poor in practice. Croffle type material (loose bits of foam) was also rejected because it may well merely float out through damaged areas. These thoughts led to the idea of making the bow cone of each hull of GRP(Glass Reinforced Plastics), foam filled. This idea is of course common practice in small dories and yachts and is actually mentioned in the Code (page 23). It also eased somewhat the Yard's task of making a somewhat difficult shape in aluminium. The GRP nose cone is structurally the equal of the aluminium hull and is bolted in place.

The other item added to enhance damage stability was the creation of sealed buoyancy tanks under the engine room formed merely by closing off the top of the lower tubular hull forming, in effect, a local double bottom. These reduce the amount of flooding under side damage within the engine room which is necessarily the largest subdivision compartment in the craft. They also avoid engine room flooding under bottom damage. They are sealed rather than vented and bilged.

The Code does not admit to any such device despite the fact that most catamarans and hovercraft are fitted with sealed spaces (e.g. the raft areas). The attraction of a sealed space is that if air cannot leak out (through a vent pipe) then water is less likely to enter if damage is in the bottom of the space. The St Malo catamaran was held up partly by the buoyant raft after her accident. It is a subject area of the Code that needs addressing.

Even with the above subdivision foam buoyancy and sealed spaces the PTC still needs action from the ballast system to "reduce the angle of heel to 10º within 15 minutes" as the Code puts it.

Since a SWATH has a small tonne per cm, a large ballast capacity and pumping system is required in order to offset the effects of large changes in payload, and still maintain a reasonable draft and trim. On the PTC this

amounts to some 20% of the full load displacement and each of the four tanks is placed at each corner of the raft in order to give the maximum lever as possible.

The tanks are each filled by a dedicated pump in 8 minutes, Fig. 8. They are emptied by gravity in 6 minutes. Control is from a panel at the engineer's position in the wheelhouse. The pumps are AC supply, and rely on at least one generator being undamaged in order to fill tanks on the high side. Alternatively the tanks on the low side can be emptied. If electricity is not available to the motorised valves the valves can be manually opened. It should be noted that the generators are sited well above the normal waterline and either generator can supply any pump.

It may seem strange that the tanks are so high up and that it is permissible to "fill tanks on the high side of the ship"; advice which is not normally given to ships operators. The reason is simply that the centre of gravity of a SWATH, including the PTC, is high up within the raft. Thus adding or subtracting ballast water at this height has very little effect on the KG. Since the variable load is also approximately at this height, changes in payload or ballast have very little effect on the GZ curves.

By similar reasoning the fuel tank is situated in the 'third bow' sited underneath the raft forward. The third bow creates an anti-slamming shape. Siting the fuel up here also overcomes the suction lift problem that would have to be overcome if the fuel were down in the lower hulls. The Ministry's requirements also ask for exploration of the extent of damage beyond the 10%L criteria to make the craft capsize or sink. This is where the buoyancy in the raft which is present on most multihulls comes into play. Under 'normal' damage this area is still above water. But the fact is that the centre portion of the raft on this craft lying between two watertight longitudinal bulkheads in the haunch area, is 21.5m long, 5.75m wide and 0.9m deep, giving a buoyant volume of 111m^3; i..e. in excess of the weight of the craft. It is unlikely that this part of the raft would ever get damaged but to preserve that final 'lifebelt' effect in case of damage at the extreme forward and aft of the raft, the raft has collision bulkheads fore and aft. The centre portion of the raft still gives 77m^3 of buoyancy.

8.   REMOTE RELEASE OF CO$_2$

Another new requirement of the Code is that the CO$_2$, (or engine room fire extinguishing system), can be released from the control station - the wheelhouse. This complicates the system considerably and many features have to be incorporated to ensure that inadvertent release of the gas is a remote risk. Before the gas is released other action such as stopping the fan and closing the fire flaps, shutting doors and hatches and checking that there are no personnel inside the engine room, have to be carried out. This is clearly more complicated and less reliable to achieve from the wheelhouse. The authors believe that this requirement of the Code is a retrograde step.

On the PTC design, remote release is arranged though not without misgivings. Indeed the HAZOP Study team drew a conclusion that safety would be enhanced if gas release was done directly at the bottle.

However, the only proviso to this is that the bottle stowage and release position should be in a sheltered location on the open deck. This was not possible to arrange on the PTC so remote release was reluctantly incorporated. Of course manual release has to be arranged anyway in case the electric remote release fails so the operator does have a choice in practice. The remote release can only be electrically armed by a key set in a break-glass box.

9. SALOON SPRINKLER

Another new item in the Code is the requirement for a sprinkler system in the passenger saloon. The PTC is so fitted but in such a small vessel it is debatable whether this will actually enhance the safety of those on board. Portable extinguishers in the saloon would suffice.

10. EVACUATION

A SWATH necessarily has a relatively high freeboard. On the PTC it is not high enough to consider a Marine Escape System (MES) (a chute) but much higher than the 1.5m Code requirement considered the most that people can be expected to jump. The usual practice in these cases is to provide a portable ladder. There are serious design difficulties with ladders such as:

1) They need to be secure when in position such that a heavy liferaft surging alongside does not dislodge it.

2) Taking into account the need to allow for the worst trim and heel situation the ladder quickly becomes longer than is man-handleable in one fixed length, so hinged or telescopic arrangements are needed - all more complication in the stress of an evacuation.

3) Evacuation is very slow down a ladder. The St Malo report highlights several real problems with ladders.

Ref: 1 page 5 mentions the concept of a fore and aft stairway recessed into the side of a craft, rather like a traditional flight of steps set into a stone jetty. It is this concept which is applied to the PTC. Fig 9 shows a mock-up of the arrangement built to prove the idea. A hinged grating hatch in the deck allows access down to the stairway. At the bottom is a small deck area on which to stand, the body still inboard of the shell. From there one can turn towards the raft and jump in.

This permanent recessed boarding point will also be useful in the general role of the craft - boarding from small boats etc.

11. DIRECTIONAL CONTROL

For designers coming from waterjet propelled craft design to a propeller and rudder arrangement, the Code posed some problems. If an engine or jet fails on a waterjet propelled craft the other engine/jet can immediately carry on satisfactorily propelling and steering the craft even if the failed jet fails hard-over. On craft steered by rudders, if one or both rudders fail hard-over, the ability to immediately continue to steer in a direction of choice, is lost. Traditionally the crew would go into the aft peak and manually centre and lock the failed rudder and then the master can regain directional control by using the other rudder. (all assuming a twin-engine-propeller-rudder arrangement). However it is not possible to do this in the 5 seconds called up in the Code.

On a waterjet propelled craft it is possible to go into the back-up steering/engine control immediately at any speed from the helm position without pause and the passengers would never notice. With a ruddered craft the master's only option is to stop until the failed rudder can be set amidships and locked. The back-up directional control asked for in the Code can then be provided by a separate steering system to the other rudder.

This is how the PTC is arranged. The rudders are not mechanically or hydraulically linked. Each has its own power pack and electric potentiometer control in the wheelhouse, but both potentiometers are driven by the same steering wheel. Hence, if one system fails, the other is totally independent. Another solution could have been to have two hydraulic pump sets (one stand by) driving both rudders together. But on a SWATH, or catamaran for that matter, this would have meant a hydraulic tie bar because a tie bar is difficult to arrange (the great distance between stocks) Hydraulic tie bars are notorious for drift giving creeping misalignment of the rudders.

12. STRUCTURES

The Code is very brief on this aspect relying on Flag authority or Classification Society input in terms of overall and local strength. The Code does however call attention to cyclic loads, fatigue and vibration.

A SWATH is a 'gangly' type of structure and therefore prone to many modes of global vibration induced from exciting forces from, for instance, propeller shafting. A Finite Element Analysis was performed by modelling the whole of the structure especially the detail of the after cone and structure above it. Stresses due to wave loading and natural frequencies in the various possible modes were calculated. Fatigue cracks usually start from points of poor detail design execution and much thought was put into the design of the structure in those areas thought likely to have a problem. The general aim in a welded structure is to have a 'clean' uninterrupted structure with as few intersections of frames and stiffeners as possible. In parts of the craft therefore, plating is stiffened by frames only, thus avoiding multiple intersections by longitudinals passing through frames.

The use of plastics for minor non-structural areas is now common practice in fast ferries using phenolics which meet the requirements of "fire-restricting material" mentioned in the Code (pages 47 and 53). Main structure is also permitted to be of a fire restrictive material providing the requirements for the following aspects are met:

- flame spread;
- heat flux;
- heat release;
- gas;
- smoke;
- 'structural strength at elevated temperatures' (page 52 of HSC Code).

The most onerous requirement is the last one relating to strength at high temperatures. It is essential that in the event of a major fire, that the structure maintains it's strength, and notably in areas associated with the evacuation routes. To the knowledge of the authors, however, nobody has created a material that meets all of these criteria, especially the last one. In the case of the PTC, GRP is used for the nose cones of the hulls.. The selection of GRP for this area of the craft is justified on two grounds. Firstly while these are structurally as strong as the main hull, they are not essential to the integrity of the main hull structure. Secondly, there is no equipment inboard of the GRP cones that is likely to start a fire, and in any case, the cones are submerged in seawater which would act as an effective coolant.'

There are structural areas on fast ferries where it makes sense to use materials other than aluminium. Plastics lend themselves to complicated shapes or in this case to the use of formed-in buoyancy. Each part of a craft can be made of an appropriate material to suit, in a composite fashion. Other writers have propounded the use of steel/aluminium composite structures. Note the meaning here of the word "composite"; not composite as in Fibre Reinforced Composites, but composite in the Cutty Sark sense (different materials for different parts of the structure).

13.   HAZOP STUDIES

To give an idea of how much work was involved during the design phase of the PTC there will have been, after the vessel is commissioned:

1) A preliminary meeting to list the risk areas to be studied in HAZOP meetings.

2) Four HAZOP meetings, the last one on board the finished craft.

On each occasion the appropriate designers in hull, mechanical, and electrical disciplines were present, plus a safety consultant to do the paperwork, plus the Safety Manager and MOD Safety Officer and MOD specialists including the operator. Each meeting took most of the day. On completion a full Safety Case document will be handed over to the Ministry to be referenced and updated throughout the lives of the vessels.

An integral part of the Safety Case Study was a Failure Mode and Effects Analysis (FMEA) as dictated by the Code. It is interesting that this relatively new facet of fast craft design and build now occupies several man weeks of paperwork and at least one full day of basin trial and one full day of sea trials even for a small craft such as the PTC.

14.   CONCLUSION

Despite its modest power, speed and dimensions, the SWATH PTC posed some interesting design problems to meet the Code. The significant additional requirements of the Code - Rescue boat, sprinkler and remote CO_2 release, have been addressed. The stability criteria have been met by a combination of subdivision, foam filled GRP nose cones and buoyancy tanks, the latter highlighting the need for the Code to address non-ventilated, non bilged watertight spaces.

ACKNOWLEGEMENTS

The authors acknowlege permission given by FBM Marine Ltd and the Ministry of Defence for publishing the paper.

REFERENCES

1. RINA Conference on High Speed Vessels for Transport and Defence - Paper 13 - London November 1995.

2. International Code of Safety for High Speed Craft - IMO London 1995.

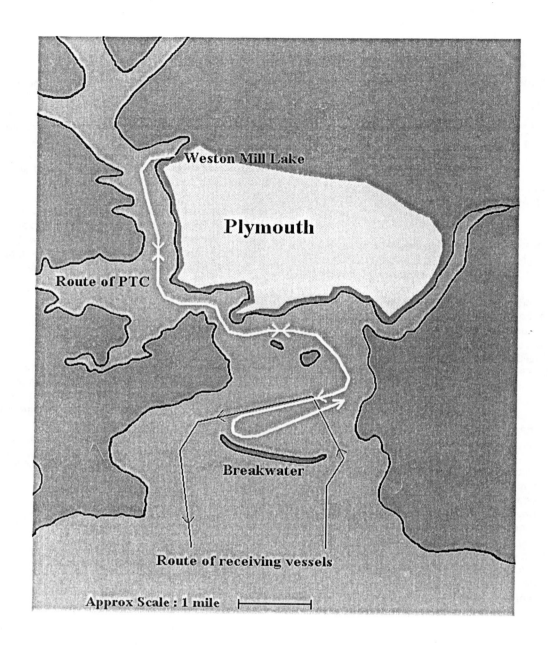

Fig. 1 The Plymouth 'Racetrack'

Fig. 2 Photograph of Typical Transfer Position on Receiving Ship

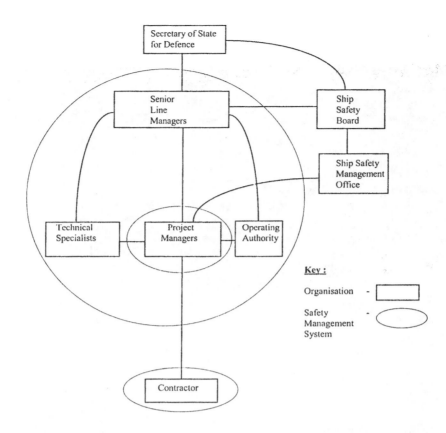

Fig. 3 Management of Safety within the Ministry of Defence

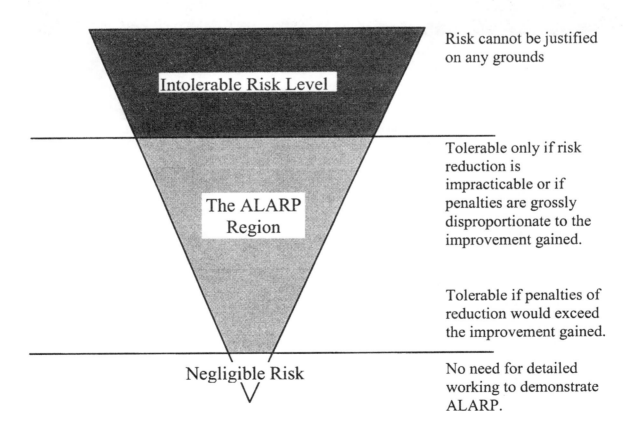

Fig. 4 Principle of "As Low As Reasonably Practical" (ALARP)

12

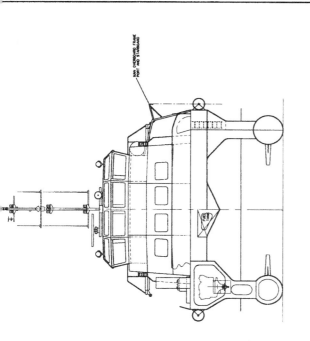

PASSENGER
TRANSFER CRAFT

General Arrangement

Principal Dimensions

LOA	23.95m
LWL	21.00m
Beam	11.10m
Draft	2.25m

Scale 1:50

FMSH-21-09-GA/01

AMENDMENT 9

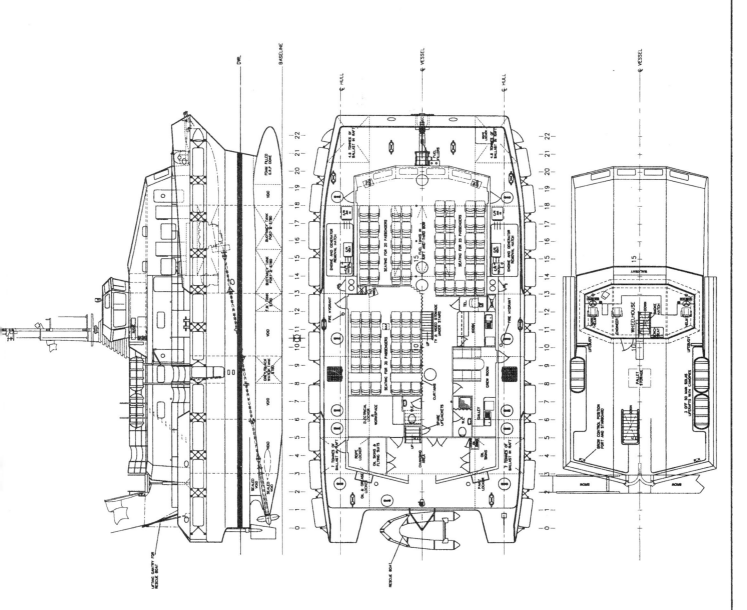

Fig. 5 General Arrangement showing watertight boundaries

Fig. 6 Artist's impression

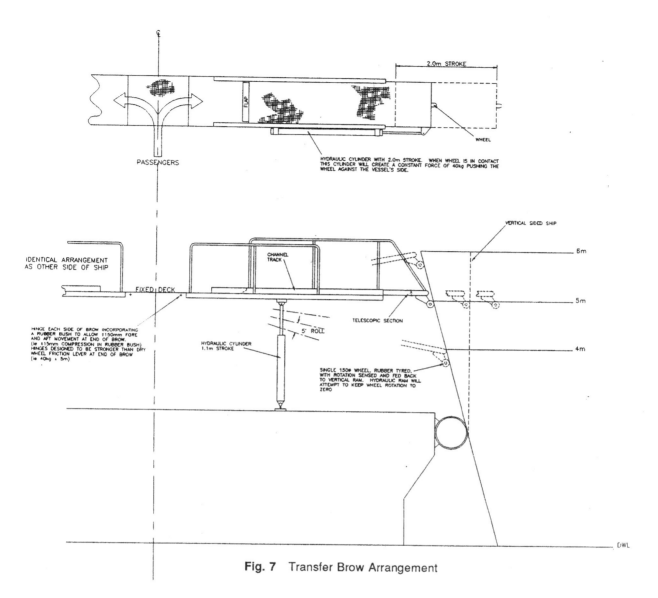

Fig. 7 Transfer Brow Arrangement

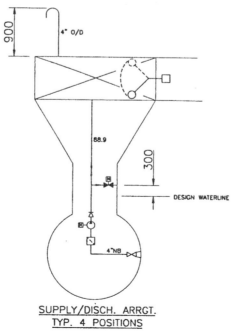

SUPPLY/DISCH. ARRGT.
TYP. 4 POSITIONS

Fig. 8 Ballast Arrangement Schematic

Fig. 9 Mock-up of Evacuation stairway to be built into the side of the PTC.

<u>**PAPER NO.7.**</u>

FORMAL SAFETY ASSESSMENT AND HIGH SPEED CRAFT

by Jim Peachey, Marine Safety Agency, UK

Paper presented at the

International Symposium & Seminar

THE SAFETY OF HIGH SPEED CRAFT

6 - 7 FEBRUARY 1997 LONDON

FORMAL SAFETY ASSESSMENT & HIGH SPEED CRAFT

Jim Peachey FRINA, Principal Surveyor
Marine Safety Agency

There are perhaps some questions about safety that passengers, crew, and others involved with a high speed craft might ask. These are:

- What are the hazards that might arise?

- Which accident scenarios present the highest risk?

- Are those accident scenarios being controlled to an acceptable level of safety?

If we assume that the craft is designed, built and operated to applicable codes, standards and regulations, then the regulator or author of those codes and standards bears a significant responsibility to ensure that all relevant hazards have indeed been addressed, and that sufficient and appropriate controls and requirements are in place to combat the resulting risks.

The crew, passengers and other organisations involved will have other questions as well. For example they will want assurance that the regulatory regime and requirements in place are not over restrictive, which might result in the stifling of technological development and a preclusion of worthwhile advances in transport service and capability.

My purpose this afternoon is to tell you about Formal Safety Assessment (FSA), an approach which should provide a rational basis to answer these questions about hazards, risks, and appropriate levels of regulation. FSA is a new approach that is being pioneered by the UK Marine Safety Agency (MSA). It is aimed at the regulators of the international shipping industry. The particular reason for me speaking here this afternoon at this conference on High Speed Craft Safety, is that the MSA is currently undertaking an FSA study of high speed passenger catamaran vessels, to "try out" this new approach.

FSA is a process to assist in the management and control of shipping safety. It is a process which is based on risk assessment, and it is a process which is systematic and holistic (i.e. embracing all aspects of safety). MSA's objective in developing and promoting FSA is to achieve its adoption by the International Maritime Organisation (IMO), and for FSA to become part of IMO's normal rule making process for international shipping.

As a process, FSA makes use of risk assessment, and also cost benefit assessment. It is aimed at enhancing all aspects of maritime safety relating both to people (their lives and their health), and relating to the marine environment and to property.

I should perhaps explain the difference between the words "hazard" and "risk", since the distinction is not always clearly understood. A hazard isn't actually an accident, but it is a situation that has the potential to become an accident. Risk, on the other hand, and in the way that we are using it (FSA is a risk based approach), has a very particular and explicit meaning. I hope most of you are already aware of this, but risk combines two aspects of a potential accident: its likelihood or probability on the one hand; and the severity or magnitude of its consequences on the other hand. When I talk about risk and a risk based approach, I mean the combination of how likely the accident is to happen, and how bad it would be if it did. Many industries have, or are adopting, a risk based approach for achieving improved safety. However, what we have proposed for the shipping industry is that this risk based approach should be used as a basis for setting the regulatory framework and requirements. I want to tell you about the FSA approach for shipping, and tell you a little about the study that we are doing at the moment of its application to high speed passenger catamaran ferries.

So what is the FSA approach? It started life almost exactly five years ago in February 1992, when the UK House of Lords committee on science and technology produced their report on the safety aspects of ship design [1]. Known as the Carver Report because Lord Carver chaired the committee, the enquiry was set up in the wake of two major disasters in the UK: the *Herald of Free Enterprise* in 1987, and the *Marchioness* disaster on the Thames in 1989, both of which claimed many lives. The Carver report concluded that modern science and technology were not being adequately applied in the many fields that affect shipping safety, and that the time had come for a radical change.

The change that Lord Carver and his committee envisaged comprised two components: firstly the adoption of safety goals based upon an assessment of risks, costs and benefits; and secondly the introduction of a ship safety case regime for every vessel operating commercially. That second part of it, the safety case idea, reflected the then recently introduced safety case regime in the UK offshore industry, wherein owners of offshore platforms were required to produce a "safety case" document which set out how they intended to achieve an acceptable level of safety. The offshore safety case document was of course to be submitted to the regulator for approval. Lord Carver's committee recognised the likely difficulties of a safety case approach for international shipping, given the huge diversity of the industry worldwide.

In our response, as the UK shipping regulator, the MSA acknowledged and agreed with that difficulty, but we saw the attraction of using scientific risk principles as a basis for a complete overview of shipping safety regulation. We noted the international nature of the industry, and therefore the need for any new approach to safety regulation to be developed in the context of the IMO, and with the agreement and co-operation of all its members. We also knew that a safety case regime for every vessel would be impractical in the foreseeable future, for two principal reasons: firstly the inevitable variations in implementation that would arise amongst the owners worldwide, and their different flag states; secondly the enormous, and quite unrealistic demands that would be put on both the regulator and the regulated in producing and assessing safety cases. The solution we developed was based on the first of Lord Carver's conclusions and is a system which uses the concept of risk assessment not on a ship by ship basis, but for deriving the regulatory framework and rules applicable to all ships of a particular type.

We use the phrase "Formal Safety Assessment" to differentiate this new concept for shipping from the safety case idea. FSA is a process, a rational and systematic risk based process for use by the regulator, i.e. the IMO internationally, and the MSA in the UK. FSA will assess the risks associated with any shipping activity and it will evaluate the costs and benefits of potential regulatory options for reducing those risks. It therefore enables an objective assessment to be made of the need for, and the content of, safety regulations. We believe that FSA is a tool that can and should be applied by the regulator to assist in that rule making process, and thus help to improve maritime safety. However, it is only a tool; FSA doesn't replace the regulatory decision making activity but it provides an objective support for it.

FSA comprises five steps, which are very simple and logical. They are first of all: identify the hazards; i.e. what is it that could go wrong. Secondly, assess the risk level resulting from those hazards. Thirdly look at what options there are for managing or controlling those risks; fourthly do a cost benefit assessment of those options; and then finally as the fifth step decide what to do based on the information about hazards, risks, options, costs and benefits generated by the preceding steps.

We see the benefits of applying the FSA discipline to the regulatory process as being very significant and including: having a consistent regulatory regime across all aspects of maritime safety; having cost effective regulation so that safety investment is targeted where it will get the best benefit; being pro-active in the regulatory approach rather than reactive, so that hazards and risk scenarios that have not yet arisen are properly addressed; being confident that the requirements that are put in place are in proportion to the severity of the risk, so that one is not over prescribing in terms of safety; and finally, having a process which can address the new risks posed by ever changing marine technology, which is particularly appropriate in the field of high speed craft.

We went to the Maritime Safety Committee (MSC) of the IMO in 1993 with our proposal for FSA. It was well received, and an international correspondence group was set up to take forward consideration of that proposal. That group now comprises thirty two different members, countries and observer organisations at the IMO, with a very broad cross section of representative IMO membership. Subsequently the IMO have recognised the importance and the potential of FSA as an approach to assist in the rule making procedure. They have agreed to put FSA as a high priority item on their agenda, and they have established a working group to develop the concept further in a practical way. Just over two years ago, we in the MSA started a major programme of research on FSA, to "put flesh" on the skeletal concept of those five steps. The output of the first of phase of that research was a fully developed methodology, a full procedure of how to apply those five steps.

We reported the FSA methodology to the IMO in the summer of last year (1996) [2]. At that MSC meeting, the working group met for the first time and drafted IMO guidelines. It was very gratifying that those guidelines reflected the framework and all the key elements of the FSA methodology that we in the UK had developed. The current draft of these guidelines [3] is out with the membership at the moment for review and comment, and the expectation and hope is that they will be approved as IMO guidelines on FSA at the meeting in May of this year.

The other thing that the MSC Committee at the IMO did in the summer of 1996 was to call for trial applications of the FSA approach. We in the UK had already decided to proceed with the second phase of research to do precisely that; which is to apply FSA to high speed passenger catamarans. We chose that type of vessel for two main reasons; It constitutes (as you know only too well), a growing sector of the shipping industry in terms of numbers, size, speed and passenger capacity of these craft. Also it embodies new and very rapidly developing technology, which means there is not an extensive base of experience upon which to base regulations.

Whilst the principal objective of this current research project is to demonstrate the practicality of the FSA approach and hence promote understanding and acceptance of FSA by the IMO, we have significant subsidiary objectives which include: To produce a risk profile for high speed catamarans, in other words ranking the risks arising from different sources according to their severity, and to propose tentative risk based regulatory requirements (though I don't know how those will turn out in relation to the existing requirements, for example of the IMO High Speed Craft Code).

Finally to assist in the review that the UK is undertaking of the safety regulation of high speed craft operating in UK waters. For the trial applications we are applying the entire five step process to high speed craft, but we have limited the scope of the work to enable it to be completed in a relatively short time and meet the deadlines for reporting it to the MSC of the IMO. So we have confined the study to the safety of people, whereas in principle FSA can and should encompass people, the environment and property and we are looking only at three particular accident categories: collision, fire and loss of hull integrity. We intend to report the results of this trial application to the IMO [4], and also to publish them later in the year, when the work is complete in July.

Step 1 of the process is essentially complete and Step 2, the assessment of risk, is currently in hand. As a prelude to the work, we have compiled a database of high speed craft, and of incidents. Operators, designers, builders and other administrations have been extremely helpful in providing access to their files, from quite a number of regions of the world where high speed craft are operated. Included in that database is recognition of the importance of the human factor in the occurrence of accidents. We have conducted a number of human factors interviews with operating staff, and those feed into the task analysis part of the hazard identification exercise in Step 1. I should also talk briefly about the concept of the generic ship, or the generic model, which is a key feature of Formal Safety Assessment in trying to assess the risks for shipping in general in a particular category of ships. One can't work on the details of a particular vessel, so there is the need for a generic model which is representative of the functions, characteristics and features that are common to all ships of the type to be defined. That definition includes not just the hardware side of things, but organisational, management and software issues as well.

So to Step 1 of the process, the hazard identification. The objective is firstly to derive a list of all possible accident scenarios together with their potential causes on the one hand and outcomes on the other. We do this by using standard hazard identification techniques which include a review of data we have collected in the database (incident data), and hazard identification meetings using "brainstorming" techniques, where one brings together a group of suitably qualified and experienced people. We included designers, builders, classification societies, operators, people maintaining and repairing craft, human factors experts, fire experts, collision experts and so forth in these meetings. We brought that group of people together, and in a structured fashion looked at the accident categories, the sub-categories of those accidents (like fires originating in different parts of the vessel), and what the causes, contributory hazards and consequences would be. That's all part of the hazard identification exercise.

Having done that and collected a large amount of information, one then structures and organises that information and screens the large number of accident scenarios to see which are the most risky in qualitative terms, using historical data on incidents and expert judgement. What's been interesting is that the historical data has shown that the risk levels for fire and loss of hull integrity, two of the accident scenarios we're looking at, are significantly lower than the risk level for collisions; but the expert judgement view suggests that the risk level associated with fire accidents is comparable with that for collision accidents. We've yet to fully test that, but what the experts are saying is that we ought as regulators to be considering the potential for major fire accidents. So the outcome of Step 1 is a large set of accident scenarios with information about the contributory causes and potential outcomes, with those accident scenarios ranked qualitatively in terms of their risk, in other words the combination of probability and consequence.

So onto Step 2 which is underway at the moment. The purpose of Step 2 is to evaluate in a quantitative way each of those significant accident scenarios identified in Step 1. Again we use both historical data and expert

judgement to do that. But it is in Step 2 that the greatest novelty of the FSA approach really appears, because the regulator cannot look at individual ships, individual routes or individual operators in assessing risks; he is doing it in a general overview. Many of the existing techniques of risk assessment are not fully appropriate in that situation. So what we have is two key features of Step 2 of the FSA process. The first looks at the relative contributions to total risk from all the different accident categories and evaluates this in terms of the frequency and the potential severity of that accident.

The second, and more interesting, attempts to identify the factors which influence the level of risk. Factors such as training, management, human failures, design, communication, regulations, maintenance; a whole host of them; many, many factors. What we believe is that there is a network of such factors which link the regulatory regime with the occurrence of accidents. It is a hierarchal network, so that, so to speak: below the accidents there are direct influences, direct causes of those accidents which can be categorised under three principal headings: human factors, hardware factors, and external factors (like the weather for example). Beneath those direct factors, there are more underlying factors which are called the organisational influences, and which relate to things like the company's maintenance, training or rostering policies. Beneath that is the regulatory context, the regulatory policy, things like conventions and codes, the port state control activity and so forth which influence the context in which the organisational factors actually work and operate.

We want to quantify those influences in Step 2, and we do that by focusing on each of the accident scenarios that we have generated, defining quite precisely the factors that are relevant to that particular scenario, and then using expert judgement to assess the relative importance of each factor and its influence in that network of factors. I accept that such generalised quantifications are actually quite a way removed from the detail of a particular craft or route or operator. But on the other hand it is no more than a structured and systematic approach to what the regulator has done in the past. So in summary, Step 2 gives us a quantification of risks, information about where risks arise from and their contribution to total risk, and a measure of the factors that influence the level of risk.

I 'll skip over Step 3, which is identification of control options, and Step 4 which is the cost benefit side of it; and say just a few words about Step 5, the decision making part. This step of course receives information from the previous four steps of FSA in terms of the hazards, risks, costs, benefits and options. That information is fed in alongside other factors that are taken into account in the regulatory context in terms of cultural, political and social factors and so forth. More importantly, part of the process we say, is that in identifying hazards, risks, costs and so forth, we take account of the person or organisation upon whom those risks, costs and benefits fall: the stakeholder if you like. There are many stakeholders: the owner, the emergency services, the crew, the passengers, people affected by noise and wash of high speed craft operations and so forth.

When we come to make the decisions as to what regulatory requirement to put into place, we suggest that the regulator should seek an equitable arrangement, in terms of those various stakeholders and the benefits, risks and costs they carry.

So to conclude, FSA represents a major cultural change in the approach to achieving improved safety at sea; from a largely reactive and piecemeal approach that we've seen in the past, to one which is integrated, pro-active, cost effective and based soundly on the principles of risk. That change will take some time to implement, but will lead, I believe, to a much improved regulatory regime and thus safer shipping at sea.

I have tried to explain what FSA is, how it arose, and the progress we've made at the IMO. I've also described our current project to test out the FSA process in relation to high speed craft.

REFERENCES

1. Safety Aspects of Ship Design and Technology, House of Lords Select Committee on Science and Technology, 1992.

2. A Methodolgy for Formal Safety Assessment of Shipping, UK Submission to IMO, MSC 66/14 and MSC 66/INF.8 February 1996.

3. Draft Guidelines for FSA Application, MSC 68/14, December 1996.

4. Trial Application of Formal Safety Assessment, Progress Report, UK Submission to IMO, MSC 68/14/2 and MSC 68/INF.6, February 1997.

PAPER NO.8.

FORMAL SAFETY ASSESSMENT FOR HIGH SPEED CRAFT: PROPULSION AND MANOEUVRING SYSTEMS RELIABILITY

AN OUTLINE OF THE START OF A RESEARCH PROJECT

by J M Forestier and R Giribone
Bureau Veritas Marine Division, France

Paper presented at the

International Symposium & Seminar

THE SAFETY OF HIGH SPEED CRAFT

6 - 7 FEBRUARY 1997 LONDON

FORMAL SAFETY ASSESSMENT FOR HIGH SPEED CRAFT: PROPULSION AND MANOEUVRING SYSTEMS RELIABILITY

AN OUTLINE OF THE START OF A RESEARCH PROJECT

J M Forestier and R Giribone
Bureau Veritas Marine Division

SUMMARY

A three-year Research Project devoted to application of Formal Safety Assessment methodology to a typical High Speed Craft started early this year with EC funding in the scope of the Brite Euram Programme.

The authors explain the main features of the project together with the most significant findings. As the work is ongoing, no definitive conclusion can be drawn at this stage. However, the following two aspects have proved of special relevance:

- IMO safety rules applicable to such kind of vessels appear to be effective when assessed by an FSA type approach.

- Due to the high level of equipment redundancy generally achieved on this type of craft, the human element becomes the main potential source of failure. This aspect has to be addressed by specific methods of investigation.

AUTHORS' BIOGRAPHIES

Mr Jean-Michel Forestier graduated in Engineering from the Ecole Nationale Supérieure de Techniques Avancées (ENSTA). In 1983 he joined Bureau Veritas in the Marine New Constructions Division and after various posts, namely in the Machinery Section, was appointed to be in charge of the Drawing Approval Department. In particular he was involved in the design approval of CORSAIRE 11000 built by Leroux & Lotz. He is currently Head of Department/New Constructions Division.

Mr Rémy Giribone graduated in Engineering from the Ecole Supérieure d'Ingénieurs de Marseille (ESIM-1973). He started as a design engineer in a company involved in subsea works where he was in charge of submarines, following which he joined Bureau Veritas to be in charge of structural analysis and mechanical design. He became increasingly involved in reliability and risk analysis, working mainly in the nuclear and chemical fields. Today, he is responsible for Risk Analysis (Marine and Offshore Activities).

1. INTRODUCTION

1.1 GENERAL

This project fits into the general trend now observed in marine field, that aims at replacing (or supplementing) existing rules by new ones, based on both risk evaluation and cost-effectiveness assessment.

The reasons why this new approach has emerged and the benefits expected by the maritime community are now clear for anybody aware of recent IMO works on FSA (see Ref. 1) and will not be developed here.

However, there is an obvious need for producing case studies and possibly guidances, in order to illustrate and make this new process more familiar to potential users.

This is the reason why Bureau Veritas with other European partners have decided to start à Brite-Euram project devoted to FSA. Amongst other possible themes, High Speed Crafts have been selected as being a category of ships in rapid expansion and about which few accident/failure data are available from in-service experience.

1.2 WHAT IS MEANT BY FSA

Since the publication of MSA (Marine Safety Agency, UK) report (Ref. 1), FSA aims and methodology have become quite clear. A summary of the main FSA steps is given in Appendix. However, when this project was conceived, some possible options were still open -for example, whether FSA should be applied to individual ships or to rule-making process... In addition to that, our intention was to focus on specific subsystems rather than dealing with general considerations about ship safety. Therefore, it resulted in a project which, *although fully compatible* with MSA's approach and hopefully useful for it, conserved its own personality, the main features of which are exposed hereafter.

2. THE GENERAL FEATURES OF THE PROJECT

2.1 AIMS

The aims of the project are to:

- develop and validate a specific methodology for future safety assessment of propulsion and manoeuvring systems of high speed craft. This methodology will be explained by means of guidelines and illustrated by worked examples. It is hoped that it will be a valuable input for IMO discussions about FSA;

- contribute to possible improvements of *existing* safety regulations applicable to such crafts (IMO-MSC 36(63) « International safety code for High Speed Craft » - May 1994);

- show how the FSA process can be extended in order to serve as a basis for improving profitability by optimising the ratio availability/costs.

The last point goes beyond FSA's scope. However, we strongly believe that, when dealing with propulsion/ manoeuvring systems for which availability is directly connected to safety, such topics as maintenance policy optimisation are the natural continuation of risk analysis and will give a sharp *incentive* to yards, and owners to get interested in these matters.

The various steps of the adopted methodology are sketched in Fig. 1.

2.2 PARTNERSHIP

According to EC's philosophy relative to research programmes, the partnership has been built up so as to encompass the main bodies concerned by HSC, in addition to Bureau Veritas (France, classification society), namely:

- Bazan   :   shipyard (Spain)

- Cetena   :   marine research center (Italy)

- DSB   :   ship operator (Denmark)

- MSA   :   administration (UK)

- MTU   :   engine builder and control system designer (Germany)

2.3 WORK PROGRAMME

The work programme has been split into the following sub-tasks:

Task 0 :   Methodology
Task 1 :   Analysis of the system
Task 2 :   Hazard identification
Task 3 :   Availability analysis
Task 4 :   Safety analysis
Task 5 :   Cost-benefit analysis
Task 6 :   Guidelines
Task 7 :   Databases
Task 8 :   Regulations

How this work programme fits with FSA's scheme, as proposed to IMO by MSA, is indicated in the Appendix.

The main findings and outcomes of the study are now being presented, taking into account that, at the time this paper is written, Task 2 is not completely finished and Task 3 has just started.

3.   MAIN OUTCOMES AND FINDINGS

3.1   TASK 0

Task 0 is entirely dedicated to the review of available methodological tools. These tools are of current use in other industrial fields such as nuclear, space, transportation and chemical plants. The aim of this review was therefore to analyse their purpose, merits and drawbacks and, for the ones selected within the scope of this project, to make them as specific as possible.

In order to make things clearer, a tools efficiency can be analysed with respect to a failure taxonomy. For convenience, failures have been classified in three categories, namely:

- functional failure: corresponding to the type of failure of a component resulting in a loss of its main function (ex. failure of local control unit of main engine, resulting in loss of propulsion);

- hazardous failure: corresponding to failure liable to generate intrinsic detrimental effects such as explosion or fire (eg. leakage from a flange on a fuel conveying pipe);

- human errors: corresponding to « ...human actions (or failure to act) that exceed some limit of acceptability » (quoted from Swain - (Ref. 2)).

This classification has clear drawbacks, as a failure can be « functional » *and* « hazardous » at the same time, and can take (or not) its origin from an inappropriate action of an operator.

However, they have been found convenient for both principle and practical reasons:

- Failure propagation modes are usually completely different:

In the case of purely functional failure, the effect is propagated only between intentionally connected components. This connection is of a purely *topological* nature.

On the contrary, hazardous failure can create unwanted connection between components having no functional links (domino effect), simply because of *proximity* or lack of *physical separation* (fire door).

- Purely functional failure results in an actual decrease of safety only if *additional* adverse circumstances are simultaneously present. For example, partial loss of propulsion can be just a matter of trouble in the case of fine weather. By contrast, this event may lead to catastrophic situations in the case of rough seas.

Hazardous failures are of special interest for hazard identification of HSC as usually this type of craft already provides for a substantially high level of functional redundancy -due to both regulatory constraints and the commercial need for a high level of availability.

Therefore, it is to be expected that common causes of failures be more related to hazardous failure - for instance, fire generation - than to purely functional ones - considering existing redundancy. Therefore this consideration has to be mitigated by the fact that, according to rules requirements, specific provisions should be enforced to prevent fire escalation. In this context, rules requirements correspond to all relevant requirements of IMO, supplemented by rules of Classification Societies.

It has nevertheless been found useful to deal with hazardous failure in a specific way, by making use of the so-called 'Zone analysis' technique, an example of which is provided in the Appendix. Of course, the zone analysis approach is not contradictory with the more commonly used FMEA, and cannot be substituted for it. It rather constitutes a complimentary tool, enabling some kind of cross-checking.

Human error analysis is of course a vast and ambitious subject. For the project under consideration, the following options have been selected.

* **evaluation of man/machine interaction**

    Due to the high degree of sophistication of control command and the presence of numerous sensors, panels, etc., it can be of interest to assess ergonomics aspects.

* **task analysis**

    Is probably the most important subject to assess both organisational and procedural aspects.

* **maintenance-induced error**

    A detailed specific methodology is currently in progress.

To end with this preliminary methodological phase, the various tools liable to be used for quantitative availability analysis have been reviewed and evaluated.

Not surprisingly, Monte Carlo simulation has proved the most suitable tool for such an assessment. As far as application to reliability problems is concerned, the Monte Carlo method can be described as an estimate of reliability based on a *simulation* of the random behaviour of the system under consideration rather than on a *modelling type approach*. The simulation generates random numbers that, under suitable assumptions, can be interpreted as occurrences of failure. As a matter of fact, no other method shows such an outstanding versatility with respect to the possibility of considering both variable hazard failure rates and complex maintenance strategy. It is therefore adopted as a reference tool for the project.

As a conclusion, Task 0 shows that some methods should be preferentially used, as more appropriate to our case.

3.2   TASK 1

Task 1 aims at gaining a *thorough knowledge of the system* in order to define relevant 'generic ships' attributes, in fact 'generic ship' should be better defined as 'functional model.

3.2.1   Model Selection

This is done by reviewing existing propulsion/manoeuvring systems in use on board in-service ship, and by performing a taxonomy.

As far as general architectures are concerned, the following types of vessels have been identified: Hovercraft, hydrofoil, catamaran, SES, SWATH, and monohull.

In the selected range of interest (speed $\geq$ 30 kn, more than 250 passengers, several units in service) the types most commonly operated are catamarans and monohulls.

As far as propulsion system is concerned, the following combinations were considered:

CODAD   (Combined Diesel and Diesel)
COGAG   (Combined Gas and Gas)
CODAG   (Combined Diesel and Gas)

For each type, there is of course a choice to be made between various technical solutions (number of shaft, propulsion types, etc.).

At last, the typical craft selected is of *CODAD type*, with *4 independent propulsion systems and 4 waterjets* (2 external are steerable, 2 are fixed *boosters*).

It is to be emphasized that, although composed from actually existing and compatible- elements the representative « generic » ship is a theoretical model.

3.2.2   Functional Description

Functions have been classified in 4 categories:

-   main;
-   auxiliary;
-   safety/monitoring;
-   other.

Rather than remaining at a purely functional *abstract* level, it has been found more convenient to directly consider *sub-subsystems* associated with functions, and breaking down sub-assemblies into *components*, whenever necessary.

As a matter of fact, the description is not purely functional but rather *techno-functional*.

The reason why this approach has been retained is that it makes subsequent FMEA and risk-related investigation easier, as far as functional failure only are considered.

An example of a typical FAT (Functional Analysis Table) of a subsystem is given in appendix, showing the current level of detail retained.

The list of subsystems considered as covering all current types of vessels is as follows:

- Main engine;
- Shaft line;
- Booster water jet;
- Steering water jet;
- Fuel system;
- Fresh water system;
- Engine sea-water circuit;
- Starting air system;
- Lub oil system;
- Air combustion system;
- Electrical power system;
- Bow thruster;
- Remote control system;
- Monitoring control system;
- Common remote control system.

3.2.3   Other Data

The other data necessary to perform a complete risk analysis comprise: the definition of the mission profile, the route, and of course, the procedural and managerial aspects. This was done by the operator DSB and will be incorporated in further stages of the study.

To summarize it can be said further to this task completion, a functional model was set up which will be the basis for all subsequent studies.

3.3   TASK 2

Task 2 can be considered as the real first step of the process of risk assessment. It corresponds to the classical hazard identification phase of any risk analysis.

It has been organized as follows:

- Statistic review;
- FMEA;
- Zone analysis.

In a first instance, a review of available casualty statistics data was made by a partner.

The review covers 166 accidents, 8 of which directly related to fire in the machine room. Those accidents never involved fatalities or even casualties. Causes were not always perfectly identified. However, main conclusions are as follows:

*   3 fires out of 8 were caused by improper maintenance;

*   fire could always be fought back before escalation took place;

*   the fact that fires mainly start in machinery room is completely consistent with general fire statistics relative to any type of vessels (72%), where it is well-known that 50% are due to oil leak and 19% to electric faults.

The 8 accidents reported above are relative to fires that initiated in the *machinery room*, which was the subject of the study.

The reported accidents can be detailed as follows:

•	Hull/machinery incidents (excluding fire):	7
•	Grounding	34
•	Fire/explosion (all in machine room)	8
•	Collision	55
•	Contact	44
•	Flooding	2
•	Miscellaneous	16
	TOTAL:	**166**

The fact that fire causes relate to improper maintenance and that fire could always be fought (e.g. wrong or right behaviour in case of an emergency situation) highlights the importance of the human element in *both negative and positive aspects*.

Besides, the need for effective fire containing bulkheads is also put forward.

Another partner's report emphasizes the occurrence of potentially critical events which, if not controlled in due time, could have led to serious consequences. The situation corresponds more or less to so-called near-misses. Such events are of great value for the risk expert as he is enabled to imagine possible accident scenarii which are not physically unrealistic. This is a way of being *proactive*.

Of course, these kinds of statistics are not easy to find in current technical literature in which even causes of accidents that actually occurred are too often vague or not reported at all.

The next step of Task 2 has been to perform systematic FMEA based on the functional breakdown already presented. As this part of the work -although essential to the analysis- is now classical as being a part of IMO regulation for HSC, we will not insist on this point.

Zone analysis has been performed for the two machine rooms and for the water jet room. A typical form is presented in Appendix.

As expected, no significant critical situation was identified, since it was basically assumed that the vessel is in compliance with IMO rules.

Therefore, it can be considered as a posteriori validation of IMO rules effectiveness, based on an FSA-type approach.

An interesting exercise would be to remove some regulatory constraints to see what impact can be inferred on the overall safety level.

(PROVISIONAL) CONCLUSION(S)

As stated at the beginning, this project is now in progress and therefore no definitive conclusion can be drawn from the results achieved so far.

However, it is clear that, for the kind of vessels considered - high level of functional redundancy, compliance with existing regulations- human element, in its various aspects, has proved to be of prominent interest. This will be considered in further details within the scope of Task 4.

Besides, the influence of redundancy and equipment reliability (including alarm/monitoring/cartrel) will be quantitatively assessed in Task 3.

It is therefore hoped that if RINA kindly offered us a new opportunity in presenting our findings in a future conference, more definitive conclusions would be drawn from this project.

To end this paper, the authors would like to stress the fact that this project is a *collective work* for which all partners put their experience and knowledge in common. They express the wish that this valuable cooperative exchange could go on.

ACKNOWLEDGEMENTS

The authors would like to thank their Partners in this Project, namely Mr Jim Peachey (MSA), S Capizzi (Cetena), Mr Pedersen (DSB), A Perez de Lucas (Bazan) and P Scharpf (MTU) for their helpful cooperation.

Their thanks also go to Mr Campogrande (EC Commission, DG XII) for his continuous support.

REFERENCES

The references here after listed do not include deliverables issued in the context of the project.

1. MSA: 'A methodology for Formal Safety Assessment of Shipping', IMO/MSC66 information paper, 1996.

2. KIRWAN B: 'A guide to practical human reliability assessment', Taylor & Francis, 1994.

3. Project: Task 0 (methodological report).

4. Project: Task 1 (general knowledge).

TABLE 1   FSA BASIC FEATURES

FSA FIVE STEPS	
1.	HAZARD IDENTIFICATION
2.	RISK ASSESSMENT
3.	RISK CONTROL OPTION
4.	COST-BENEFIT ASSESSMENT
5.	DECISION-MAKING RECOMMENDATIONS

GENERAL INTEGRATION OF THE PROJECT IN FSA SCHEME

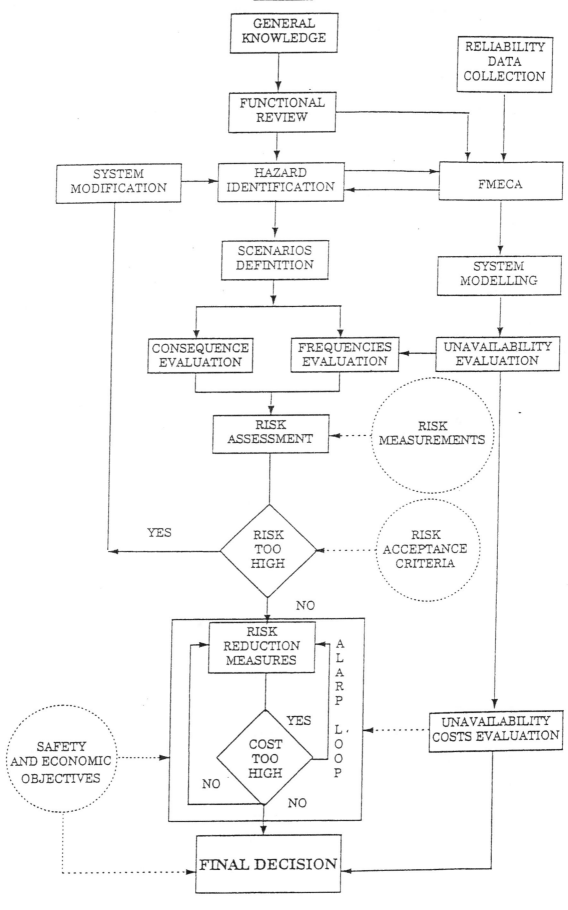

Fig. 1

ENGINE ROOM Forward

ZONE:	Item	Assembly concerned	Initiating event	Triggering event	Potential aggravating factors	Mitigation factors		Emergency response	Likelyhood	Severity	Remarks
						Location and separation rules	Means of detection				
	MENG/FS	Engine fuel oil circuit (EFC)	Fuel oil spray (HP)	contact with hot surfaces:				engine stop (fans closure)			
	MENG/LOS	Engine lube oil circuit (ELOG)	Lube oil spray (HP)			* § 7.5.5 HSC Rules					(localisation of potential leak point far of potential hot surface)
						specific flanges (if P>1,8bar)					
				Engine it self (MRNG)			speed detection				As AUT then carter temp. < flam. temp.
				main switchboard (EPS/MS)		flameproof enclosure					
				main electric generator (EPS/MGS)			speed detection				Asf AUT then carter temp. < flam. temp.
				main electric generator silencer and exhaust gas pipe (EEGC)		coating					hot surface = bellows
				pumps (all)		flameproof enclosure	speed detection				
				other main engine (MENG)			speed detection				
				air electric compressor (SAS/COMP)		flameproof enclosure					
	FWS	Engine fresh water pump (EFWP)									not relevant for single failure analysis

Fig. 2 Zone Analysis (example)

7

FUNCTIONAL ANALYSIS TABLES

TABLE 2

1. **SUB-SYSTEM NAME:** SHAFT LINE [SL]

2. **SUB-SYSTEM DESCRIPTION:** The sub-system comprises all constituting elements of the shaft line which allow torque transmission from engine to waterjet, and RPM regulation.

3. **FUNCTIONAL SCHEME**

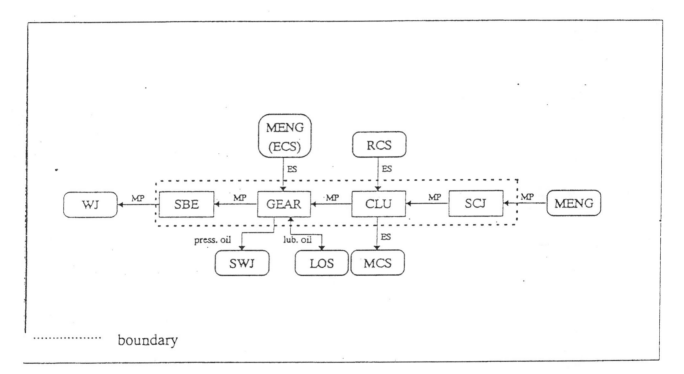

.... boundary

CLU : Clutch
ECS : Engine Control System
LOS : Lube Oil System
MCS : Monitoring Control System
MENG : Main Engine
RCS : Remote Control System
SBE : Shaft Bearing
SCJ : Shaft/Cardan Joint
SWJ : Steering Water Jet
WJ : Water Jet

TABLE 3 FUNCTIONS

ID	Sub-system Function	Operational Mode	Back-up
M2a	Transmit torque from engine to waterjet	All.	Local
M2b	Regulate engine RPM	All.	Local

TABLE 4 ASSOCIATED COMPONENTS

ID	Component	Function
SCJ	Shaft/Cardan Joint	Transmit torque from diesel engine to gear box
CLU	Clutch	Allow engine/shaft connection/disconnection.
GEAR	Gear	Reduce engine RPM as to fit waterjet requirements.
SBE	Shaft Bearings	Fix shaft to hull and allow shaft rotation along axis.

TABLE 5 FUNCTIONAL CONNECTIONS WITH OTHER SUB-SYSTEMS

	Type of connection	Input from	Type of connection	Output to
1	Mechanical power	MENG		
2	Electrical signal	RCS		
3	Electrical signal	MENG (ECS)		
4	Lub oil	LOS		
5			Mechanical power	SWJ or BWJ
6			Pressurised oil	SWJ
7			Electrical signal	MCS
8			Dirty luboil	LOS
9				
10				

FMECA Worksheet

Unit : **High Speed Craft**

System : Propulsion and Manoeuvring System

FAT Ref.: **Figure 1**

FMECA Level: 1

Analyst : S. Capizzi

Ship's Operational Mode: Manoeuvring (harbour)

Date : 25/10/1996

N°	Item Description			Failure Description		Failure Effect		Corrective Actions	Probability of Failure	Severity Category	Criticality Level	Actions/ Remarks
	Name	SBD Id	Function	Mode	Cause	Local	End					
2-5	Fuel System	FS	[A1] Store and supply fuel to diesel engines.	Complete loss of function.	Fuel tanks empty	Loss of fuel supply to the two propulsion lines of relevant engine room.	Significant reduction (50%) of Craft' propulsion and manoeuvring capabilities.	Use Fuel system of the other engine room.	Extremely Remote	Minor	Low	Each fuel tank is equipped with a suitable low fuel level alarm.
				Complete loss of function.	Pipe fracture or joint failure.	Loss of fuel supply to the two propulsion lines of relevant engine room.	Significant reduction (50%) of Craft's propulsion and manoeuvring capabilities. Fire risk increased.	Use Fuel system of the other engine room.	Remote	Major	Medium	It is recommended to carry out a detailed FMEA (Level 2) of the Fuel System.
2-6	Fresh Water System	FWS	[A2] Store and supply of fresh water to diesel engines expansion tanks.	Complete loss of function.	Fresh water pump failure.	Loss of all engines cooling.	Total loss of Craft's propulsion and manoeuvring capabilities.	Engines shut down. Local inspection and system repair.	Reasonably probable	Major	Medium	It is recommended to carry out a detailed FMEA (Level 2) of the Fresh Water System.
					Pipe fracture or joint failure.	Loss of all engines cooling.	Total loss of Craft's propulsion and manoeuvring capabilities.	Engines shut down. Local inspection and system repair.	Remote	Major	Medium	See above.
2-7	Starting Air System	SAS	[A3] Production and storage of compressed air for starting the propulsion diesel engines.	Complete loss of function.	Low air pressure.	Stopped engines would not be able to be restarted.	None	Local inspection and system repair.	Extremely Remote	Minor	Low	
2-8	Lubricating Oil System	LOS	[A4] Storage, supply and charge of diesel engine lub oil.	Complete loss of function.	Pipe fracture or joint failure.	Loss of all engines lubrication.	Total loss of Craft's propulsion and manoeuvring capabilities.	Engines shut down. Local inspection and system repair.	Remote	Major	Medium	It is recommended to carry out a detailed FMEA (Level 2) of the Lubricating Oil System.

Rev. [0]

Fig. 3 F M E C A (example)

PAPER NO.9.

GLOBAL SAFETY APPROACH

by V Farinetti, L Grossi and A Gazzo
Fincantieri - Naval Shipbuilding Division, Italy

Paper presented at the

International Symposium & Seminar

THE SAFETY OF HIGH SPEED CRAFT

6 - 7 FEBRUARY 1997 LONDON

GLOBAL SAFETY APPROACH

by V Farinetti, L Grossi and A Gazzo
Fincantieri - Naval Shipbuilding Division

SUMMARY

Safety is the major issue to be taken properly into consideration when designing, building and operating a fast ferry.

It cannot be regarded as an incoherent set of different requirements to be analysed and complied with. Better and optimized results are achieved by examining all aspects concerning safety with an integrated approach.

AUTHORS' BIOGRAPHIES

Mr Vincenzo Farinetti, born in 1948, is presently design manager of Auxiliary Naval Vessels and Fast Ferries at the Naval Shipbuilding Division of Fincantieri. He joined the Company in 1974 and since then he has been involved in data processing (including structural analysis and computer graphics), basic design of surface combatants, project management (as PM of the latest destroyers for the Italian Navy), and manager of the Shipyard Technical Department. He is the chairman of the Marine Commission of the Italian National Standardization Board. Mr Farinetti has a degree in Mechanical Engineering from University of Genoa; a degree in Naval Architecture from University of Genoa, and a post-graduate certificate in Computer Science from University of Turin.

Mr Luigi Grossi, born in 1952, graduated in Naval Architecture and Mechanical Engineering in 1977 at Genoa University and was an Engineer officer onboard Italian Navy Ships until 1979. He was a researcher at the Hydrodynamic Department of Cetena from 1979 to 1986, working on propeller and hull forms design and joined Fincantieri in 1987. Mr Grossi was an ITTC Member of the Propulsor Committee from 1985 to 1990 and is currently manager of the Hydrodynamic, Acoustic and Naval Architecture Department of Fincantieri - Naval Shipbuilding Division.

Mr Angelo Gazzo, born in 1966, attended the Maritime High School in Genoa from 1981 to 1986 after which he was an Engineer Officer in the Technical Department of the Italian Navy until 1987. He joined Fincantieri Naval Shipbuilding Division in 1988 and was involved in Hull form design and Hydrostatics calculations, following the design and construction of the DESTRIERO project and other ships for the Italian Navy. In 1994 he joined the Naval Architecture Department to follow the design of the new high speed craft.

1. INTRODUCTION

The most important threats to safety belong to three main categories: hull damage, fire and major failure of on-board systems. Most of these occurrences lead to ship evacuation and therefore escape paths and evaluation means must always be available in any "reasonable" case.

This rather simple requirement asks for the adoption of design criteria that must be clearly defined at the beginning of the basic design phase, which spans from hull form selection, to garage and passenger area arrangement; from assessment of reliability of systems and equipment to material selection for the outfitting.

The present rules relevant to High Speed Craft do not define any precise "global safety" assessment of the vessel. With "Global Safety Approach" the authors intend to underline the importance of a higher level of view of all aspects connected to safety with the aim of reaching a better harmonisation of all safety requirements with a functional ship configuration.

These criteria have been applied to the high speed Ro-Ro/Passenger vessels MDV 1200 PEGASUS and SUPERSEACAT recently built (or presently under construction) by Fincantieri. Main particulars of the vessels are indicated in the annexed Tables 1 and 2 and sketches of SuperSeaCat are at Figs. 1-4.

In the development of these ships, not only the IMO HSC Code safety requirements have been taken into account, but additional studies have been carried out, and peculiar technical solutions adopted in order to ensure the best well balanced safety in respect to the requirements of low weight and high speed.

In the following sections particular emphasis will be addressed to:

- Vessel basic architecture and damage stability assessment.

- Reliability of components and failure effect analysis.

- Selection of materials.

2. VESSEL ARCHITECTURE AND DAMAGE STABILITY ASSESSMENT

2.1 VESSEL ARCHITECTURE

Particular care has been taken in the choice of some basic features connected to the overall safety of the ship's watertightness, intact and damaged stability.

These features are related to: hull shape, bulkhead subdivision, openings with risk of sea water ingress.

Hull Shape

The selected hull shape, a deep-V monohull with rather low figure of the length/beam ratio allows a high GM value and wide righting arm diagram in the intact ship condition and it is intrinsically free from major asymmetric flooding.

The high beam value allows easy U-turns inside the ship, with loading and unloading by stern doors.

Bulkheads

A larger number of transverse bulkheads have been selected, in order to prevent the flooding of the garage deck in case of two contiguous damaged compartments. No longitudinal bulkheads have been utilized to avoid asymmetric flooding and therefore all safety devices (evacuation slides, rescue boats and rafts) are readily deployable in any damage occurrence.

Openings

No bow visor has been installed and therefore the structure of the ship is not impaired and it is intrinsically "fool proof", in this respect.

Funnels are utilized for exhaust gas instead of side exhaust openings, therefore there is no danger of sea water ingestion in rough sea conditions (and of smoke on the quay when manoeuvring alongside).

2.2   DAMAGE STABILITY

The ship has been designed in order to fulfil MSC.36(63) HSC Code requirements, but the presence of the wide garage deck and high speed involved, have suggested to Fincantieri to perform additional analysis considering the risk of larger damages in the fore part of the ship and the possible presence of water on the garage deck.

Damage of Fore Part

The ship has been designed to fulfil stability requirements with two continuous damaged compartments.

A further damage case (not requested by Rules) has been examined, considering the maximum damage of fore compartments of the ship.

In this case the ship can survive with a maximum of four contiguous damaged compartments (about 40% of ship's length) fulfilling the damage stability criteria (SOLAS 90).

In the further case of damage of the bottom of the ship (maintaining intact the garage deck) the ship could float with even more flooded compartments.

Water on Garage Deck

In order to consider the event of trapped water on garage deck in damaged conditions an extensive model test campaign has been carried out at the Danish Maritime Institute according to the method described in the Appendix "Model Test Method" to the Annex "Stability Requirements Pertaining to the Agreement" as amended during the Solas Conference 3.46 London, 29th November 1995.

After a preliminary damage stability analysis, two damage cases of the ship in full load were chosen for testing:

- the damage of the two engine room compartments to which corresponds the minimum GZ curve area;

- the damage corresponding to the midship damage with the lowest freeboard after damage. In this case there is the maximum risk of trapped water on the garage deck. Anyhow the present HSC Code does not have any minimum damage freeboard requirement.

The model was tested in both damage cases with lateral waves of 4m significant height. The survival criteria were fully satisfied with a very high safety margin; in fact after more than 60 minutes (in full scale), no water on the garage deck was observed.

Additional Damage Stability Investigations

In order to investigate the limits of survivability of this type of hull forms, the test campaign continued by reducing freeboard and increasing the height of the center of gravity far outside the range of the existing ship.

A complete description of test conditions and test results is related in Ref. (1) in which there are also the results of damage stability calculations with SOLAS-90 formulation and with additional water on garage deck, with the "Regional Agreement" requirements.

The main conclusions of this test campaign can be summarized as follows:

- The "existing" ship is extremely safe with respect to damage stability fulfilling the survivability criteria of model tests and static calculations prescribed with SOLAS-90 and "Regional Agreement Water on Garage Deck".

- The tests with parametric investigation of survivability in respect to freeboard and GM both reduced far beyond the range of the existing ship showed that the ship never capsized even with a certain amount of accumulated water on the garage deck.

- For this type of hull form static calculations with water on the garage deck as prescribed by the "Regional Agreement on Specific Stability Requirement" give considerably worse survivability results than the model test ones.

- The good results of survivability of the ship in damage conditions is due, in the opinion of the authors, partially to the hull forms but more to the high number of watertight bulkhead subdivisions.

- The results obtained during this test campaign demonstrate the intrinsic damage safety of a high speed monohull, in line with previous experimental results of tests carried out for conventional Ro-Ro ferries (2).

3. RELIABILITY AND FAILURE EFFECT ANALYSIS

A fast ferry is supposed to operate almost round-the-clock, hopefully for a good part of the year, close to her maximum performances and with a high margin of safety.

To fulfil these very demanding requirements several factors must be identified and properly evaluated, like:

- a sound structure, possibly as simple as possible;

- well proven components and systems;

- exhaustive simulations and analyses;

- efficient and tested operating procedures;

- serious training of personnel;

to mention some of the most important.

3.1. ELECTROMAGNETIC COMPATIBILITY

While it is needless to mention the impact of reliable components on vessel operativity, it is worth discussing and analysing the importance of the correct working conditions of the electro/ electronic systems that connect, manage and control the various components onboard a vessel.

A possible malfunction of these systems and equipment could cause the same effect, if not worse, of a real failure.

The origin of these possible malfunctions is usually due to electromagnetic interference (EMI), which impairs the electromagnetic compatibility (EMC) of the various equipment.

By compatibility we mean the capability of each system to operate without degradation or malfunction, so as to allow the ship to fulfil her tasks.

The criteria to be followed in order to verify the electro-magnetic compatibility of the systems installed onboard are described in the so-called EMC Control Plan.

EMC control requires the adoption of EMI minimising technique and the identification of possible correction measures after the ship test.

The main activities concerning the EMC control are:

- Criteria definition: it represents the instructions for the bodies of individuals involved with the realization of the vessel regarding criteria and techniques to be adopted in specific areas.

- Project development: it is the application of said criteria and techniques of the EMC Control Plan.

- Installation survey: to verify the compliance to the Control Plan, in particular as regards bonding and cable separation.

- EMI test: this activity involves the following phases:

a) onboard check of the correct operation of the various equipment;

b) check of dangerous areas for the personnel, if any.

The results are recorded in the EMC Test Report where the corrective steps to be undertaken are also described.

3.2. FAILURE MODE AND EFFECT ANALYSIS (FMEA)

The International Code of Safety for High Speed Craft (HSC Code), in Annex 4, requires a Failure Mode and Effect Analysis to be performed for each high speed craft before entering into service.

The FMEA study should be performed for the following systems:

- directional control;

- propulsion;

- electrical power generation and distribution;

- stabilization.

taking into account the typical operational modes within the normal design environmental conditions of the craft, i.e.:

- normal seagoing conditions at full speed;

- maximum permitted operating speed in congested waters;

- manoeuvring alongside.

The main objective is to provide a comprehensive and documented investigation which establishes the major failure conditions of the craft and assesses their impact with regard to safety of the vessel, its occupants and the environment.

It contains the following sections:

- an explanation of the applied methodology;

- a description of the craft and its operative profile;

- a description of the systems;

- an explanation of the work hypothesis and system block diagrams;

- conclusions and recommendation;

- the test programme.

All system block diagrams and FMEA worksheets, produced during the study, will be included in the final report.

Failure Mode and Effect Analysis is based on a single failure concept under which each individual failure is considered as an independent occurrence with no relation to other failures in the system, except for the subsequent effect that it might cause.

As required by the Code the FMEA is performed at two different level of detail: the first one is a functional failure analysis of the craft's main systems, the second one is a more detailed FMEA investigation of all those systems whose individual failure can cause hazardous or catastrophic effects and where a redundant system is not provided.

The analysis is carried out with the aim of defining the major failure conditions that may exist in systems and equipment and to comment on a qualitative assessment for the probability of such failures and their possible effects.

Following the Code requirements, both local and end failure effects are evaluated and the severity of end effects are classified in accordance with the categories proposed by the Code.

Failure detection devices and alternative modes of operation are indicated.

The analysis includes the review of any FMEA provided by equipment suppliers.

Finally, a trial programme is drawn up with the aim to confirm the scope and findings of the FMEA by simulating failures of the system being analysed.

In accordance with the Code Requirements the programme includes all systems and system elements whose failure would lead to major or more severe effects, restricted operations and any other corrective action.

4.   SELECTION OF MATERIALS

A major hazard onboard a vessel is represented by fire. This is particularly true in the case of high speed passenger ferries, where there is a high concentration of people, in presence of areas of major fire risk, like engine rooms and garage. To this respect, the HSC Code is emphasizing fire and smoke safety by imposing precise and tough rules about smoke emission of materials to be adopted onboard a fast ferry, being those materials either to be used in service spaces like engine rooms or garage area (basically in case of fire insulation) and in passenger area (paints, lining material, carpeting, non metallic partitions and so on).

These rules have entered into force very recently (1.1.1996) and they differ from similar rules to be adopted for "SOLAS vessels". Therefore, in general, materials suitable to be used onboard a traditional ship cannot be employed in a high speed craft, because they have to meet the requirements of different specifications.

Moreover, due to the novelty of the governing rules and to the dimensions of the market (for sure increasing, but not as big as the one of conventional ships), they are not yet completely developed by the industry and hence are difficult to be found on the market in a large variety.

As an example, the previous MSC/ Circ. 581 - "Guidance for Fire Test Procedures on Smoke and toxic products generated big combustible materials on fire", has been superseded by HSC41(64) - "Interim Standard for Measuring smoke and toxic products of combustion" and this new rule is much more demanding than the previous one, while the so-called Fire Restricting materials have to comply with the new rule MSC 40(64) "Standard for qualifying Marine Materials for HSC as Fire Restricting Materials".

5.   CONCLUSIONS

A Category "B" High Speed Craft is supposed to survive after a "reasonable" accident occurrence like a two compartments hull damage, a failure of a major component, an incipient fire.

This "survival capability" must be ascertained at the design stage, in order to be in position to perform the necessary modifications (if any) to meet this requirement.

In its global approach to the safety problem, Fincantieri decided to investigate fields which are not, so far, of usual routine like, inter alia:

-    model testing of damage stability in rough sea of a fast ferry to evaluate water ingress in Ro-Ro deck;

-    definition of design methodologies and test procedure to ascertain Electromagnetic Compatibility of the systems onboard;

-    direct involvement, with Suppliers, in research to define materials for outfitting, in line with the new safety requirements.

6.   ACKNOWLEDGEMENTS

The authors want to thank Mr M Schindler and the Danish Maritime Institute for the good work performed carrying out the tests and the analysis of damage stability.

REFERENCES

1.   SCHINDLER, M: 'Damage Stability Tests of a Model Representing a Fast Ro-Ro Passenger Ferry', RINA Rapid Marine Transport Group London, 6-7 February 1997.

2.   Confitarma (Italian Association of Ship Owners) - Italian Research on Ro-Ro Passenger Safety - August 1995.

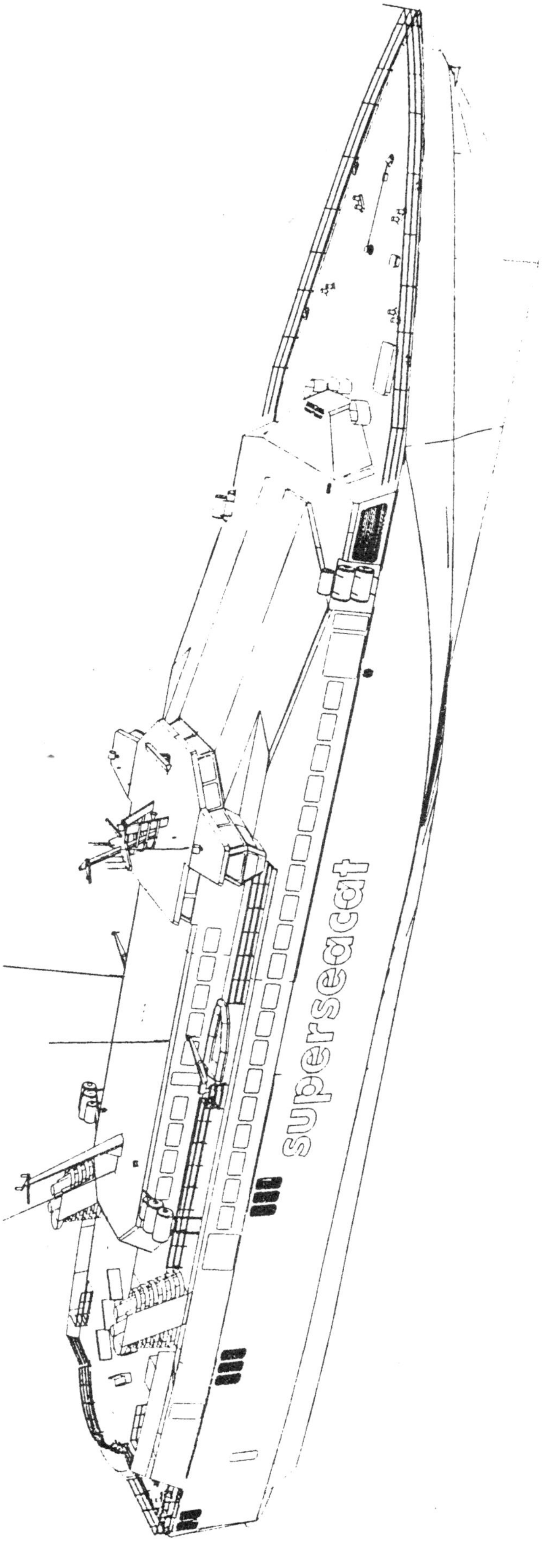

FIG. 1 - PERSPECTIVE VIEW

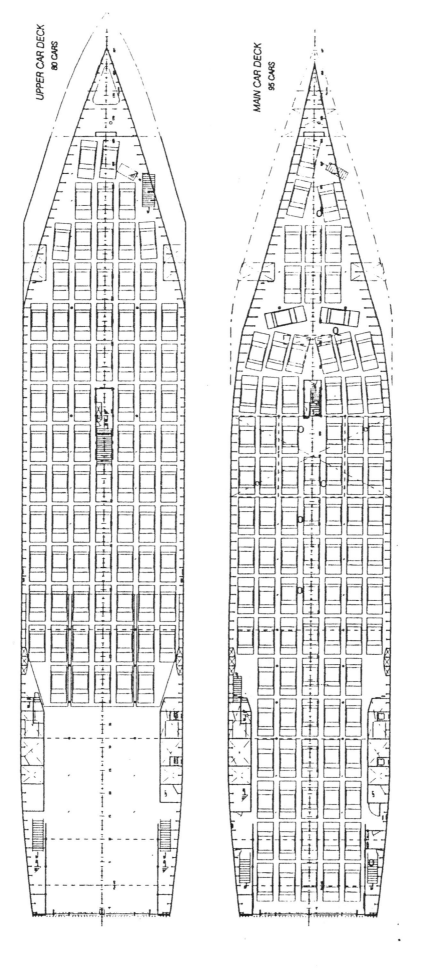

UPPER CAR DECK
80 CARS

MAIN CAR DECK
95 CARS

FIG. 2 - LOWER DECKS

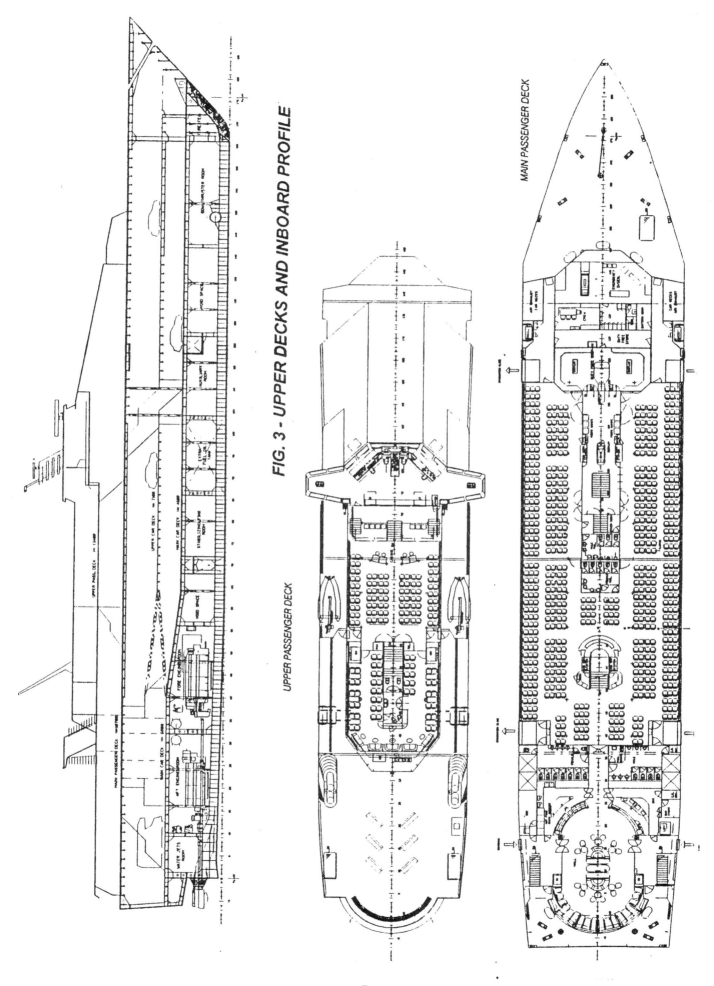

FIG. 3 - UPPER DECKS AND INBOARD PROFILE

UPPER PASSENGER DECK

MAIN PASSENGER DECK

7

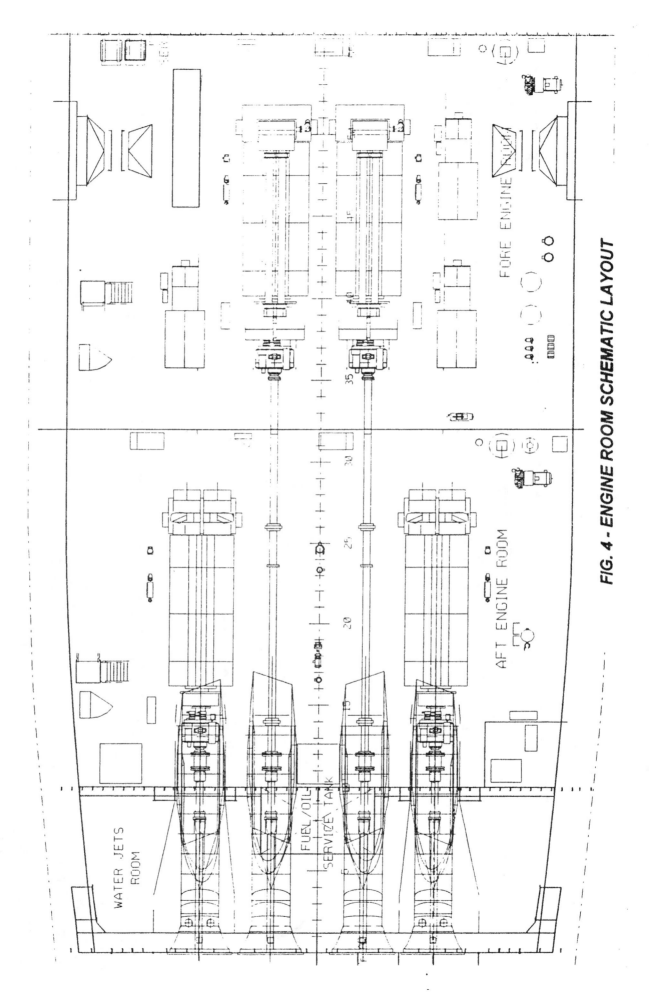

FIG. 4 - ENGINE ROOM SCHEMATIC LAYOUT

WATER JETS ROOM

FUEL/OIL SERVICE TANK

AFT ENGINE ROOM

FORE ENGINE ROOM

TABLE 1

MDV 1200 PEGASUS

MAIN PARTICULARS

SHIP TYPE	**Monohull Deep-Vee**
HULL MATERIAL	**High Tensile Steel**

DIMENSIONS

- Length overall	about 95. m
- Length between pp	82. m
- Moulded beam	16. m
- Depth	10.5 m

TRANSPORT CAPACITY

- Passenger	600
- Cars	170
- Coaches	up to 6
- Design Deadweight	400 tonnes

PROPULSION

- Engines	4 x MTU 20V1163TB73
- Propulsors	4 x Kamewa 112
- Reduction Gears	4 x Renk PLS 250
- Speed	36 knots

CLASSIFICATION SOCIETIES

- Registro Italiano Navale
- Germanischer Lloyd

TABLE 2

SUPERSEACAT

MAIN PARTICULARS

SHIP TYPE   Monohull Deep-Vee

HULL MATERIAL   Aluminum Alloy

DIMENSIONS

- Length overall   about 100. m
- Length between pp   88. m
- Moulded beam   17.1 m
- Depth   10.7 m

TRANSPORT CAPACITY

- Passenger   800
- Cars   175
- Design Deadweight   340 tonnes

PROPULSION

- Engines   4 x Ruston 20RK270
- Propulsors   4 x Kamewa 112 S II
- Reduction Gears   4 x Renk PLS 250
- Max Speed (full load)   about 40 knots

CLASSIFICATION SOCIETIES

- Registro Italiano Navale
- Det Norske Veritas

PAPER NO.10.

RECENT DEVELOPMENTS IN FIRE SAFETY FOR HIGH SPEED CRAFT

by T Eidal, Det Norske Veritas AS, Norway

Paper presented at the

International Symposium & Seminar

THE SAFETY OF HIGH SPEED CRAFT

6 - 7 FEBRUARY 1997 LONDON

RECENT DEVELOPMENTS IN FIRE SAFETY FOR HIGH SPEED CRAFT

Tormod Eidal
Det Norske Veritas AS, Norway

SUMMARY

Important aspects for fire safety on high speed craft are discussed. Special emphasis is given to areas where regulations in the International Code of Safety for High Speed Craft deviate from earlier regulations, or from the requirements for conventional ships. The paper focuses on the philosophy behind accepting Fire-Restricting Materials and the fire test procedures and criteria that govern the use of such combustible materials. The basis and main requirements for fire-resisting divisions and fire fighting systems are presented. Some examples of novel types of materials and systems which are accepted by Det Norske Veritas AS are included.

AUTHOR'S BIOGRAPHY

Mr Tormod Eidal has been working as Plan Approval Surveyor in the Fire Safety Section at Det Norske Veritas AS head office in Oslo, Norway, since 1992. His main tasks have been within fire safety for high speed craft. Mr Eidal gained his MSc from the Department of Marine Systems Design at the Technical University of Norway in 1991.

1. INTRODUCTION

The IMO Code of Safety for High Speed Craft (HSC Code) came into force 1 January 1996. The development and introduction of this new international regulation has made it possible to construct larger types of fast ferries than what was accepted in the previous Dynamically Supported Craft Code (DSC Code) adopted in 1977. With respect to fire safety, the new Code has lead to a boost in the development of new solutions in areas such as construction and outfitting materials and fire extinguishing systems.

Det Norske Veritas (DNV) has a strong position among the classification societies with respect to classification of high speed craft. Most of the large high speed ferries that have been built in recent years have been classed by DNV. This has given the society important experience in interpretation of the requirements in the HSC Code and knowledge about practical arrangements and solutions that comply with the Code requirements. This paper describes some of the most important and interesting developments with respect to fire safety for high speed craft in recent years.

2. FIRE SAFETY PHILOSOPHY FOR HIGH SPEED CRAFT

Conventional passenger ships in international trade are obligated to comply with the Regulations in the International Convention for the Safety of Life at Sea (SOLAS), 1974, as amended. The HSC Code is based on the understanding that compliance with the SOLAS Convention is not the only possible way of ascertaining a satisfactory safety level for transportation at sea.

The Code takes into account that high speed craft are of lighter displacement than conventional ships and that low weight is an essential parameter for the viability of such craft. Based on this, the Code allows for use of non-conventional shipbuilding materials, provided that a safety standard which is at least equivalent to that of conventional ships is ensured. Equivalent safety standards for high speed craft are achieved by management and reduction of risk, passive protection in the event of an accident and by restricting service areas to particular routes with satisfactory infrastructure and rescue facilities.

Two different categories of vessels are described in the Code:

1) Category A passenger craft, or assisted craft, are craft of similar type to the ones originally foreseen when the DSC Code was developed. Such vessels are not to carry more than 450 passengers and are to comply with strict requirements to operation areas and availability of rescue assistance.

2) Category B passenger craft, or unassisted craft, may be operated in areas where rescue assistance is not readily available and may carry any number of passengers. Such vessels are to be provided with a safe refuge on board, and are to comply with increased requirements to fire-resisting divisions and redundancy of important systems, including propulsion and fire fighting.

Basic principles and conditions which underlie the regulations of the fire safety chapter in the HSC Code are listed in item 7.1 of the Code. This paper focuses on three of the most important principles for fire safety of high speed craft:

1) Reduce risk of fire and its consequences by enforcing strict requirements to fire technical properties of combustible materials and to limit the amount of such materials.

2) Reduce possibility for a fire to spread from its place of origin to other parts of the vessel by subdividing the craft by fire-resisting divisions.

3) Extinguish any fire in its space of origin by ensuring that appropriate fire fighting equipment is available.

These are areas where there recently have been developments in requirements and areas where new technical solutions are being introduced.

3. RESTRICTED USE OF COMBUSTIBLE MATERIALS

3.1 COMBUSTIBLE MATERIALS IN SOLAS AND THE DSC CODE

The basic principles governing the fire safety Regulations for conventional passenger ships in the SOLAS Convention may be divided into two main groups; passive fire protection and active fire protection. Passive fire protection includes principles like restricted use of combustible materials and subdivision of the vessels by fire-resisting decks and bulkheads to prevent fires from spreading from their places of origin. Correspondingly, active fire protection includes factors like detection and extinguishing of fires in their spaces of origin.

In accordance with the above notion of passive fire protection, the SOLAS Convention requires that construction materials for passenger ships are to be steel or equivalent materials. Steel or equivalent material is understood to mean a non-combustible material, which either by itself or due to insulation provided, is able to maintain integrity and structural properties equivalent to those of steel when tested in a standard fire test for the relevant time period. Non-combustible materials are materials which comply with the test criteria in IMO Res.A.799(19).

The SOLAS Convention restricts the use of combustible materials also for other purposes than construction materials. Regulations include limitations on amount and calorific value of combustible veneers, requirements to low flame spread properties of surface facings and requirements to fire technical properties of insulation materials, furniture etc. Restrictions vary depending on category of space.

The DSC Code generally required that hulls were to be constructed of non-combustible materials. Similarly, insulation materials, ceilings, linings and furniture were to be non-combustible. Surface facings and furniture upholstery were to have low flame-spread properties.

The Code did, however, permit the use of combustible construction materials provided that "additional precautions" were taken to ensure equivalent fire safety standards were achieved. A number of high speed craft with combustible composite hulls have been constructed to the DSC Code based on this rather vague allowance. The actual amount of additional precautions taken for these vessels has varied widely, while some vessels have no fire safety compensation for the use of combustible construction materials at all.

3.2 COMBUSTIBLE MATERIALS IN THE HSC CODE

3.2.1 Basic requirements to combustible materials

The requirements regarding fire properties for materials used in the construction and outfitting of fast ferries have been transferred from the DSC Code to the new HSC Code. In principle, all materials which were accepted in the previous Code are also acceptable in vessels built to the HSC Code. The exception being that the previous allowance for combustible construction materials based on undefined additional safety precautions has been removed, and replaced with detailed test requirements for all combustible materials.

Test standards for furniture, suspended textiles, deck finish materials and bedding components are referred to in part 7.4.3 of the Code. Item 7.4.3.6 states that "Materials used in the craft, when exposed to fire, should not emit smoke or toxic gases in quantities that could be dangerous to humans as determined in tests of a standard developed by the Organization". A draft version of this standard, applicable to both high speed craft and conventional ships, was adopted by IMO in Resolution MSC.41(64) "Interim Standard for Measuring Smoke and Toxic Products of Combustion". A revised version of this document was discussed at the 41st session of the IMO sub-committee on fire protection (FP41) and will be included in the coming Fire Test Procedure Code.

3.2.2 Fire-Restricting Materials and Full Scale Testing

As an alternative to conventional non-combustible materials and low flame spread surfaces, the HSC Code allows the use of combustible materials for virtually all purposes, provided they comply with requirements of a totally new class of materials called *Fire-Restricting Materials (FRM)*.

The acceptance of this class of combustible materials is based on two main principles:

1) The recognition that new types of materials are necessary for novel types of craft and that overall safety standards can be maintained with the right use of such materials.

2) The recognition that function based fire test requirements can provide a more accurate picture of the actual fire hazard involved in using combustible materials than conventional small scale indicative tests.

Traditionally, non-combustible materials are required in ships and fast ferries because these materials do not contribute to, or significantly increase the heat release from a fire in a vessel. The basic philosophy behind FRM is that these materials are to have fire properties which ensures that a realistic initial fire scenario in one location will not result in a critical situation for the craft or for the people on board.

FRM are defined in item 7.2.2 of the HSC Code as those materials which have the following fire properties:

1) they should have low flame-spread characteristics;

2) limited heat flux, due regard being paid to the risk of ignition of furniture in the compartment;

3) limited rate of heat release, due regard being paid to the risk of spread of fire to an adjacent compartment; and

4) gas and smoke should not be emitted in quantities that could be dangerous to the occupants of the craft.

The Code defines the concept of *Local Fire* as the standard fire to which FRM are to be tested. The test method referred to for this local fire is *"Fire tests - Full-scale room test for surface products"* adopted by the International Organization for Standardisation (ISO) by ISO 9705.

This test is a function based large scale test for determining the fire properties of surface products. The materials which are to be tested are mounted to the walls and ceiling of a test room (2.4 x 3.6 x 2.4 m) as intended used. An ignition source consisting of a propane gas burner is located in one of the corners of the room. Initially the burner has a net heat output of 100kW, roughly corresponding to the heat produced by fire in a large paper bin. After 10 minutes the heat output is increased to 300kW, corresponding to the heat released from the burning upholstery of a chair. Total test period is 20 minutes. The fire development in the room is monitored by measuring heat flux, rate of heat release and production of smoke and gases. The material properties of the tested product determine the progress of the test fire and the time before flashover occurs in the test room. Products with good fire properties do not lead to flashover. Test set-up is shown in Figure 1.

The test method is function based in that the ignition source and the surface products simulate a realistic fire scenario starting in the corner of a small room. It is different from conventional surface material tests in that it takes into account the effects on the materials behind the surface when the actual combination of materials are exposed to a realistic fire. It is important that the surface product is tested on the same combination of backing materials as intended for use in the actual application.

The test method is conservative in that the ignition source is larger, and applied for a longer period of time, than what can normally be expected in a high speed craft. Furthermore, the ignition source is located in a corner, which is the most critical location, and the test room is smaller than most spaces on board a fast ferry. A flashover develops more easily in a small room than in a larger space.

ISO 9705 does not contain any acceptance criteria. Because of this, IMO has developed resolution MSC.40(64) "Standard for qualifying marine materials for high speed craft as fire-restricting materials". A material complies with this Standard if the following six acceptance criteria are fulfilled:

1) the time average of heat release rate (HRR) excluding the HRR from the ignition source does not exceed 100kW;

2) the maximum heat release rate (HRR) excluding the HRR from the ignition source does not exceed 500kW averaged over any 30 s period of time during the test;

3) the time average of the smoke production rate does not exceed 1.4 m²/s;

4) the maximum value of the smoke production rate does not exceed 8.3 m²/s averaged over any period of 60 s during the test;

5) flame spread must not reach any further down the walls of the test room than 0.5 m from the floor excluding the area which is within 1.2 m from the corner where the ignition source is located; and

6) no flaming drops or debris of the test sample may reach the floor of the test room outside the area which is within 1.2 m from the corner where the ignition source is located.

The acceptance criteria listed above have been developed to cover all requirements to fire properties for fire-restricting materials. The limitations on heat release assure that the material does not lead to flashover. Together with requirements to flame spread this will reduce the possibility that a fire will ignite furniture in the space or spread to adjacent compartments. The requirements to smoke production rate ensure a reasonable sight length in case of fire and make evacuation easier. The test method allows measurements of toxic gas production, but IMO has decided not to include criteria for such gases in the Standard. This was based on the judgement that strict requirements to heat release, flame spread and smoke production in practice also limit the development of toxic gases.

3.2.3   Small Scale Testing of Fire-Restricting Materials

There has been some uncertainty among authorities and building yards with respect to need for small scale testing in addition to ISO 9705 for FRM. From the above paragraph it should be clear that no such additional small scale testing is necessary. However, the HSC Code also refers to a different test standard for the material class. This is the *"Fire Tests - Reaction to fire - Rate of heat release from building products (Cone calorimeter method)"* adopted by ISO as specified in ISO 5660. The Cone calorimeter method is a small scale test in which heat release and smoke production are measured.

IMO has recognised that full scale testing is not suitable or practicable for all areas where fire-restricting materials can be used. Resolution MSC.40(64) therefore states that materials used for furniture and other components should be tested to ISO 5660 in stead of ISO 9705. The test set-up is shown in Figure 2.

A major problem with the use of the Cone calorimeter test is that IMO so far has not been able to adopt uniform acceptance criteria. Several proposals have been submitted to the Organisation, but presently none have gained enough support to be adopted. The IMO member states have considered that the experience with the test method is not sufficient to decide on acceptance criteria at this stage. There is also a fundamental question as to at what level requirements fire-restricting materials tested to ISO 5660 should correspond. Should requirements to furniture frames etc. be equivalent to those for combustible construction materials or can less stringent requirements be applied since the amount of material used for this purpose is normally very limited compared to the use of construction materials?

Work has been done to establish computer based models to predict large-scale performances of materials in accordance with ISO 9705 based on test results from the Cone calorimeter method. The intention has been that with increased experience, the much simpler and cheaper small scale test could normally be sufficient to classify most construction materials as FRM without the need to carry out expensive and time consuming full scale room tests. Experience so far suggests that there is still a long way to go before such models based on small scale testing will provide sufficiently accurate predictions of large scale test results in general, if indeed this is ever achieved.

One area in which the Cone calorimeter method has already proven its usefulness is in comparison of fire properties for similar materials. Requiring full scale testing in accordance with ISO 9705 for all versions of very similar materials may be considered unnecessarily onerous. According to DNV Rules, several similar versions of the same material may be accepted, based on a full scale test of the most critical version, provided tests, in accordance with ISO 5660, document that the similar versions are less critical. A combustible sandwich material with different outer surface facings is an example of what may be considered similar versions of the same material in this connection.

3.2.4 Fire-Restricting Materials Recently Approved by DNV

Several companies have DNV type approvals for their light weight, non-load carrying, bulkhead panels based on testing in accordance with ISO 9705 and ISO 5660. Imi-Tech Corporation (Plano, Texas) is the supplier of a flame-resistant polyimide foam which has been DNV type approved as a fire-restricting material. The foam may be used as comfort insulation on high speed craft and is stated to have a total weight of 8.4 kg/m^3.

No combustible material suited for the construction of main load carrying structure has so far been approved by DNV in accordance with the new regulations. However, several companies and yards are involved in the development of such materials and a break through may come in the near future.

4. REQUIREMENTS TO FIRE-RESISTING DIVISIONS

4.1 PHILOSOPHY AND MAIN PRINCIPLES

The SOLAS Convention divides all areas on conventional passenger ships into 14 different categories with respect to fire safety. Separate tables describe requirements for segregation of these categories with fire-resisting divisions for decks and bulkheads respectively. For vessels built to the DSC Code, fire insulation was only required to enclose fire hazard areas such as engine rooms and car decks and to protect the wheelhouse from other enclosed spaces.

Subdivision of craft by fire-resisting divisions is an important part of the passive fire protection principle in the HSC Code. Fire-resisting divisions are to reduce the possibility for a fire to spread from its place of origin and to make fires easier to extinguish. The divisions shall protect passengers and crew from smoke and heat and, if necessary, make it possible to evacuate the craft.

The HSC Code divides spaces on high speed craft into the following 6 groups based on fire risk:

a) Areas of Major Fire Hazard.
b) Areas of Moderate Fire Hazard.
c) Areas of Minor Fire Hazard.
d) Control Stations.
e) Evacuation Stations and External Escape Routes.
f) Open Spaces.

Table 7.4-1 in the Code describes the required structural fire protection times for separating bulkheads and decks of passenger craft based on these categories. The periods listed are minimum times for Category B craft. Requirements to minimum structural fire protection times are linked to the documented time for evacuation of the vessel. For Category A craft which can be quickly evacuated, protection times may be reduced to 30 minutes in areas where the table specifies 60 minutes.

Fire-resisting divisions on ships constructed to the SOLAS Convention are to be tested in accordance with IMO Resolution A.754(18) *"Recommendation on fire resistance tests for "A", "B" and "F" class divisions"*. SOLAS describes the time-temperature curve for the *"Standard fire test"* to which such divisions are to be tested. For high speed craft, testing in accordance with the *Standard fire test* is only relevant for areas of major and moderate fire hazard (Group A and B). For all other areas on high speed craft the concept of *Local Fire*, as described in connection with requirements to FRM, is the dimensioning fire scenario.

Strict requirements to reduce fire risk apply to areas where only *Local Fire* is foreseen. Passenger Lounges are accepted as areas of minor fire hazard based on restrictions to the use of combustible materials and based on the principle that such spaces are open areas with no sleeping berths and with people present who will detect and extinguish a starting fire at an early stage.

A consequence of the *Local Fire* philosophy is that there are no requirements to fire insulation of structure inside, or enclosing, minor fire hazard areas. Spaces of little fire risk need not be protected to withstand a *Standard fire test* and are allowed to collapse if they are exposed to a fire of such magnitude. The requirement that control stations are to be structurally fire protected from areas of minor fire hazard is an exception from the general philosophy. Main load-carrying structures inside areas of major and moderate fire hazard are to be fire insulated to avoid collapse in case of fire for the relevant test period.

Category B craft differ from other passenger vessels in that such craft are required to maintain main functions and safety systems, including propulsion and control, after fire in any one compartment on board. This makes it necessary for Category B craft to be provided with a minimum of two independent main engine rooms, separated by fire-resisting divisions.

4.2 TEST REQUIREMENTS FOR FIRE-RESISTING DIVISIONS

Fire-resisting divisions for high speed craft are defined in item 7.2.1 of the HSC Code. The most notable differences between such divisions and *"A" class divisions* in the SOLAS Convention, are the acceptance of combustible materials and the possibility to test for less than 60 minutes. FRM may be used in lieu of non-combustible materials for fire-resisting divisions in the same way as for all other parts of the construction and outfitting of high speed craft. Fire tests can normally be ended after 30 minutes unless the division is to be used as a 60 minutes fire division in Category B craft.

IMO has developed resolution MSC.45(64) "Test Procedure for Fire-Resisting Divisions of High Speed Craft" to describe how fire divisions for fast ferries are to be tested. This resolution uses IMO Resolution A.754(18), as adopted for conventional ships, as a basis. In resolution MSC.45(64), testing of fire-resisting divisions is described in three separate parts; non-load bearing fire-resisting divisions, load bearing fire-resisting divisions with structural metal core and other load bearing fire-resisting divisions.

Recommendations for testing of non-load bearing divisions and for testing of metal core divisions are similar to those of IMO Resolution A.754(18). Aluminium is the most commonly used construction material for high speed craft and the requirement to maximum temperature rise in the structural core of aluminium divisions is often the critical factor with respect to fire insulation.

Testing of load bearing divisions without a structural metal core deviates from testing of conventional fire-resisting divisions. Such divisions may be constructed of combustible materials. Evenly distributed loads are applied to non-metallic decks and bulkheads during fire testing. Criteria for maximum deflection and rate of deflection are to be fulfilled in addition to the conventional criteria for fire-resisting divisions.

It should be noted that the above requirements to load-carrying capability of fire-resisting divisions are independent of requirements to FRM. This test need only be carried out on a FRM if such materials are used as the load-carrying core in fire-resisting divisions.

4.3 FACTORS TO BE CONSIDERED AND SYSTEM EXAMPLES

4.3.1 Important Factors

In conformity with the construction of high speed craft, weight is of prime importance when shipyards decide on fire insulation systems. Weight considerations often convince yards to use more complex and expensive insulation systems on fast ferries than on conventional ships. For car ferries the optimalization of the structural fire protection on vehicle deck is of critical importance, as this is normally the biggest area where fire insulation is needed.

The extensive use of aluminium in high speed craft makes special considerations necessary compared to conventional steel constructions. Great care must be put into design of all types of penetrations, fastening of steel doors and fire dampers etc. in aluminium structure. Most aluminium alloys lose half their structural capacity at about 250°C and melt at approximately 660°C. A local defect in fire insulation for a steel division may result in a limited hot area on unexposed side, whereas a similar weakness in a system protecting an aluminium construction may initiate a breach in the integrity of the division and lead to a possible collapse of the structure.

At the time of writing, no DNV Type Approval Certificate has been issued to a load bearing fire-resisting divisions with a non-metallic core. However, we are aware of yards who plan to carry out tests for such constructions in the near future.

4.3.2 Examples of fire insulation systems which are type approved by DNV

Figure 3 shows a non-combustible cassette type system primarily designed to protect aluminium structure bounding car decks for 60 minutes. The presented system is developed by Scan-Isolering AS (Porsgrunn, Norway) and is one of several such DNV approved cassette systems. This particular system is stated to have a total weight of 6.3 kg/m² for bulkheads and 5.0 kg/m² for decks. Similar systems are also available for non-load bearing bulkheads where HSC Code Table 7.4-1 requires that divisions are fire protected from both sides.

Ceramic fire insulation blankets are widely used in small craft and in areas where the complexity of aluminium structure makes use of cassette systems impractical. Several such fire insulation systems are type approved by DNV.

5. FIRE EXTINGUISHING SYSTEMS

5.1 SPRINKLER SYSTEMS IN ACCOMMODATION AREAS

The HSC Code requires public spaces, service spaces,

storage rooms and similar areas to be protected by a fixed sprinkler system. This requirement is valid for all types of fast passenger ferries and was not included in the previous DSC Code. IMO has developed Resolution MSC.44(65) "Standards for fixed sprinkler systems for high speed craft" which is recommended for use when designing such systems for accommodation areas on passenger vessels.

Resolution MSC.44(65) describes different alternative sprinkler systems which should be permitted in high speed craft. Both manual and automatic systems are accepted. Automatic systems are divided into wet pipe systems, dry pipe systems and combination systems. Different minimum areas for simultaneous operation of sprinklers apply for the different types of systems. The largest minimum protection area is required for manual systems (280 m²), while the smallest area is required for automatic wet pipe systems (150 m²).

The sprinkler standard specifically states that equivalent systems complying with IMO Resolution A.755(18) "Guidelines for approval of sprinkler systems equivalent to that referred to in SOLAS regulation II-2/12" (revised in Resolution A.800(19)) are accepted as alternatives to manual and automatic sprinkler systems of conventional type. DNV have type approved several types of water fog/mist systems for accommodation areas based on this document. These are extinguishing systems which use smaller water droplets at higher pressure than conventional sprinkler systems. Droplet size, water pressure and application rate varies widely between the different systems. A sprinkler head from Marioff Hi-fog Oy (Vantaa, Finland) is shown in Figure 4. This system operates at a pressure of up to 120 bar at the sprinkler heads and has an application rate of minimum 1.3 l/min/m² for public areas with ceiling height of less than 2.5 meter.

Advantages with water fog/water mist sprinkler systems include possible weight savings, less water damage if the system is activated and possible benefits in installation and testing compared to conventional systems.

5.2 FIRE EXTINGUISHING SYSTEMS FOR AREAS OF MAJOR FIRE HAZARD

5.2.1 Fixed fire fighting in machinery spaces

The HSC Code requires all areas of major fire hazard to be protected by a suitable fixed fire extinguishing system which is possible to operate from the wheelhouse. Where gas is used as the extinguishing medium, a second discharge is to be available. An alternative fixed fire fighting system may be installed in lieu of gas capacity for a second discharge. Previously, Halon 1301 was the preferred extinguishing gas for fast ferries, combining high fire fighting efficiency with low installation weight. Halon does not constitute a danger for crew or other personnel, but is not allowed in new vessels because of its harmful effects on the environment. The CO_2 systems used in most high speed craft today have the disadvantages of being lethal to people present in the protected space and of having relatively high installation weight compared to Halon because of the high required gas concentration.

A number of new agents and fire fighting systems are being proposed as alternatives to Halon and CO_2. New inert gas mixtures are being introduced, extinguishing fires by diluting the oxygen in the air in a similar way as CO_2, but being less harmful to people present. Examples of such gas mixtures are Inergen and Argonite, which both are type approved by DNV. Similarly, much research has been put into finding safe agents which can replace Halon with respect to fire fighting properties, without being harmful to the environment. Examples of such systems are Envirogel, FM200 and Halotron. The Swedish Administration has informed IMO that Halotron is accepted as a replacement gas for Halon on Swedish vessels. Guidelines for approval of equivalent fire extinguishing systems for machinery spaces are currently under development in IMO.

Water fog/water mist systems are being offered also for areas of major fire hazard. Such systems have been accepted in engine rooms of several DNV classed vessels. The IMO document MSC/Circ.668 "Alternative arrangements for Halon Fire-Extinguishing Systems in Machinery Spaces and Pump-Rooms", with amendments, describes recommended requirements for approval of such systems.

5.2.2 Fixed water spray systems for car decks

Car decks are required to be protected by an approved pressure water-spraying system in accordance with Resolution A.123(V) "Recommendation on Fixed Fire-Fighting Systems for Special-Category Spaces", originally adopted by IMO for conventional passenger ferries. In accordance with the HSC Code's basic principle of maintenance of main safety functions in case of fire in any one compartment, DNV requires for Category B craft that the minimum recommended protection area and application rate is to be met even with any one pump room out of function.

Item 7.8.2 in the Code states that other fixed fire fighting systems may be accepted on car deck areas, provided equivalent fire fighting ability is shown in full scale flowing petrol fires. The lack of a recognised test standard to document equivalence has been a main obstacle in accepting novel types of extinguishing systems so far. A draft proposal for such a test method has been submitted to IMO at FP41 by the Swedish Administration. Several high pressure water fog systems have already been installed in high speed craft based on testing in accordance with this document.

6. CONCLUSIONS

The regulations of the HSC Code provides a viable alternative to more conventional requirements with respect to obtaining a satisfactory safety level for transportation at sea. Successful application of the Code relies on building yards and operators of high speed craft following its requirements carefully. It is of similar importance that classification societies and national maritime authorities recognise the differences in safety philosophy for the HSC Code and SOLAS, and not impose customary interpretations for conventional ships on high speed craft.

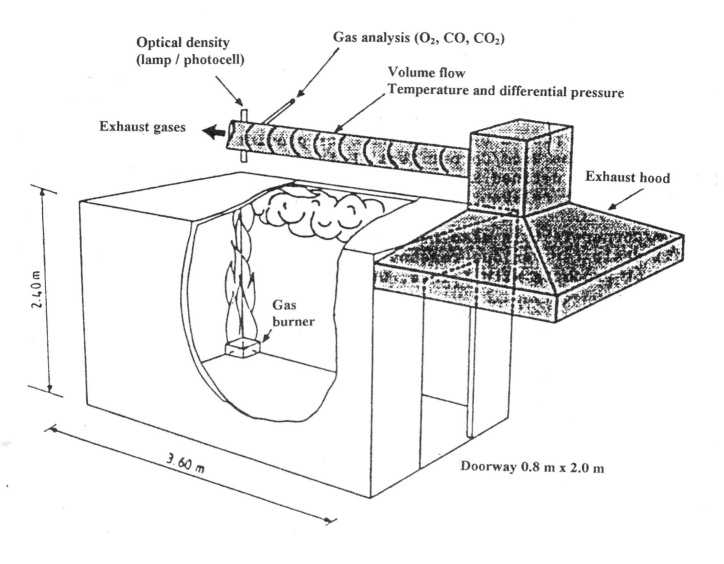

Fig. 1 Test set-up for ISO 9705, Full-Scale room test for surface products

7

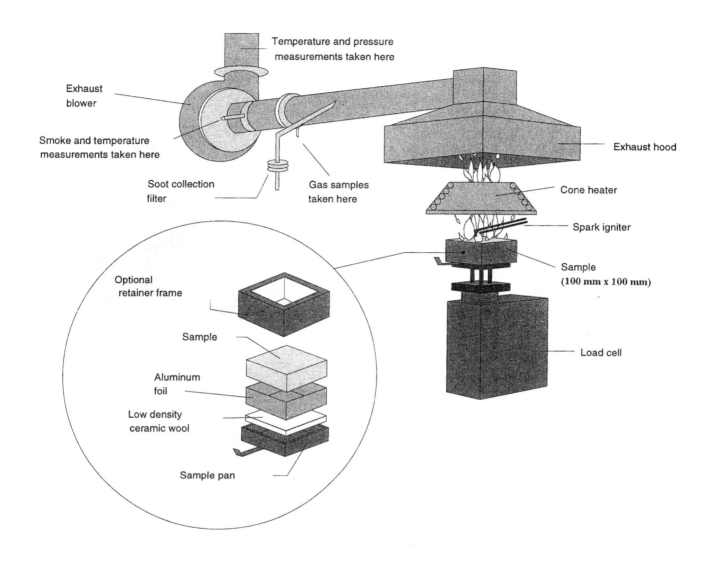

Fig. 2 Test set-up for ISO 5660, Cone calorimeter method

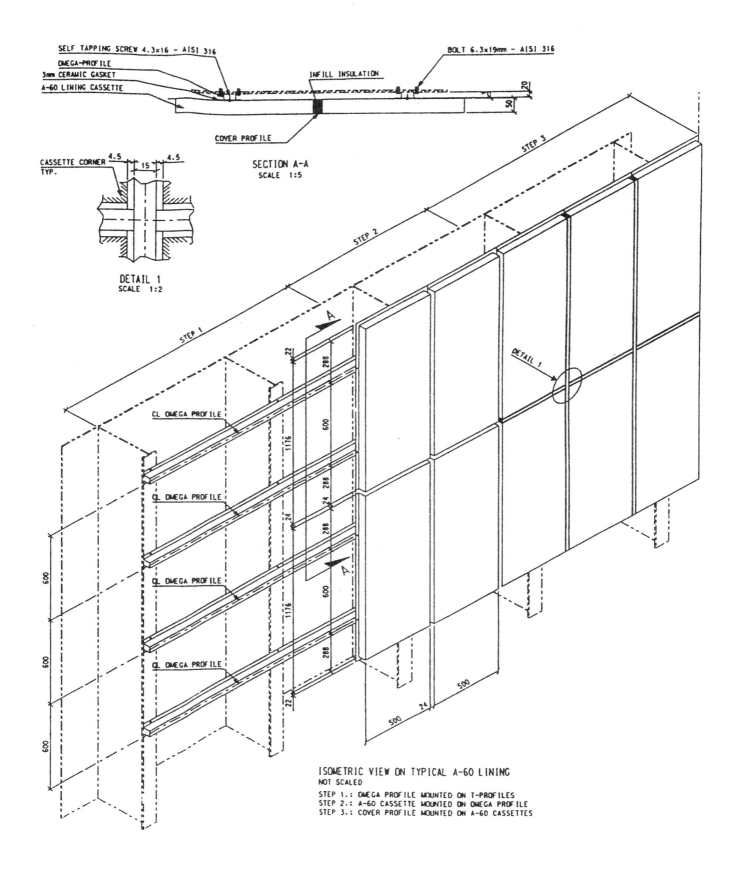

SELF TAPPING SCREW 4.3x16 - AISI 316
OMEGA-PROFILE
3mm CERAMIC GASKET
A-60 LINING CASSETTE
BOLT 6.3x19mm - AISI 316
INFILL INSULATION
COVER PROFILE

SECTION A-A
SCALE 1:5

CASSETTE CORNER
TYP.
4.5   15   4.5

DETAIL 1
SCALE 1:2

STEP 3
STEP 2
STEP 1

A
DETAIL 1

CL OMEGA PROFILE
CL OMEGA PROFILE
CL OMEGA PROFILE
CL OMEGA PROFILE

ISOMETRIC VIEW ON TYPICAL A-60 LINING
NOT SCALED
STEP 1.: OMEGA PROFILE MOUNTED ON T-PROFILES
STEP 2.: A-60 CASSETTE MOUNTED ON OMEGA PROFILE
STEP 3.: COVER PROFILE MOUNTED ON A-60 CASSETTES

Fig. 3   Typical cassette system for 60 minutes fire protection of aluminium structure bounding car decks (Scan-Isolering AS)

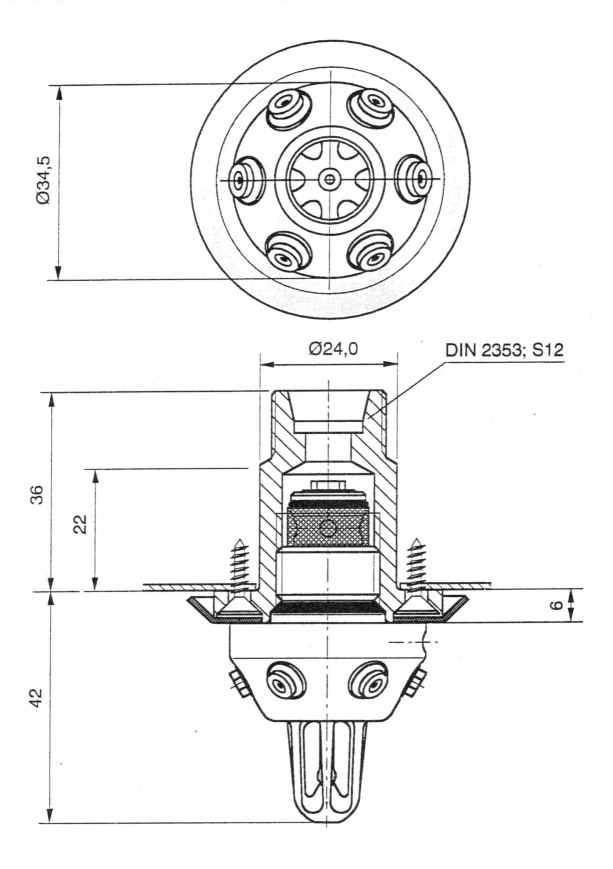

Ø34,5

Ø24,0   DIN 2353; S12

36

22

6

42

Material:
Brass / chrom plated

Assembly body weight 100 g
Sprinkler head weight 130 g

Fig. 4   High pressure water fog sprinkler head for accommodation areas (Marioff Hi-fog OY)

PAPER NO.11.

AN OVERVIEW OF SOME STRUCTURAL DESIGN ASPECTS OF THE IMO HSC CODE

by Professor T Jastrzębski, DSc, PhD, MATMA, MISSC
Technical University of Szczecin, Poland

Paper presented at the

International Symposium & Seminar

THE SAFETY OF HIGH SPEED CRAFT

6 - 7 FEBRUARY 1997 LONDON

AN OVERVIEW OF SOME STRUCTURAL DESIGN ASPECTS OF THE IMO HSC CODE

Professor Tadeusz Jastrzębski, DSc, PhD, MATMA, MISSC
Technical University of Szczecin, Poland

SUMMARY

Since the new IMO Code for High Speed Craft was published in 1994, the various safety aspects of fast ships which are covered by the Code have been discussed in several publications. This paper is mainly devoted to the implications of the Code for the hull structural design and safety.

In the paper at first a definition of high speed is analysed in the relation to the ship types. Then the safety requirements for the ship hull structure are described and the hull strength in service and in damage conditions are briefly discussed. Requirements for structural fire safety and materials are also summarised. In a separate chapter the general craft layout is discussed and illustrated. Finally some considerations are given to a possible application of the risk analysis in hull structural design of fast craft.

AUTHOR'S BIOGRAPHY

Professor Tadeusz Jastrzębski graduated from the Technical University of Gdańsk (TUG) in 1960 with a Master of Science in Naval Architecture. He obtained his Philosophy Doctorate from the Technical University of Szczecin (TUS) in 1986 and Doctorate of Science from TUG in 1994. Since 1996 he has been a Professor of Naval Architecture at the TUS. He is currently Head of the Ship Structure and Mechanics Department in the Ocean and Ship Technology Institute of the Technical University of Szczecin (Poland). In the years 1960-74 he was a Chief Designer in the Ship Design Office of the Gdynia Shipyard; in 1974-77 he was Head of the Design Office in the Oran Shipyard (Algeria), and in 1977-79, a Chief Surveyor in the Polish Register of Shipping. His present scope of activity is research and teaching on ship structural design.

Professor Jastrzębski is the author of a number of research and technical papers on ship structural design, structural materials, design philosophy and high speed craft design. He is a member of the Association Technique Maritime et Aéronautique (France), the International Ship and Offshore Structures Congress, the Polish Association of Naval Architects, the Scientific Board of Polish Register of Shipping and the Scientific Board of the Shipbuilding Research Centre in Gdańsk, Poland.

1. INTRODUCTION

The adoption of the International Code of Safety for High Speed Craft (HSC Code) [1] in 1994 and its coming into force on the 1st January 1996 and replacing the former 1977 IMO Dynamically Supported Craft Code (DSC) [2] constitute the important moments in development of structural design of fast craft. Both before this date and after - several papers were published on the general safety philosophy forming the HSC regulations. Also various design and service aspects of high speed craft in the light of the Code requirements were discussed in some publications [3,4,5]. This paper deals mainly with one field of influence of the HSC which concerns the design and safety criteria for the hull structure of fast craft.

The influence of the regulations of the new Code on the safety is today far greater than it was in the case of the DSC. This influence may be observed in decisions of designers who are forced to follow the requirements of the Code itself as well as the new classification rules. In the latest editions of the Classification Societies rules for the high speed craft the HSC requirements are practically totally included into the rule requirements, like in the Rules of UNITAS (Bureau Veritas, Germanischer Lloyd and Registro Italiano Navale) [6], Det norske Veritas [7] or Lloyd's Register [8].

The general assumptions of the safety philosophy of high speed craft has been clarified in the Preamble to the HSC. It is worth recalling those safety aspects influencing directly the ship hull structure. First of all the new unified definition of high speed and the fact that the Code application was extended to the craft of any size (not only to the ships up to 50m of the length) and to the various ship hull configurations (not only to the dynamically supported craft) constitute the starting point for all design actions. It is taken into consideration in the Code that fast craft are built not only with light materials but also with steels. The loads in collision conditions at the high speed are to be very carefully considered. Some requirements regarding general layout of the ship are also worth paying attention, taking into consideration the strength and integrity of a structure and fire safety. For the first time the basis of the probabilistic approach, which may be used when the craft safety is investigated, is given in the Code. The HSC comprises in total nineteen Chapters; in Chapters from 1 to 7, and Chapters 9, 15 and 16, there are requirements which refer to the hull structure of the fast craft.

2. HIGH SPEED DEFINITION AND SHIP TYPES

The HSC applies to the following high speed craft:

- passenger craft carrying more than 12 passengers (Category A and Category B craft);

- cargo craft of 500 gross tonnage and upwards.

There are no restrictions concerning the ship structural types, so the Code covers: air-cushion vehicles (ACV), hydrofoil boats, surface effect ships (SES) and the others. The Code does not apply to some special type craft like craft of war, troopcraft, craft not propelled by mechanical means, wooden craft of primitive built, pleasure craft not engaged in trade, fishing ships and those navigating in some specific areas.

A main parameter defining the applicability of the HSC is still the speed - the parameter discussed in many papers, for example in [9], and lately in [10]. High speed in the Code is defined by the volumetric Froude Number, and the limit speed is given as:

$$v > 3.7 \cdot \nabla^{0.1667} \qquad (1)$$

where v - speed in metres/second, and ∇ - volume of displacement in cubic metres. The question is how the new Code criterion corresponds to the earlier classification and distinction of vessels into 'fast' and 'slow' craft. And what about the inclusion of existing craft in one or another group of craft? To know the answer a relation between ship displacement and the ship length $\nabla = f(L)$ for different types of fast craft was analysed and simplified linear expressions were found and new Code criterion was expressed as a function of the craft length in the following approximate form:

- hydrofoils: $\qquad v > 7.2(0.9 + 0.10L)^{1/2} \qquad (2)$

- monohulls: $\qquad v > 7.2(1.3 + 0.11L)^{1/2} \qquad (3)$

- hovercraft $\qquad v > 7.2(0.5 + 0.12L)^{1/2} \qquad (4)$

- catamarans, SES: $\quad v > 7.2(0.6 + 0.13L)^{1/2} \qquad (5)$

- SWATH: $\qquad v > 7.2(0.9 + 0.19L)^{1/2} \qquad (6)$

where v is the speed in knots and L is the craft length in metres.

In Fig.1 the old and new IMO criteria are compared. It is clearly shown that the IMO HSC has covered a wider area of craft population since the limit lines of applicability and influence on the ship structure design were lowered for all craft types except SWATHs. The last type due to its displacement/length relation may be in some cases formally excluded from new IMO Code requirements.

3. SAFETY REQUIREMENTS RELATED TO HULL STRUCTURE

A few Chapters of the HSC refer to the fast ship hull structure details. The requirements are formulated directly, like in Chapter 3 "Structures", or the requirements are connected with the other general design criteria or the criteria related to the craft equipment.

In Chapter 2 the design criteria for buoyancy and stability are given. To satisfy those criteria, in the both - intact and damage conditions - a careful analysis which sometimes provokes deep changes in the structure and in the ship layout, is required. The initial metacentric height (0.15 m) can be assured by precise verification of the centre of gravity and this is achieved by selection of the material and dimensions of hull members in the specified hull regions. The structure is required to be capable of sustaining all increased loads in the damage conditions without loss of buoyancy and dangerous degradation of stability. In the analysis of the damage conditions the side and bottom extent of damage should be assumed as shown in Figs. 2 and 3.

Separate Chapter 3 is devoted especially to the hull strength. It concerns all hull and superstructure members which determine the overall and local ship strength. Those strength members should be made of the materials adequate for intended use of the craft. It may be assumed that the application of the materials in accordance with the Classification Rules meet this requirement. For the dimensioning of hull members all possible static and dynamic loads which can act on the craft under operating conditions are to be taken into consideration. Criteria of the structure stability and deformations, assuring the watertightness and safe operation of the craft are to be satisfied. The cycling loading should not impair the integrity of structure and hinder normal crew duties and operation of machinery and equipment. Designers should address their projects to the Administration for acceptance of the specification of design loading conditions and the safety factors according to the craft operation. In some cases full-scale trials may be required to prove that the design assumptions are adequate to the expected service conditions.

Large parts of the hull structure and its details are strongly influenced by the ship machinery and various equipment elements. It concerns directional control systems such as air or water rudders, foils, flaps, steerable propellers or jets, yaw control ports or side trusters (Chapter 5), anchoring, towing and mooring equipment (Chapter 6), machinery installations such as engines and power transmissions (Chapter 9) or the stabilisation systems such as rudders, foils, flaps, skirts, fans, water jets and other (Chapter 16). Although the HSC does not precise any detailed structural recommendations, it is clear that the structure should assure a safe and reliable work of those systems and installations satisfying the strength and stiffness of the adjacent supporting structure.

The growing interest in exploitation of fast craft in the ice areas is observed together with increasing number of countries involved in the development of high speed transportation systems. There are no special safety restrictions in the IMO HSC for the operation of fast craft in the areas where the ice on the water surface and some accretion is likely to occur. Some operators and designers express their doubts in this matter. The code has an ice accretion requirement, but there are no other restrictions against fast craft in areas such as the Baltic Sea. Some words about structure, speed, etc, would be very welcome in the code. It should be clearly stated that the adoption of the high speed craft structure to the ice condition is left to the Administration and Classification Societies requirements. The HSC concerns only accretion condition of external ship surfaces of the craft in specified areas of icing. According to the Code requirements it is necessary to take into consideration the additional loads on decks and superstructures subjected to the accretion. This is equivalent to 30 kg/m² on exposed weather decks and gangways and 7.5 kg/m² on the projected lateral area of each side of the craft above the waterline. Those conditions are to be included when the stability calculation of the craft are performed. They are also important from the strength point of view.

4. DESIGN LOADS, ACCELERATIONS AND PRESSURES

The HSC supplies the following - important from the design point of view - requirements concerning loads acting on the structure of the fast craft:

-   pressures due to the effects of passenger weight (Chapter 2);

-   additional moments due to the wind pressure (Chapter 2);

-   accelerations in service and collision conditions (Chapter 4).

In the case of a passenger craft the required design load is calculated taking into consideration the distribution of 4 passengers per square metre of a mass of 75 kg each. The vertical centre of gravity is equal to 0.3m above seat for seated persons and 1.0m above deck for standing ones. The assumed distribution of passengers is used for intact stability calculations. It is required that in any loading condition in still water the uncontrolled passenger movements will not produce the inclination greater than 10° (so called "angle of panic") in both - the displacement and non-displacement mode and including the effect of wind pressure.

The total moment due to wind action is to be calculated on the base of the windage area A_v, which is considered as the projection of the lateral surface of the hull, superstructure and various structures above the waterline, the wind pressure P_v and the lever of windage area z. The wind forces and moments may be calculated by the following formulae:

$$F_v = A_v \, P_v \qquad (7)$$

$$M_v = 0.001 \, P_v \, A_v \, z \qquad (8)$$

The acceleration - one of the most important design parameters - is the subject of Chapter 4 of the HSC. For passenger craft, the vertical accelerations at the longitudinal centre of gravity should not superimpose the value 1.0g unless special precautions are taken with respect to passenger safety. In the light of the data from service and theoretical studies [11,12] this condition will not always be easy to be fulfilled.

A passenger craft is to be designed in such a way that even at the collision load the assumed safety of passengers and crew is assured. Collision loads are calculated

taking into consideration:

-   type of the craft;

-   size of the craft: main dimensions, displacement;

-   speed;

-   material of hull structure.

The collision design load is calculated for the condition of craft head-on collision at operational speed with a vertical rock with maximum 2m height above the waterline - Fig. 4. The design deceleration may be calculated by the formula:

$$a_{col} = 1.2 \, \frac{P}{g\Delta} \qquad (9)$$

where P is the load depending on the kinetic energy E, the hull material factor M, the ship length factor c_L, and the height factor c_H which is a function of the craft type (catamaran, surface effect ship, monohull, hydrofoil, air-cushion vehicle) and the relation of main dimensions of a craft. In the formula (9) Δ denotes the craft displacement, being the mean of the lightweight and maximum operational weight, and g - the gravitational acceleration.

5. FIRE SAFETY AND STRUCTURAL MATERIALS

The fire safety is one of the most important criteria in the design of fast craft. That is why Chapter 7 of the HSC is specially devoted to this criterion. The requirements of this chapter influence on the hull structure mainly in the following areas:

-   layout of accommodations and compartments;

-   internal subdivision of the ship by fire-resisting boundaries;

-   selection of structural materials.

The fast craft hull should be divided into separate fire-resisted spaces by bulkheads and decks with adequate strength and stiffness. They should have also required thermal properties to minimise the rise of the temperature on the side of a wall which is opposite to the fire.

For the purpose of detailed design considerations the classification of spaces is proposed according to the fire hazard risk:

1. Areas of major fire hazard - like machinery spaces, open vehicle spaces and others.

2. Areas of moderate fire hazard - auxiliary machinery spaces, crew accommodations etc.

3. Areas of minor fire hazard - cargo spaces, public spaces etc.

4. Control stations.

5. Evacuation stations and external escape routes - external stairs, muster stations etc.

6. Open spaces.

Depending to the space category, but independently to the material type, the fire-resisting boundaries of spaces should be generally constructed to resist exposure to standard fire conditions for a period of 30 min for areas of moderate fire hazard and 60 min for areas of major fire hazards.

The fire-resistant structure refers to the hull, super-structure, structural bulkheads, decks, deckhouses and pillars should be constructed of non-combustible materials. Normally the steel has adequate fire and structural properties. Other materials may be also used such as aluminium alloys, but in this case some thermal insulation is needed. Main load-carrying structures within major and moderate fire hazard areas should be able to keep their load capability in such a way that there will be no collapse of the construction of the hull and superstructures being exposed to fire for the appropriate fire protection time. In the case of the aluminium structure its insulation and installation should be such that the temperature of the load carrying part of the structure (the core) does not rise more than 200° above the ambient temperature in accordance with the required times (30 and 60 min). The special attention should be paid to the structures made of combustible materials (wood, FRP). After discussion with specialists of fire protection, it is the author's opinion that some further work on the application of these materials is needed to influence some existing chapters of the code. Their insulation should be such that their temperatures will not rise to a level where deterioration of the construction will occur.

6. GENERAL CRAFT LAYOUT

According to the requirements in Chapter 4, all passenger and crew accommodations should be designed and arranged so as to protect the passengers and crew from unfavourable environmental conditions. It is also necessary to minimise the risk of occurring of overloading of structure and occupants in normal service, collision and emergency conditions. This criterion is to be taken into consideration when the general layout of accommodations is designed and safety in, and escape from, the public spaces is considered. The free access to the lifesaving and emergency equipment should be also assured.

The safety requirements determine also special "collision space", located in the fore part of the ship. The public and crew spaces should be located beyond this space. The length of the space - x_{col} measured as shown in Fig.5, from the extreme forward end of the effective hull girder of the craft, may be calculated from the formula:

$$x_{col} = v^2 / (20\ a_{col}) \qquad (10)$$

where: v - craft speed in w m/s and a_{col} - the design collision deceleration defined by Equation 9. The example of the influence of the speed and material on the length of collision space is shown in Fig.6 for two models of monohulls.

In the design process it is required to verify if all mounting of the large mass equipment such as main engines, auxiliary engines, lift fans and others is capable of withstanding the collision design deceleration a_{col} without fracturing.

Special attention is given in Chapter 4 to the seating construction - their installations, attachments and disposition which in some way can influence the adjacent hull and deckhouse structures. The internal craft arrangement and construction should also fulfil the Code requirements concerning the noise levels, which generally are not to exceed:

- in crew and passengers' accommodations - 75 dB (A);

- in operating compartments - 65 dB (A).

As it was yet mentioned in the former chapter the general layout and destination of the ship accommodations is strongly influenced by the fire safety criteria. Some requirements of the HSC may be surprising for designers and passengers. For example, on fast craft the enclosed spaces such as cinemas, discotheques and similar spaces are not permitted. Those are typical repose spaces on the passenger ferries and normally they make the sea journey more attractive.

Some influence on the hull structure design may have also the requirements of Chapter 9 - "Machinery". The machinery should be of design and construction to minimise any danger to persons on board. Main engines, auxiliary machinery, boilers, piping and other installations should be well mounted and insulated to protect the ship from the noise, nitration (fumes), temperature in the engine room as well as in the adjacent compartments.

To analyse the correct work of the machinery systems a failure mode and effect analysis is required. The installations should be designed to operate when the craft is upright and when inclined under static and dynamic conditions (the list up to 15° and rolling 22.5° and simultaneously inclined by pitching 7.5° by bow or stern). Control of the machinery should be from the craft's operating compartment. The machinery space is to be adequately ventilated. Both requirements may, in some measure, influence the general layout of the ship. An important item, from the internal disposition point of view, is the arrangement of the power transmissions. It is strongly required to construct the surrounding hull structure with sufficient strength, stability and fatigue characteristics. It means that the general ship arrange-ment may be subjected to those criteria too.

4

One of spaces of the special attention in the Code is the operating compartment. Chapter 15 is devoted to the layout of that space. In the special operating conditions of fast craft, at high speed, all crew members' decisions have to be taken in very short time, so the design and layout of the operating compartment should be arranged in such a way as to permit operating crew members to work without unreasonable difficulty, fatigue or deconcentration. The proper field of vision from this compartment is one of the criteria to be fulfilled. The view all round the horizon should be assured and the operating compartment is to be located above all other superstructures. Sometimes two separate compartments are needed to respect that requirement. The internal structure should not to obstruct the visibility and crew members' operation. The permitted blind sectors and the view of the sea surface from the operation station are precisely defined in the Code as shown in Fig.7.

7. APPLICATION OF PROBABILITY CONCEPT AND RISK ANALYSIS

In the HSC, for the first time in the international rules which regard the means of the marine fast transportation, the probability concept together with the risk analysis is proposed to be used in normal design practice. The advocated practical method of analysis is that which is the failure mode and effect analysis (FMEA). This is the method of an examination of the craft's systems to determine whether any reasonably probable failure or improper operation can result in a hazardous or catastrophic effect.

When the Code was adopted the use of the probability concept was devoted to be used mainly for systems and equipment. But the probabilistic concept of safety may be extended to hull strength members as well as to a hull girder. It seems to be a question of time only to adopt the probability concept in classification rules design procedure for most of marine craft including the high speed craft. The increasing interest for application of semi-probabilistic and probabilistic approaches in practice calls for the data of probabilistic characteristics of materials, loads and the structural details. More and more operating craft and some research projects promise to supply those data.

The HSC puts in order and define the most important terms and numerical values to be used in design practice when the probabilistic concept is used. The FEMA method is explained and the example procedure is given. The method is based on the single failure concept under which each system at various levels of a system's functional hierarchy is assumed to fail by one probable cause at a time. The effects of the postulated failure are analysed and classified according to their severity. An example of the set of failures modes are given in the Code in relation to the ship systems and equipment. It might be interesting to complete these data with an exemplary set of the hull structure items as shown in Table 1.

8. CONCLUSIONS

In the paper the most important aspects of the implication of the IMO HSC for the hull structure design and safety of fast craft were presented. This implication is much deeper then in the case of the DSC. It concerns practically all design aspects and criteria: high speed definition and craft classification, design loads, general layout, hull structural details, structural materials and fire safety. The basis of the probabilistic concept are also given for the first time.

Any further critical analysis of the HSC regulations requires next parametric verification and calculations of the Code in the design process. It is well known that some requirements of the Code are now investigated in several research and design centres and they will certainly be a subject of future publications and discussions on conferences and in the forum of the IMO.

ACKNOWLEDGEMENT

The author wishes to acknowledge Mr. Zbigniew Sekulski for his assistance in preparing this paper.

REFERENCES

1. International Code of Safety for High Speed Craft (HSC), International Maritime Organisation, 1994.

2. Code of Safety for Dynamically Supported Craft (DSC), Inter-governmental Maritime Consultative Organisation, 1977.

3. BLYTH, A G: 'Implementing the IMO High Speed Code', International Symposium: High Speed Vessels for Transport and Defence, London, 1995.

4. CLEARY, W A: 'Fast ships and regulatory safety', International Symposium: High Speed Vessels for Transport and Defence, London, 1995.

5. OKKENHAUG, S, CVERKMO, M: 'Code of Safety for High Speed Craft - Future Safety Requirements', 12th Fast Ferry International Conference, Copenhagen, 1996.

6. 'Rules for Classification of High Speed and Light Craft', Det norske Veritas, 1995.

7. 'Rules for the Construction and Classification of High Speed Craft', Bureau Veritas, NR 396 UNITAS AS ROO E, 1995.

8. 'Lloyd's Register's Rules and Regulations for the Classification of Special Service Craft', to be published in 1996.

9. BLYTH, A G: 'What is a lightweight ship?', Fast Ferry International, June 1991.

10. JASTRZEBSKI, T: 'Further consideration of a 'High-Speed Craft' definition', Fast Ferry International, September 1994.

11. JASTRZEBSKI, T, SEKULSKI, Z: 'Some Notes on SES Hull Structural Design according to Classification Rules', Second International Conference on Fast Sea Transportation FAST'93, Yokohama, 1993.

12. SCHLACHTER, G, JASTRZEBSKI, T et al: 'Surface-Effect Ships', Committee V.4, International Ship and Offshore Structures Congress, St. Johns, Canada, 1994.

TABLE 1 Example of a set of failures modes of ship hull structure and equipment

	Failure mode	Example of appearance
1	2	3
1	Fracture	Structural material
2	Excessive deflection	Element, region, hull
3	Permanent deformation	Element, hull
4	Lost of bonds	Welding and other joints
5	Vibration	Element, hull
6	Fails to open	Doors, windows manholes
7	Fails to close	
8	Internal leakage	Closing appliances. tanks, deckhouses, hull
9	External leakage	

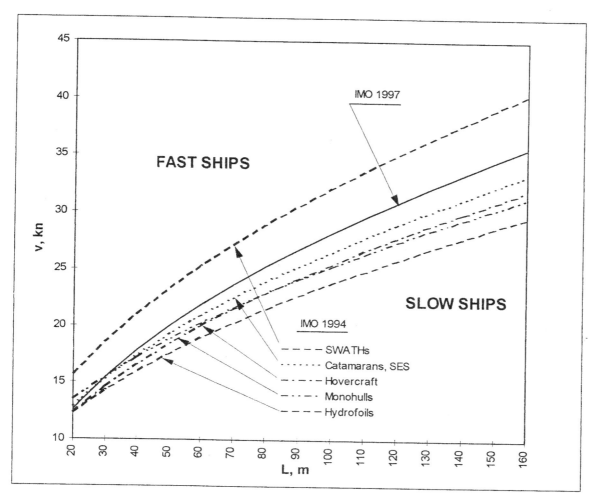

Fig. 1 Comparison of new and old IMO criteria for fast craft

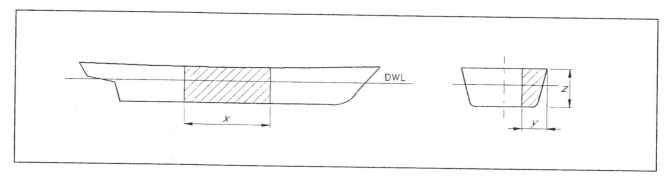

Fig. 2 Assumed side damages according to IMO Code'94:
  x - longitudinal extend: *min* $(0.1L, 3 + 0.03L, 11.0$ m$)$
  y - transverse extend: *min* $(0.2B, 0.05L, 5.0$ m$)$
  z - vertical extend: $z = H$

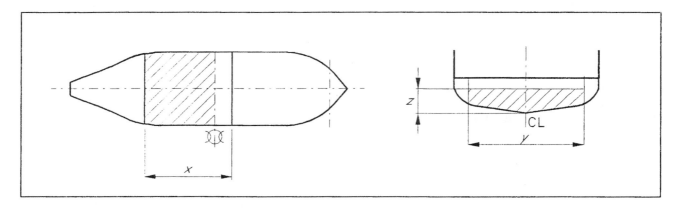

Fig. 3 Assumed bottom damages according to IMO Code'94:
  x - longitudinal extend: *min* $(0.1L, 3 + 0.03L, 11.0 \text{ m})$
  y - transverse extend: *min* $(B, 7.0 \text{ m})$
  z - vertical extend: *min* $(0.02B, 0.5 \text{ m})$

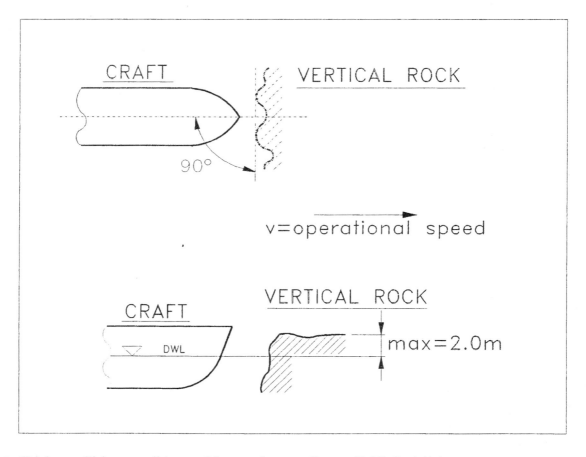

Fig. 4 Design collision conditions of fast craft according to IMO Code'94

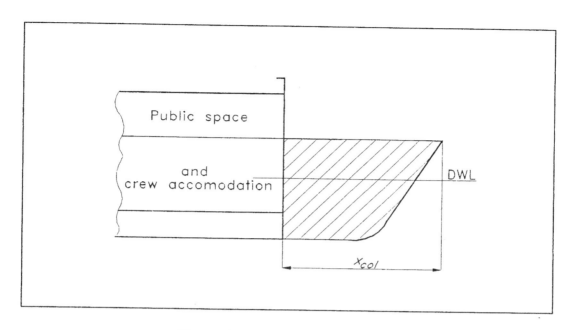

Fig. 5 Collision space of fast craft

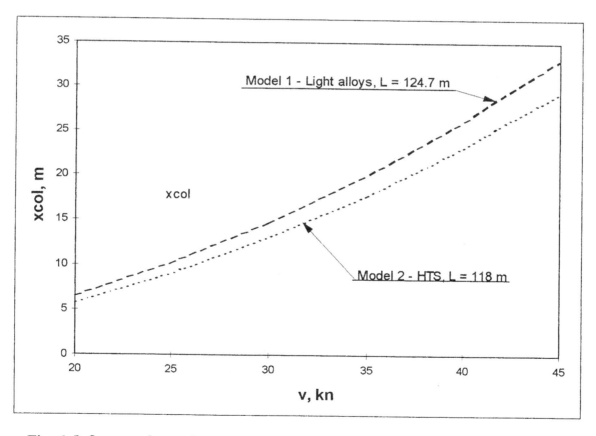

Fig. 6 Influence of speed and material on length of collision protection space x_{col}

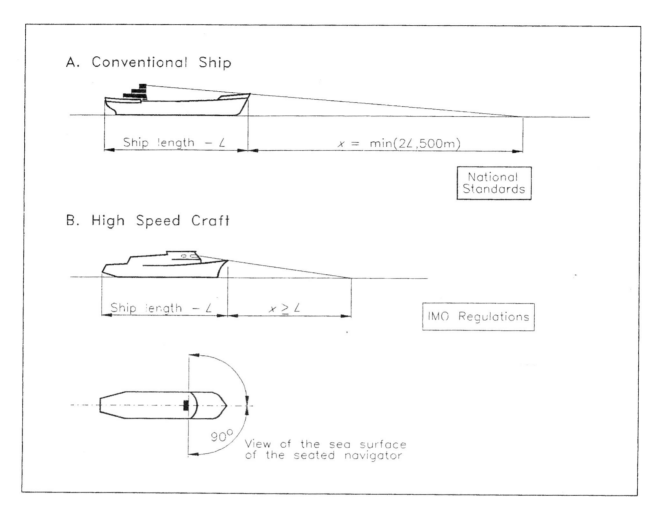

Fig. 7 Required fields of vision from operating compartment

UNDERWRITING HIGH SPEED CRAFT

by R Bryce, Hart, Fenton & Co Ltd, and
D Taylor, Clifford Chance, UK

Paper presented at the

International Symposium & Seminar

THE SAFETY OF HIGH SPEED CRAFT

6 - 7 FEBRUARY 1997 LONDON

UNDERWRITING HIGH SPEED CRAFT

Robert Bryce, Hart, Fenton & Co Ltd, and
David Taylor, Clifford Chance

SUMMARY

High speed transportation at sea is developing rapidly, with challenges both technical, operational and regulatory. There are now approximately 1,200 substantial vessels in operation, including 34 large car and passenger fast ferries, with developments into deep sea cargo transportation now visible.

It is apparent that underwriters, both hull and P&I, are perhaps only now concentrating on an appreciation of the differences between the risk attaching to High Speed Craft ("HSC") as opposed to conventional vessels. Until now, HSCs have tended to be underwritten "on the back of" conventional fleets. Given the rate of development, it is important to consider the underwriting criteria, which are now being contemplated.

This appraisal will consider the technical issues relating to HSC as they impact upon the assessment of the underwriting risk.

AUTHORS' BIOGRAPHIES

After training and working as a shipwright in Sydney, Mr Robert A Bryce joined Incat Designs as a draughtsman. In 1989 he moved to the U.K. and joined Aluminium Shipbuilders as Technical Co-ordinator for the construction of the wavepiercer "CONDOR 9". In 1992 he joined Hart Fenton as a designer and more recently worked in a project management role. He is presently working towards chartered engineer accreditation and CEDR mediator accreditation.

Mr David Taylor, MA (Oxon) is a marine insurance lawyer with Clifford Chance with more than 25 years experience. He worked for the Chamber of Shipping as legal manager in the 1970's and has experience as a manager of a P & I Club. He has represented interests at IMO, UNCTAD and IUMI. He is a Titular Member of the Comité Maritime International (CMI) and is Honorary Secretary of the Association of Average Adjusters. He has made a special study of HSC.

1. INTRODUCTION

Historically HSC have not received special underwriting attention. Recently the Ocean Hull Committee of IUMI, under its Chairman Peter Chrismas, a Lloyd's Underwriter, has been giving attention to the underwriting criteria appropriate to HSC, raising the question of whether HSC should be underwritten as a discrete category, rather than as an add on to a conventional fleet. As with any maritime operator the HSC operator has a deep concern at the level of premium and the level of deductible. It is evident too that the pressure to maintain operating schedules and to fund borrowings are especially important, given the characteristics of the hull and machinery and the competition pressures.

2. THE INDUSTRY

HSC have been operating commercially since the mid 1950's with the development of Rodriquez' hydrofoils and similar craft in the former USSR. The Hovercraft in the 1960's and 1970's gave the first example of car and passenger HSC however it was not until after the boom period of the late 1970's and 1980's of the aluminium catamaran that the concept of large car passenger HSC really took root.

Since the Hoverspeed GREAT BRITAIN won the Hales Trophy in 1990 more than 34 of the larger car and passenger craft have been constructed. At present there are approximately 1200 HSC of all types, plying trade on different short sea routes around the world.

For the many technical professionals in the industry insurance issues are not important. However, the underwriting risk is of concern to Owners, Operators, and Insurers and influences the economic viability of the industry.

3. WHY SHOULD HIGH SPEED CRAFT BE RATED DIFFERENTLY FROM CONVENTIONAL CRAFT?

3.1 INSTALLED POWER

The amount of installed power in an HSC, when expressed as a ratio against displacement, is necessarily far greater than for conventional vessels in order to produce the required high operating speeds.

The main propulsion machinery typically is either medium speed or high speed marine diesels or gas turbines. The duty cycles for these HSC are very rigorous and significantly more so than for conventional vessels. Water jet propulsion involves an even greater level of technology, bringing with it the prospect of increased cost of installation and increased cost of repair.

The desire to achieve maximum performance produces a pressure to reduce onboard equipment to a minimum to save weight and space and underwriters will be playing close attention to hull stress monitoring systems, which DNV is developing and voyage data recorders as developed for example by the P & O subsidiary, Broadgate Ltd.

Underwriters will inevitably recognise that there is only a very short operating history of the larger and more highly rated machinery now being installed. This contrasts sharply with the well tried and developed propulsion technology of conventional vessels, with the wide availability of repair facilities for conventional vessels.

3.2   HULL MATERIAL - DESIGN

Predominantly HSC have been constructed from either marine grades of aluminium or fibreglass reinforced plastics (FRP). Some of the larger craft are composites of steel hulls and aluminium superstructures. These materials impact upon a hull risk. Whilst aluminium is easier to work, the correct welding of it is critical to ensure structural reliability. Fatigue properties are also a factor. One of the key issues for underwriters is the lack of skilled fabricators and welders of the material. The lack of convenient skills and resources increases the prospect of a Constructive Total Loss (CTL) because of this dramatically increased cost of either transporting the skills and resources to the damaged craft or vice versa.

The limitation for fibre reinforced composites is similar, but compounded by the necessity of a controlled environment for fabrication and repair. Such facilities are in even more limited supply than those appropriate for repairing aluminium. The scarcity of these resources increases, inevitably, the potential cost of repair.

Aluminium can be scrapped and recycled, thus leaving a residual value in the hull. So far as FRP composite hulls are concerned, it would be necessary to bury or sink a hull manufactured of these composites and this is likely to produce environmental hostility and consequently increase disposal costs. Moreover the residual value is likely to be nil. Indeed, the hull is likely to create a disposal liability.

The research in Japan into the development of a Tecno Superliner - an ocean cargo carrier - makes it clear that specially constructed terminals will be necessary and indeed are already necessary to protect the relatively fragile hull on berthing and unberthing, as well as being necessary to ensure that the time gained by the passage at speed is not lost by slow and inefficient discharge of cargo and the same is true for passenger craft.

The nature of the design and construction of HSC make it likely that there will be significant builders' risks and repairers' liability issues.

3.3   ROUTES

Some routes are more HSC friendly than others in that the cost of speed has to be weighed against the return on capital after the reduction of operating costs. Passenger demographics, waterborne traffic density, weather forecasting services and environmental conditions, as well as

the availability of engineering skills, repair and maintenance facilities will all impact upon the underwriting risk and ultimately the commercial viability of the service.

The practical operating differences between Category A and Category B craft as specified in the High Speed Code highlight the various risk levels which exist in the HSC industry. The more immediate evacuation methodology of Category A craft places great reliance on the effectiveness of the local rescue services whilst the more "get the craft home" methodology of Category B craft places the reliance on the craft systems and crew. It is therefore apparent that passenger liability risks differ between these Categories.

3.4   ENVIRONMENTAL CONDITIONS

The environmental aspects of the operating route have broad ranging implications not only for passengers and their comfort but will also influence the viability of cargo craft operations.

Some years ago the claims history for cargo damage in containers in conventional craft operating in the high 20 knot speed range forced operators to reduce operating speeds to minimise damage to container cargo. Speed reductions proved very effective without adversely affecting the service.

The challenge for high speed cargo operators amongst all the other commercial issues relating to running costs will be to ensure that their craft do not subject their cargoes to excessive motions in the seaway. This will not only be reflected in cargo damages but also in wear and tear, or artificial ageing of the suspension systems of motor vehicles or to components within machinery or electronic equipment being transported. Cargo underwriters and P & I Clubs will want to look closely at the level of risk in respect of cargo transported in HSC's. Such cargoes will very likely also be very high value in order to justify carriage by HSC rather than by conventional craft.

Operating restrictions, in the form of weather and time constraints, are imposed upon the operation of these craft by the High Speed Craft Code, implemented by Flag and Port State Authorities, and the rules of the Classification society with which the vessel is classed. It is important that commercial imperatives to meet or maintain operating schedules, especially when the route is subject to wide seasonal variations in demand, do not tempt operators to turn a "blind eye" to those restrictions. Some recent unfortunate conventional ro-ro disasters have included contributory factors such as steaming at high speeds in adverse weather in an attempt to maintain a schedule.

The weather/sea conditions will always be an issue, since the basis of HSC has been and remains that they are craft of restricted service by reason of their Class Notation.

It is interesting to note that a Scandinavian P & I Club has recently announced a new cover for cruise and passenger vessel members "CCL 96" ("Cruise and Consequential

Loss Cover"). The cover provides indemnity for specified consequential losses eventuating from total or partial cancellation of consecutive voyages. This may well have a particular application for HSC's.

3.5 REPAIR COSTS AND REPAIR FACILITIES

It is clear that HSC require repair facilities which very few drydock and ship repair facilities around the world presently provide. For an insurer this becomes an issue when in the event of a casualty a craft has to be towed some distance to an appropriate repair facility.

We have discussed above in 3.2 some of the issues relating to hull materials. It is important to reflect upon the issues of repair facilities.

Experience has shown that poor aluminium repair techniques contribute to and speed up the deterioration of hull areas subjected to high fatigue conditions. Therefore the skill and expertise of a repair facility will be of interest to the insurer. When considering the repair options for an FRP/composite hull or structure the present limited spread of expertise and facilities have important implications for the insurer.

There have been recent occasions when HSC have had to be towed considerable distances to appropriate facilities. The towage costs and possible consequential damages to the craft resulting from the tow become issues. The fact that HSC are of light displacement, limited underwater profile and high windage mean that controllability during the tow will be important. The lighter structural scantlings of an HSC will influence the available weather window for the tow, as well.

3.6 STATUS AND EXPERIENCE OF THE OPERATORS

It is already evident that HSC are performance critical and require highly trained officers, both deck and engineering. These craft are also maintenance sensitive and require meticulous monitoring by superintendents.

Planned maintenance procedures to meet machinery manufacturers' specifications will be considered a basic necessity. The practice of entering into manufacturer maintenance contracts are likely to become of interest to operators if insurers view such contracts as confirmation that the machinery is maintained to the highest standards.

In October/November 1993, IMO adopted the International Safety Management Code (ISM Code) with the intention of providing an international standard for the safe operation and management of vessels. The general requirements of the High Speed Craft Code specifies the implementation of the ISM Code for high speed craft operations. A European Council Directive required compliance by high speed craft operators by 1 July 1996. The procedures and practices which the ISM Code requires should already be common practices of the prudent operator. If current underwriting attitudes are anything to go by, it is unlikely that the insurance market will "reward" operators with reductions in premiums because an Operator has ISM certification. Rather, this certification will be considered as a minimum requirement.

The ISM Code will put greater pressure on those companies acquiring secondhand craft as to commit financial resources to maintain appropriate levels.

4. SPEED

It is unarguably the case that a vessel travelling at high speed, making contact with either the ground, another vessel or fixed or floating objects, is significantly more susceptible to extensive damage than a conventional vessel. The areas where HSC have up to now and extensively operated are high traffic density areas, requiring very high levels of human operation, as well as technical operation. A human failure or a response to a technological failure, resulting from the greater operating speeds of machinery, components and the craft, mean that the margin of error is significantly reduced for HSC's when compared with conventional vessels.

5. SAFETY

Passenger safety is an important and emotive issue. The increasing size of craft and passenger numbers have implications for liability and are discussed in Schedule A.

When viewing the safety aspects which are designed into these craft and the requirements for their validation, for example of passenger evacuation procedures, it is clear that in some instances the risks when compared with conventional vessels have been improved.

By virtue of the restrictions or limitations imposed upon length of service and operation of HSC certain risks are reduced. The description that HSC are "eggshells on razor blades" can be put in perspective when the extent of the massive damage suffered to the bottom of the hull of the tanker "SEA EMPRESS" is considered.

The HSC Code which came into force in January 1996 is not without its problems, but is an improvement over the DSC Code which it replaces. The issue of the application retrospectively of the HSC Code to older craft is more complex. The insurance market will be anxious that best practice is implemented. However, older craft do have problems in complying with the HSC Code and this issue is not helped by variations in interpretation by Survey Authorities and indeed governments.

6. RATING

Underwriters consider two main factors in establishing the premium level of a conventional vessel and generally consider the propulsion machine is a neutral factor.

HSC differ in that the propulsion machinery is a critical factor. Accordingly, the premium for a HSC could be expressed as the product of:

Machinery	-	$ per kW.
Hull	-	S per GRT.
Total Loss	-	% of the sum insured.

This equation is further influenced by the fact that a Constructive Total Loss (CTL), where the cost of repairing the vessel is more than its insured value, will occur at a lower percentage of damage on HSC as opposed to conventional vessels because the cost of repairs using appropriate materials and labour costs will be significantly higher than for conventional vessel.

7. POLICY FORMS

While HSC are insured in differing markets, such as London, Scandinavia and the United States, as yet dedicated policy wordings have not emerged, although it is the prediction of the authors of this paper that in due course the need for dedicated wording will become apparent as the risks become better appreciated. The industry is at a stage of development which produces a unique opportunity for builders, operators and insurers to develop a level of understanding which would enable underwriters to acquire a very accurate appreciation of risk to their own benefit and to the benefit of owners and operators of HSC.

8. LIABILITY AND LIMITATION

The principle of limitation of liability is dealt with under a number of regimes including the following:

- The 1957 Limitation Convention.

- The 1976 Limitation Convention.

- The Athens Convention 1974.

- The Warsaw Convention.

- The Hague and Hague Visby Rules.

- the Hovercraft (Civil Liability) Order 1986.

It is likely that, so far as passengers are concerned, the Athens Convention will apply (probably up to the global limit provided under the 1957/76 Conventions). However, it should be noted that the 1976 Convention, although applicable in Britain, may not be applicable with respect to

"air cushioned vehicles" i.e. hovercraft, SES, air cushioned catamarans or ground effect craft, in other jurisdictions.

Hovercraft have historically been dealt within accordance with the Hovercraft (Civil Liability Order 1986 which, in the UK, makes the 1976 Convention applicable but the Warsaw Convention (as used with respect to airline passengers) is incorporated with respect to passengers and their baggage.

Most limitation regimes provide for circumstances in which the right limit liability can be lost and, generally speaking, negligence of some other form of misconduct is the basis on which the right to limit liability is lost, (see example in Schedule A).

9. CONCLUSION

The present underwriting market is "soft" and has recently described as about to go into "free fall" "...reductions and coverage concessions are available to anyone who asks for them and underwriters are not making distinctions for quality. Existing underwriters follow the levels (of premium) down in order to protect market share and new entrants retaliate in order to gain market share that they did not have in the first place". (John Hickey, President of the American Hull Insurance Syndicate Act 1996 - "Insurance Day")

"Fairplay" September 1996 reports from the IUMI Conference in Oslo that "underwriters are falling over each other to write premiums and maintain market share, but everybody wants the other fellow to be more responsible on rate assessment and quote higher premiums.

It is, therefore, vital that owners/operators and the insurance industry share their experience - their operating, technical and financial management experience - to enable underwriters to make an accurate assessment of the risk and establish rates which realistically represent the level of risk. All sections of the industry; owners, operators, classification societies, industry groups/ representatives should maintain a vigorous dialogue to ensure that the risks are properly understood. This would enable underwriters to set rates at a level which are economically and technically sound and allow the industry to provide a service to all its customers and achieve a decent financial return for all.

H.S.C LIMITATION AND SAMPLE CALCULATIONS

1. THE VESSELS CONSIDERED

For the purposes of the examples given, three vessels have been considered. Two are typical of vessels of around the 80 in length and the third, "STENA EXPLORER", is of the new HSS type.

2. THE 1976 CONVENTION

The calculations have been made on the basis of the 1976 Convention which is a two tier system. The first tier is the limitation fund available for claims relating to death or personal injury of people other than passengers together with claims relating to damage to property.

This first tier is split internally between the death/personal injury and the damage to property elements. Where both elements exist in one case then the exposure relating to each is combined to make an overall fund but claims relating to death or personal injury rank higher than claims relating to damage to property and a specific tranche of the combined fund is therefore reserved for death and personal injury claims only. The total exposure with respect to both death or personal injury to persons other than passengers and with respect to damage to property is calculated in accordance with Article 6 of the 1976 Convention and this calculation is a function of the gross registered tonnage of the vessel measured in accordance with the 1969 (Universal Measurement System) Tonnage Convention.

In addition to liability for death or personal injury to persons other than passengers and damage to property, the 1976 Convention also provides for a limit of liability with respect to claims for death or personal injury of passengers. This separate liability is covered by Article 7 of the 1976 Convention and is based on the number of passengers which the vessel is certified to carry rather than the number of passengers who actually claim or the vessel's tonnage. The limitation amount is 46,666 SDR[1] multiplied by the number of passengers which the ship is authorised to carry according to the ship's certificate.

However, the limit of liability for claims with respect to death or personal injury to passengers is capped maximum level of 25,000,000 SDR regardless of the number of passengers that the ship is authorised to carry. At the exchange rate for the SDR for 30 May 1996 this represents about £23,550,000 or US$36,150,000. This separate and additional liability to passengers only continues to increase for vessels certified to carry passenger numbers between 1 and 536 when the maximum exposure is reached because 46,666 SDR multiplied by 536 passengers achieves and exceeds the 25,000,000 SDR cap.

In circumstances where, on one distinct occasion, claims with respect to death or personal injury to personnel other than passengers, damage to property, and death or personal injury to passengers all co-exist then the limits of liability prescribed by Articles 6 and 7 of the 1976 Convention must be added together to calculate the maximum exposure.

3. THE ATHENS CONVENTION

Limitation of liability to passengers is also covered by the Athens Convention. This provides for limitation of liability for claims with respect to death or personal injury of passengers on a per passenger basis at the same rate per passenger as that provided under Article 7 of the 1976 Convention (46,666 SDR per passenger). However there are a number of differences between the Athens Convention and the 1976 Convention which are worthy of note. For instance, while the amount per passenger is the same as Article 7 of the 1976 Convention the Athens Convention allows any ratifying state to increase the per passenger amount and a number of states (including the UK) are known to have done so. Also, while the Athens Convention limitation amount is calculated on a per passenger basis it is calculated on the basis of the number of passengers actually claiming (rather than the number of passengers which the vessel is certified to carry). Effectively therefore, the Athens Convention sets up a separate limitation fund for each passenger claiming and there is no global limit such as the 536 passenger limit which applies under Article 7 of the 1976 Convention. However, Article 19 of the Athens Convention does allow owners to invoke any global limit provided for by any other limitation convention which owners would otherwise be entitled to invoke.

4. 1976 AND ATHENS CONVENTIONS COMPARED

Therefore, in jurisdictions where both the Athens Convention and the 1976 Convention apply, the global limits for passenger claims would remain as prescribed by Article 7 of 1976 Convention because the global limit of 25,000,000 SDR prescribed in the 1976 Convention can be invoked under the Athens Convention.

However, in a jurisdiction which applies the Athens Convention but not the 1976 Convention (or any other global limitation regime) then the exposure to passenger claims could conceivably increase beyond this limit. This would be particularly important for the most recent HSCs with passenger numbers vastly in excess of the 536 passenger level.

Although the possibility for the amount per passenger to be increased and the absence of a global limit results in the possibility of increased potential exposure, in practice, the Athens Convention tends to work favourably for Carriers and Insurers because the per passenger amount is separate for each passenger claiming (any excess fund from a claim by one passenger is not available for use by other passengers whose individual funds may have been exhausted) whereas the 1976 Convention creates a common fund based on the maximum number of passengers which the vessel is certified to carry and which is available for distribution amongst those passengers who claim even if relatively few passengers do actually claim.

Because per passenger amounts under the Athens Convention vary from state to state, the maximum potential exposure to passenger claims under that regime has not been included in the calculations shown.

---

[1]SDR - The Unit of Account used for calculation of the limitation fund. It is a theoretical currency whose value is determined daily by the International Monetary Fund on the basis of a basket of currencies, ie a range of national currencies.

HSC LIMITATION FUNDS

SAMPLE CALCULATIONS

"SEACAT SCOTLAND" (WAVEPIERCING CATAMARAN)

LOA	74 m		
Limitation Tonnage/GRT	3,003		
Passengers	431		
		£	US$
1976 Convention	Personal Injury & Property Fund	2,043,198	3,136,374
	Passenger Fund	18,946,489	29,083,464
	Total Fund	20,989,687	32,219,838

"CONDOR 12" (WAVEPIERCING CATAMARAN)

LOA	81 m		
Limitation Tonnage/GRT	4,112		
Passengers	750		
1976 Convention	Personal Injury & Property Fund	2,565,537	3,938,181
	Passenger Fund	23,550,000	36,150,000
	Total Fund	26,115,537	40,088,181

"STENA EXPLORER" (LARGE CATAMARAN)

LOA	126 m		
Limitation Tonnage/GRT	19,638		
Passengers	1,500		
1976 Convention	Personal Injury & Property Fund	9,878,283	15,163,479
	Passenger Fund	23,550,000	36,150,000
	Total Fund	33,428,283	51,313,479

NB:

1.   SDR rates used (30 May 1996) £0.942; US$1.446

2.   It should be noted that there is no relationship between the fund and the insurance rate. The fund is the Limitation fund, ie the amount to which the Owner can limit his liability under the maritime law of limitation.

Calculations are based on published data.

PARTIES TO THE 1974 AND 1976 CONVENTIONS

1974 Athens Convention:

Argentina, Bahamas, Barbados, Belgium, China, Egypt, Some of the Federal States of Germany, Georgia, Greece, Jordan, Liberia, Luxembourg, Malawi, Marshall Islands, Poland, Russian Federation, Spain, Switzerland, Tonga, United Kingdom[1], Ukraine, Vanuatu, Yemen,[2].

1976 Convention on Limitation of Liability

Australia, Bahamas, Barbados, Belgium, Benin, Croatia, Denmark, Egypt, Finland, France, Georgia, Germany, Greece, Japan, Liberia, Marshall Islands, Mexico, The Netherlands, New Zealand, Norway, Poland, Spain, Sweden, Switzerland, United Kingdom[3], Vanuatu, Yemen.

---

1.   Ratification by the UK is also effective in respect of: Bailwick of Jersey, Bailwick of Guernsey, Bermuda, British Virgin Islands, Cayman Islands, Falkland Islands, Gibraltar, Hong Kong, Isle of Man, Montserrat, Pitcairn, St. Helena and Dependencies.

2.   Yugoslavia was one of the original signatories to the Athens Convention but the present situation requires clarification.

3.   See footnote 1

PAPER NO.13.

REVISED REQUIREMENTS FOR CLASSIFICATION OF HIGH-SPEED CRAFT

by M Cooper and A Mak
American Bureau of Shipping, Singapore

Paper presented at the

International Symposium & Seminar

THE SAFETY OF HIGH SPEED CRAFT

6 - 7 FEBRUARY 1997 LONDON

REVISED REQUIREMENTS FOR CLASSIFICATION OF HIGH-SPEED CRAFT

M Cooper and A Mak
American Bureau of Shipping, Singapore

SUMMARY

With the significant boom in the fast ferry market of the last several years the industry has seen catamaran design grow to 100 metres in length and 40 knot capability. Similarly, monohulls have also kept pace with 80 to 130 metre vessels, capable of 50 knots, currently under construction.

Although ABS has accepted high speed craft into class for many years, this paper provides the background to its latest classification requirements, to assure continued safe operation based on up to date experience gained from the new generation of fast ferries.

The focal point of this paper is on two key design related topics of the revised requirements in the ABS Guide for High-Speed Craft. The first will discuss the hull requirements including prediction of global and local loads acting on the structure, the strength criteria in response to these loads, specific concerns with critical areas and construction quality-control. The second part will discuss the machinery requirements unique to high- speed craft including propulsion and auxiliary systems and associated safety issues.

AUTHORS' BIOGRAPHIES

Mr Martyn Cooper served a four year student apprentice-ship with a small shipyard on the East Coast of England, after which he spent several years in the company's drawing and design offices. Subsequently he moved to a South Coast manufacturer of lifeboats where he was employed as a design draughtsman. In 1979 he embarked upon a degree course at the University of Newcastle-upon-Tyne and after graduating joined Lloyd's Register of Shipping as a Surveyor, where, in 1988, he was promoted to Senior Surveyor.

In 1992, Mr Cooper joined the London Office of the American Bureau of Shipping as a Senior Engineer, and in 1996, he was transferred to the Pacific region where he is currently dealing with the structural and statutory review of all vessel types, in particular, the Classification and Statutory certification of high speed craft.

Mr Andrew Mak is a Singaporean who, in 1980, obtained his Diploma in Marine Engineering from Singapore Poly-technic, and in 1988, a degree in Mechanical Engineering from Nanyang Technological University of Singapore. Work experience included employment with the Neptune Orient Line as a Marine Engineer serving on an oil tanker, a bulk carrier and a container vessel. After obtaining his degree he served in the Republic of Singapore Navy as a Project Engineer. His responsibilities included the provision of engineering support in matters related to mechanical equipment and systems of naval craft, the assessment of modifications and the drawing of specifications for the procurement and implementation of such systems.

Mr Mak joined the American Bureau of Shipping as a Machinery Engineer in 1990, obtaining his seniority in 1996. He is responsible for the plan approval of machinery and electrical drawings of all types of vessels, including high speed craft to ABS and statutory requirements.

1. INTRODUCTION

In order to better consider the Classification of High Speed Craft, it is first important to have an understanding of what this vessel type is considered to be. As a prelude to the discussion of classification issues, the following section is offered to introduce the definition of high-speed craft and the forms which they typically take in present day practical use.

1.1 DEFINITIONS

There are many definitions of high speed craft, but in general the following are those accepted in the industry today:

a) The crafts with speed V kn $\geq$ function $(L_{WL})^{1/2}$, where L_{WL} is the load water line length in metres.

Figure 1 shows a graph of drag/lift versus speed [1]. This indicates the economically feasible upper speed limit of displacement type craft. At speeds higher than 2.35 $(L_{WL})^{1/2}$ the wave-making resistance increases such that the power requirements make it no longer feasible for normal form displacement craft to operate in the true displacement mode.

This definition of high speed applies to all craft, including those that do not meet the definition in b) below:

b) Vessels with speed V m/s $\geq 3.7 \nabla^{1/6}$ or V kn $\geq 7.193 \nabla^{1/6}$, where ∇ is the volume of displacement, in cubic metres, corresponding to the design waterline.

These define the relationship between speed and volumetric displacement as one of the conditions to be met if a high speed craft is to qualify for compliance with the IMO High-Speed Craft Code [2] as an alternative to the previous SOLAS 1974 [3], requirements.

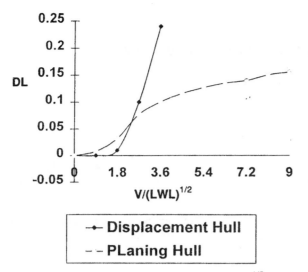

Fig. 1 Drag/Lift V. Speed/(Length)$^{1/2}$

The IMO High-Speed Craft Code defines both high speed and light displacement limits. This definition excludes some truly high-speed craft that have speeds in excess of 2.35 $(L_{WL})^{1/2}$ but less than 7.193 $\nabla^{1/6}$.

The original ABS Guide for High-Speed Craft [4], published in 1990, applied to high-speed craft with Vkn≥ 2.35 $(L)^{1/2}$ and up to 61m in length.

1.2 HIGH SPEED CRAFT HULL FORMS (CRAFT TYPES)

High speed craft fall into five basic groups:

• Semi-planing and Planing Monohulls.
• Multi-hull Craft.
• Hydrofoil Craft.
• Air Cushion Supported Hulls, and
• Small Waterplane Area Twin Hulls.

It should be noted that SWATH craft, are considered by some not to be a true high-speed craft. Nevertheless they show some of the characteristics of this type of craft and have therefore been included in the list. Typical cross sections of the various craft types are given are shown in Figure 2.

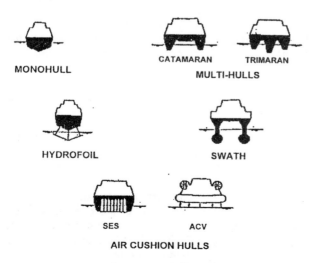

Fig. 2 Craft Types

1.3 MEANS OF INCREASING SPEED

To clarify the various types of high-speed craft hull forms, it is helpful to consider the means by which the normal form, true displacement type vessel can be modified to attain higher speeds and be economically feasible. The means must eliminate the extremely high wave-making resistance that is associated with normal form true displacement craft with speeds greater than

$$V \text{ kn} = 2.35 \ (L_{WL})^{1/2}.$$

Three basic measures are used:

a) **Dynamic Lift**

Dynamic lift on the bottom of a planing surface is created by the upward dynamic reaction of the fluid against the moving planing surface.

This lift reduces the amount of water the moving craft displaces, so that the weight of the vessel (supported entirely by displacement of water when stationary) is, when moving, carried partly by displacement of water and partly by dynamic lift. This reduction in displacement will in turn reduce the wave-making resistance and the required horsepower.

Dynamic lift makes planing craft and hydrofoils economically feasible high-speed craft.

b) **Hull Configuration**

Wave-making resistance is primarily a function of vessel displacement and L/B ratio. However, there is an upper limit to L/B for mono-hulls due to stability considerations.

This is not the case with multi-hull craft where the use of two or more narrow hulls reduces the wave-making resistance while the multi-hulls assure stability generally better than the mono-hull.

Multi-hulled craft take one of several forms, depending on whether they are commercial or naval, and depending on the sea states likely to be encountered. For commercial applications catamarans are the most common form of multi-hulls, although trimarans and quadrimarans are also used.

c) **Air Cushion**

This form of reducing wave-making resistance is similar to dynamic-lift in that it reduces the displacement of the moving craft, however the lift in this case is achieved by an air cushion created generally by pressurized air, fan-driven out of the bottom of the hull.

Air cushion craft are either:

1. of the amphibious air cushion (ACV), supported entirely be an air cushion retained in a flexible skirt, or

2. surface-effect craft (SES), with two rigid structural side walls.

2

Combinations of dynamic lift, hull configuration and air cushion methods are sometimes used.

For example, the surface-effect craft depends on displacement and dynamic lift to attain its maximum off-cushion speed; at maximum on-cushion speed it is supported by displacement, dynamic lift and air cushion. Likewise hydrofoils depend on displacement and dynamic lift until they reach their minimum on-foil speed, after which they are entirely foil supported.

High-speed catamarans depend primarily on a long slender hull configuration to reduce wave-making resistance, but in some cases they can also benefit from dynamic lift attained by chined hulls.

2.   ABS GUIDE

The ABS Guide for High Speed Craft, published in 1990, recognised the differences between the traditional steel displacement craft and those of the high-speed craft, which by its nature, is of lighter construction and behaves entirely differently in service. Hull requirements given in the Guide were established from ABS in-house standards applied over many years to class many high speed craft.

Hull structural requirements were primarily developed for semi-planing and planing monohulls less than 61 metres in length. But they were also applicable to hydrofoils and surface effect craft in their hull-borne modes of operation, as well as to the hulls of semi-planing multi-hull craft. Approval of the special multi-hull features of catamarans, such as transverse strength; and the special features of air cushion vehicles and hydrofoils were based on internal ABS standards.

Many high speed passenger ferries have been classed in accordance with the Guide, these include many monohulls, a number of catamarans and air cushion vehicles and hydro-foils (Table 1 shows a list of some of the recent classed ferries). Also, many patrol boats have been approved in accordance with the Guide. Certain navies, coastguard and similar authorities specify compliance with the Guide for High Speed Craft.

TABLE 1 - RECENT ABS CLASSED VESSELS

PASSENGER & PASSENGER/VEHICLE FERRIES

INCLUDES RECENT CLASSIFICATION OF:

85.3 x 14.5 x 9.5m	RODRIQUEZ NO. 25	SCATTO	Passenger/Ro-Ro	40 kn Monohull
85.3 x 14.5 x 9.5m	RODRIQUEZ NO. 255	GUIZZO	Passenger/Ro-Ro	40 kn Monohull
79.5 x 23.0 x 10.2m	SEC		Passenger/Ro-Ro	50 kn SES

SWATHS/CATAMARANS (MULTI-HULLS)

71.0 x 24.0 x 14.86m	TAGOS-19		USN Surveillance	SWATH
68.0 x 31.7 x 18.75m	AGOR-23		USN	SWATH
44.5 x 20.0 x 7.0m	-		USCG Cutter	SWATH
40.0 x 16.2 x 6.25m	PAMESCO		Passenger Ferry	SWATH
38.6 x 15.6 x 6.0m	NICHOLS		Passenger Ferry	Catamaran
40.0 x 10.1 x 4.0m	KVAAAERNER FJELLSTRAND		Passenger Ferry	Catamaran
22.0 x 7.6 x 2.1m	SABRE CATAMARANS		Passenger Ferry	Catamaran

SWATHS/CATAMARANS (MULTI-HULLS)

CURRENTLY UNDER PLAN APPROVAL:

140.0 x 21.0 x 12.6m			Passenger/Ro-Ro	42 kn Monohull
40.0 x 10.0m			Passenger	37 kn Catamaran
110.0 x 18.25 x 11.2m			Passenger/Car	44 kn Monohull

3. THE 1997 GUIDE FOR HIGH-SPEED CRAFT

The Guide [5] has been revised, enhanced and updated for 1997. This was to:

- ensure advancement with industry;

- incorporate advances in technology;

- incorporate those parts that were previously available only to ABS staff;

- to give the hull design loads in a more parametrically complete but flexible format.

3.1 APPLICABILITY

The **1997 Guide** is now applicable to high speed mono-hulls, multi-hulls, surface effect ships and Hydrofoils. The craft may be for commercial or governmental use and having Vkn $\geq$ 2.35 (L)$^{1/2}$ within the following limits:

Vessel Type	Applicable Length
Mono-Hull	$\leq$ 130m
Multi-Hull	$\leq$ 100m
Surface Effect Ship (SES)	$\leq$ 90m
Hydro Foil	$\leq$ 60m

The materials of construction covered by the Guide are steel, aluminium and fibre reinforced plastics.

3.2 NEW HULL CLASSIFICATION NOTATIONS

Careful consideration was given to the class notation, taking into account ship owners requirements and an apt description of the craft and its intended use. The basic notation indicating that the craft has been approved on the basis of the new Guide is:

$$✦A1 \ HSC \ ✦AMS$$

The meanings of the notation symbols are:

✦A1 HSC   indicates the hull is built under ABS survey in accordance with the Guide, including material testing, and in accordance with ABS hull approved plans, for unrestricted service.

✦AMS   indicates machinery is constructed and installed under ABS survey in accordance with the Guide and found satisfactory after trials.

In addition, craft that are built to special requirements contained in the Guide for a restricted service may be classed with an appropriate notation, e.g. **Ro-Ro Passenger Craft (A)**.

Alternatively, special purpose craft may be distinguished with an additional notation that is a description of a particular service, e.g. **Harbour Service**.

Geographical and Wave Height limitations may also be recognised in the class by an additional notation, e.g. **Coastal Service Less than 25 Miles.**

4. REVISED STRUCTURAL REQUIREMENTS FOR MONOHULLS

4.1 VERTICAL ACCELERATION

Fundamental to the calculation of the dynamic design pressure equations in the Guide, is the determination of the vertical acceleration at the longitudinal centre of gravity of the craft.

The equation given in the 1990 Guide was based on the standard equation developed by Savitsky and Brown [6]. The ABS modified equation considered a significant wave-height of L/12 and the average highest 1/10 acceleration in that condition.

In line with the need to update classification requirements to meet the changing industry and international legislation, the equation to determine the accelerations at the longitudinal centre of gravity of the craft was revised. The revised equation for a monohull is given as:

$$n_{cg} = 0.0078 \ ((12 \ h_{1/3})/B + 1.0 \ ) \ \tau \ (50\text{-}\beta) \ \frac{V^2 B^2}{\Delta}, \quad g's$$

where

n_{cg} = average of the 1/100 highest vertical accelerations at LCG, g's;

$h_{1/3}$ = significant wave height, m, for the sea state being considered;

B = maximum beam at the waterline in metres;

τ = running trim at V, in degrees, generally not to be taken less than 3°;

β = deadrise at longitudinal centre of gravity, degrees;

V = vessel speed, kn;

Δ = displacement at design waterline in kg.

This revised equation is now based on average of the 1/100 highest vertical accelerations and also recognises that service speeds can vary with different significant waveheights. Figure 3 shows typical speed versus wave-height envelope, at 0.6g & 1g, for a 35m monohull.

4.2 DESIGN BOTTOM SLAMMING PRESSURE

From this basic revision, the bottom design pressures p_b, which is given in the Guide as a function of the accelera-tion, can now be based on the speed of the craft and the significant wave height of the sea conditions, in which the vessel will operate.

4

This is a very important feature of many craft, e.g. ferries, which operate in a very limited environment, as it enables the hull structure of the craft to be designed to the local sea conditions and for operational limits on speed at increasing waveheights to be assigned (Figure 4).

In addition to this the structural design can be based on varying strength co-efficients based on the designer specified or Guide minimum required significant wave heights for the specific areas of operation. This is particularly applicable to service craft such as rescue and crew boats, which require to operate in more severe conditions than passenger craft.

4.3 DESIGN BOTTOM HYDROSTATIC PLUS WAVE PRESSURE

Due to the Guide now covering craft with a greater range of lengths, the bottom hydrostatic pressure equation has also been revised. This is now given as:

$$P_d = 9.81 (H + d)$$

where

P_d = bottom design pressure based on hydrostatic forces, kN/m^2;

H = wave parameter, $0.0172 L + 3.653$, m;

d = stationary draft moulded, m, but generally not to be taken as less than $0.04L$;

L = scantling length.

Figure 5 shows a plot of p_b and P_d along the length of the craft.

4.4 DESIGN SIDE PRESSURE

The previous Guide addressed the side pressures in a quasi dynamic/hydrostatic manner. The new Guide now considers the design loads in the following manner:

a) **Slamming** pressure based on the acceleration and the hull geometry at the position considered.

b) **Hydrostatic** pressure based on the draft and wave loadings.

c) **Pitching** pressure in the forward region based on the length of the craft and hull geometry at the forward end.

The pressures are shown plotted along the length of the craft in Figure 6.

4.5 DECK PRESSURE

The deck pressures in the Guide are those that ABS have previously established. However, in recognition of the light loadings on internal decks on passenger craft, a new category of loading has been introduced for this type of deck.

In addition, a category for concentrated loads has also been introduced, which takes into account the location of the load in the length of the craft, and the possible effects from the accelerations at that location.

4.6 PRESSURES FOR MULTI-HULL CRAFT

The various equations for a monohull are suitably modified to take into account the hull form of the multi-hull craft. In particular the value of B, beam at waterline, is taken as the sum of each hull. In addition, an equation for obtaining the wet/crossdeck design pressure has been included.

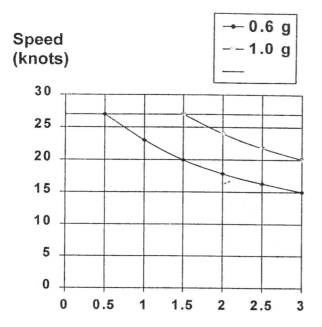

Speed (knots)

— 0.6 g
-- 1.0 g

Significant Waveheight (m)

Fig. 3 Speed v. Significant Waveheight

Significant Wave Height (m)	Maximum Speed (Knots)
≤ 0.5	27
≤ 1.0	23
≤ 2.0	18
≤ 3.0	15
Above 3 metres	Seek Shelter at Slow Speed

Fig. 4 Typical Operational Restrictions for a High-Speed Craft

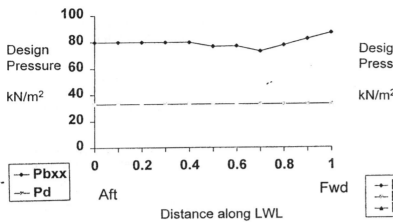

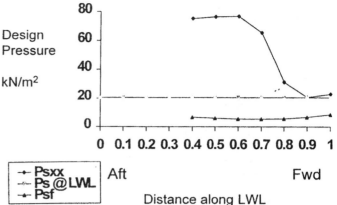

Fig. 5 Typical Bottom Pressure Distribution along the Length of a 35m Monohull

Fig. 6 Typical Side Pressure Distribution along the Length of a 35m Monohull

4.7 GLOBAL STRENGTH

The section on global strength has been totally revised. Previously, the guide only considered monohulls of normal proportions up to 61 metres in lengths, for the following:

1. hull girder section modulus and inertia in the displacement mode, and

2. hull girder section modulus, taking into account slamming, for craft with speeds over 25 knots.

The revised Guide, in addition, considers the following:

3. hull girder strength, taking into account craft with restricted operation and/or the speed of the craft, and

4. for craft over 61 metres in length, hull girder strength taking into account still water and wave bending moments and shear forces.

The global strength of twin hull craft such as catamarans and SES are now addressed and formulae are given to determine adequate transverse strength. The equations take into account bending and shear forces applied to the craft, and torsional strength of the cross deck structure, due to the pitching moments of the two hulls.

The various requirements for global strength, for monohull and multi-hull are shown in Figure 7.

5. DIRECT ANALYSIS

The Guide provides standard accepted formulae for determining the scantlings of plating and associated secondary stiffening, primary members such as girders and transverses etc. However, on occasions it may also be required that designers carry out additional two or three dimensional Finite Element Analysis to show the adequacy of a primary system, particularly when considering the main hull framing in the slamming region. A typical 3D half model of one compartment of a catamaran is shown in Figure 8 and the some of the loads that can be applied to it are shown in Figure 9.

Further, the Guide also requires, for craft over 61 metres in length or when the speed of the craft exceeds 45 knots, that direct analysis is performed to show adequate global and local hull strength. The analytical models, their boundary conditions and loadings should ideally be discussed and agreed with the Bureau before the analysis is carried out.

6. SPECIAL FEATURES

In recognition of the fact that high speed craft have now moved from the area of a relatively small type of marine transport to much larger multi-role vessels, ABS has endeavoured to include in the Guide information and requirements on those features that were previously considered as novel. One such area was the consideration of car decks and shell closing arrangements. The Guide considers the fitting of vehicle decks and the associated bow, stern or side shell doors.

7. CRITICAL AREAS OF CONSTRUCTION

As this type of craft increases in size and speed, structural continuity and detail design, which were not problems in smaller craft, become ever more important in keeping areas of stress concentration as low as possible.

With the increase in overall length of high speed craft that has been seen over the last few years structural continuity has become of paramount importance, to ensure that the associated increases in hull girder deflections do not cause local structural failure and low resistance to fatigue.

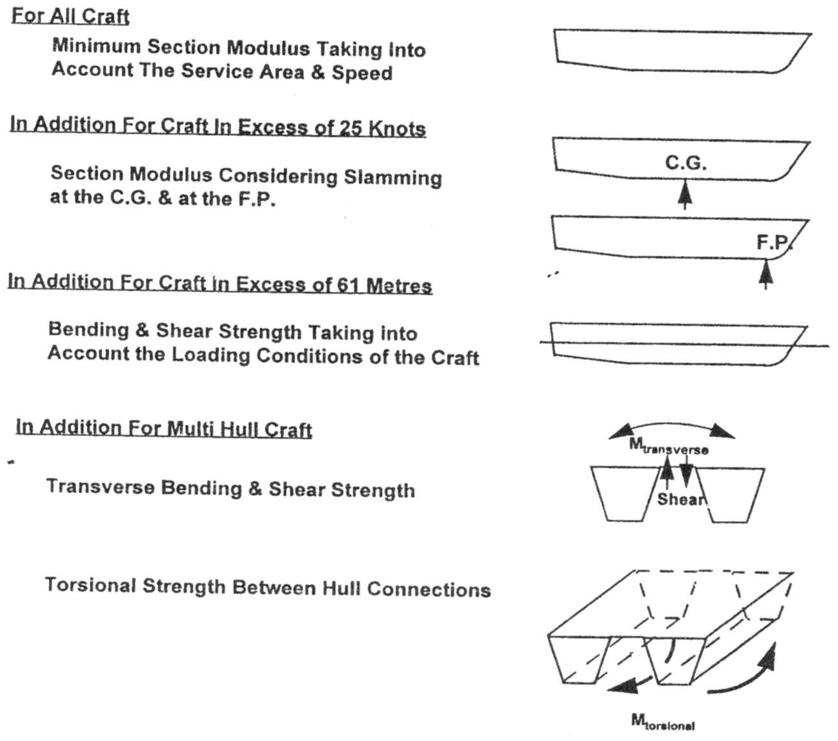

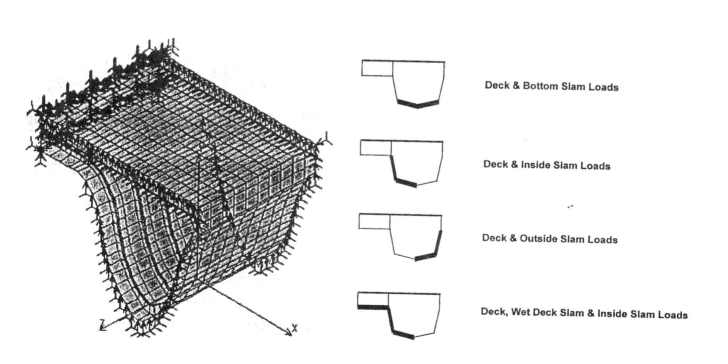

For All Craft

   Minimum Section Modulus Taking Into
   Account The Service Area & Speed

In Addition For Craft In Excess of 25 Knots

   Section Modulus Considering Slamming
   at the C.G. & at the F.P.

C.G.

F.P.

In Addition For Craft In Excess of 61 Metres

   Bending & Shear Strength Taking Into
   Account the Loading Conditions of the Craft

In Addition For Multi Hull Craft

   Transverse Bending & Shear Strength

$M_{transverse}$

Shear

   Torsional Strength Between Hull Connections

$M_{torsional}$

Fig. 7   Global Strength

Deck & Bottom Slam Loads

Deck & Inside Slam Loads

Deck & Outside Slam Loads

Deck, Wet Deck Slam & Inside Slam Loads

Fig. 8   Typical 3D Half Model

Fig. 9   Typical Model Loads

7

General layouts of the craft should take into account the arrangement of primary structural members and loss of local and overall strength due to deck openings.

Some of the global areas that should be carefully considered in the design of any high speed craft are:

- the hull connections of multi-hull craft;

- the contribution to overall strength by superstructures;

- the positioning of transverse bulkheads and web frames in the hull and superstructure, and

- deck supporting arrangements.

Some of the areas of detail design that require particular attention are:

- support of pillars;

- end connections of secondary stiffening;

- through structure continuity of primary members;

- cut outs in plating for windows, doors. etc., and

- support of chines and knuckles of hull shell plating.

By careful design and application of well proven systems the potential problem areas in the new generation of larger high speed craft can be avoided.

8.   REVISED MACHINERY REQUIREMENTS

8.1   OVERVIEW

The contents of the machinery section of the Guide have been totally revised. New sections include:

- Conditions of Classification of Machinery.

- Gas Turbines.

- Internal Combustion Engines and Reduction Gears, and

- Shipboard Control and Monitoring Systems.

Remaining sections have been extensively revised and in some cases expanded. These sections include:

- Electrical Installations.

- Pumps and Piping Systems.

- Fire Extinguishing Systems, and

- Propulsion Shafting, Propellers, Waterjet and Lift Devices.

- Steering.

The purpose of the revision is to keep pace with the latest technology (particularly with the craft increases in length from 40 metres to 120 metres), and address the unique machinery features of these craft. In some cases, changes to our requirements were brought about by international concern and the publishing of the IMO HSC Code. The new Guide has been produced in a 'stand alone' format, e.g. the machinery sections of the new Guide are designed to minimise cross references to other ABS Rules.

8.2   CONDITIONS OF CLASSIFICATION OF MACHINERY

In view of the increases in size, speeds and therefore complexity of this type of craft, a new section has been introduced. This section, Conditions of Classification of Machinery, comprehensively outlines the minimum data and plans for all machinery and the associated systems to be submitted to ABS for approval, before the construction of the craft commences. In the previous Guide, the plans were listed within the individual sections, the new format allows for easier reference. It also specifies definitions used in the Guide for the purpose of review. This covers all systems including machinery and electrical installations, periodically unattended machinery spaces, fire protection and extinction.

8.3   GAS TURBINES

Gas turbine requirements are included in the Guide to cater for the latest trend in development of high-speed craft. Minimum installation requirements for low flash point fuels typically used for the gas turbines are also covered in this section.

8.4   ELECTRICAL INSTALLATION

The format of the electrical requirements has been revised extensively for the following reasons:

- to be of a uniform format with ABS Steel Vessels Rules, and

- to incorporate applicable requirements of HSC Code.

For example, requirements of each section are sub-divided into the major parts, such as general, system, installation, machinery and equipment, specialised installations, specialised craft and services. This makes for a quick and easy reference to each topic.

8.5   PUMP AND PIPING SYSTEMS

This section has been revised to incorporate some of the latest requirements from the Steel Vessels Rules which are also applicable to high speed craft, this includes the requirements for installation of plastic pipes. It has also been revised to include requirements of HSC Code which are also considered applicable to high speed craft classification, examples of which are the installation arrangements and requirements for bilge systems, including alternative arrangements such as the submersible pump installations (typically used in many high-speed craft designs).

8.6 PROPULSION SHAFTING, PROPELLERS, WATERJETS AND LIFT DEVICES

Since weight is one of the important concerns in high-speed craft, designers and builders are selecting shaft materials with properties that exhibit superior strength and corrosion-resistance over the conventional carbon steels. Requirements in the new Guide allows for shaft diameter reduction if these superior materials are used.

Requirements of waterjets and lift devices, which are typically found on high-speed craft, are now also incorporated in this section.

8.7 FIRE SAFETY

Due to the nature of construction and operation of high speed craft, the following fire safety measures are incorporated in the new Guide, for passenger craft on international voyages:

a) Enclosed spaces in the accommodation, such as toilets, stairway enclosures and corridors are fitted with automatic smoke-detection system and manually operated call points.

b) Main propulsion machinery rooms are supervised by TV cameras from a manned space (typically the navigation bridge).

c) Fixed fire fighting systems are to be provided for propulsion machinery spaces (area of major fire hazard). Where gas such as CO_2 is used, the quantity of gas is to be sufficient for two independent discharges.

d) Fixed fire detection and alarm systems are to be provided for any machinery space containing an internal combustion engine, gas turbine, or switchboards of aggregate capacity exceeding 800 kW.

e) Public spaces and service spaces, storage rooms and similar spaces are to be protected by manually operated fixed sprinkler systems.

8.8 SHIPBOARD CONTROL AND MONITORING SYSTEM

Depending on the operating preference, the machinery spaces for high-speed craft are typically unattended. The alarm monitoring panels for the main and auxiliary engines are located in the wheelhouse. The fire fighting station, with controls and alarms for fixed fire detection system, firefighting systems, sprinkler systems, fuel oil pumps and valves and ventilation systems shut-downs are also typically located in the wheelhouse. The section on Shipboard Control and Monitoring applies different requirements for shipboard automatic or remote control monitoring systems, based on the length and gross tonnage of the craft, and also incorporates the applicable requirements of the HSC Code.

Craft complying with this section of the Guide will be given an additional class notation **ACCU** or **ABCU** notations.

9. CONCLUSION

This paper has covered some of the revised areas in the ABS High Speed Craft Guide. The Guide has now been published as a stand alone document, and covers all aspects of the latest trend in high speed craft classification. In doing so ABS, in line with its mission, hopes to serve the public interests, as well as shipbuilding industry, in the advancement of the various types of high speed marine vehicles in the market place today.

REFERENCES

1. SAVITSKY, D: Naval Engineering Journal, ASNE, Ch.4, Feb 1985.

2. International Code of Safety of High Speed Craft (HSC), International Maritime Organisation, 1994.

3. International Convention for the Safety of Life at Sea 1974 (with amendments). International Maritime Organisation, 1994.

4. Guide for Building and Classing High-Speed Craft, October 1990, American Bureau of Shipping.

5. Guide for Building and Classing High-Speed Craft, February 1997, American Bureau of Shipping.

6. SAVITSKY, D and WARD BROWN, P: 'Procedures for Hydrodynamic Evaluation of Planing Hulls in Smooth and Rough Water', Marine Technology, Vol. 13, No. 4, Oct 1996.

SUMMARY REPORT OF DISCUSSIONS

by David Anderson

International Symposium & Seminar

THE SAFETY OF HIGH SPEED CRAFT

6 - 7 FEBRUARY 1997 LONDON

SUMMARY REPORT OF DISCUSSIONS

by David Anderson

SESSION I - STABILITY

In the chair: Mr A G Blyth (Blyth Bridges Marine Consultants, Member RINA Safety Committee, Member RINA Small Craft Group, Member RINA Rapid Marine Transport Group.)

PAPER NO 1

DAMAGE STABILITY TESTS OF A MODEL REPRESENTING A FAST RO-RO PASSENGER FERRY

Presented by M Schindler

Mr A G Blyth, from the chair, expressed surprise that the model tested did not capsize even though expected to do so from calculations based upon the Stockholm Agreement. He wondered what improvements if any could be incorporated in the method of calculation.

Mr S L Pollard (P&O European Ferries) sought details of how control was exercised over the value of GM during the experiments. He commended the use of model experiments because these often demonstrated that older vessels could comply with the requirements of SOLAS '90, whereas according to direct calculations they did not.

The author said the model was fitted with an elevator which enabled an internal weight to be moved in order to control KG, and hence GM and GZ. He said control of the freeboard after damage could be exercised by increasing the extent of damage together with changes in permeability.

Prof D Vassalos (University of Strathclyde) commented that the calculations envisaged under the Stockholm Agreement related to static conditions, and therefore, could not be used to study the evolution of the flooding process and the subsequent behaviour of the ship.

In addition, although the Stockholm Agreement was based upon the results of model experiments, these related to ships having normal proportions and geometric properties, most of which had side casings and bulkheads on the vehicle deck. He expressed his doubts that the results of such experiments could be used to investigate the damage stability characteristics of all types of Ro-Ro vessels, and he sought the authors view on the validity of attempts to do so.

The author responded saying a number of factors were involved in the improved damaged stability inherent in this high speed ship concept, which he hoped would be explained as the result of future work.

PAPER NO 2

COMPARISON OF TYPICAL DAMAGED STABILITY CHARACTERISTICS OF CATAMARAN AND FAST MONOHULL TYPES

Presented by J C Lewthwaite

Mr T A Armstrong (Australian Shipbuilders Association, Australia) referred to the statement in Section 1 of the paper, which he assumed related to ST MALO and CONDOR 11 where the length of the actual damage suffered by these vessels exceeded that assumed under the HSC Code, which the author had suggested might be inadequate. He pointed out that neither of these craft were certified under the HSC Code at the time of their accidents, and indeed, the latter vessel was on builders' trials at the time.

He questioned the low value of the tolerable damaged length for catamarans proposed in paragraph 4.2 of the paper and suggested this might be influenced by the semi-SWATH characteristics of the catamaran form considered by the author. He said Ref 1 of his own paper presented to this Symposium suggested a value of 0.65 L, which he believed could be exceeded in the case of a high speed catamaran having a large centre hull.

Concerning the author's conclusion that the current damaged length requirements in the HSC Code should be doubled, he wondered whether this increase should also apply to vessels operating under SOLAS '90, because many of these operated at high speeds.

The author expressed the view that future high speed craft may well have hull forms similar to those involved in the major accidents so far, and must therefore be built in accordance with the HSC Code.

He agreed that catamarans could tolerate a greater extent of damage than a corresponding SWATH, and said that both types of vessel could tolerate more than 50% damage amidships.

Mr P Werenskiold (MARINTEK, Norway) expressed support for an increase in damage length within the HSC Code. He cited the case of a 40m catamaran which grounded on a 2m rock when proceeding at 37 knots. Damage extending 5m from the bow was sustained by one hull; structural deformation extended to the upper deck. An evaluation of the data relating to this incident resulted in Fig 1 which showed the estimated extent of damage to one hull of a catamaran travelling at 40 knots.

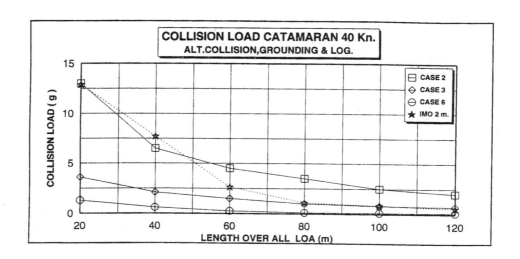

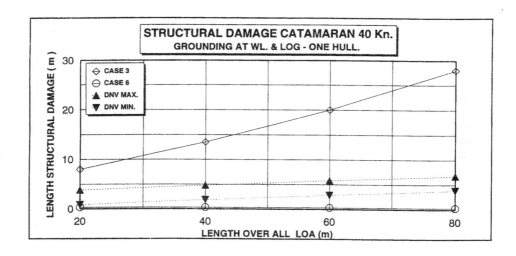

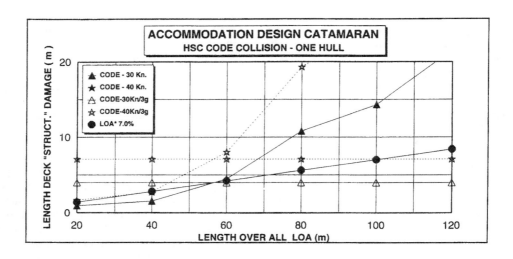

Fig. 1 One hull damage length

He agreed with the author's estimates of damage length if both hulls were to be involved in the collision.

The author was grateful for support of his contention that a damage length envisaged within the HSC Code, 10% or 6% depending on the length of the craft, was insufficient.

PAPER NO 3

DYNAMIC STABILITY OF PLANING SHIPS

Presented by S L Toxopeus, J A Keuning and J P Hooft

Prof D Vassalos asked how the authors had taken into account the change in attitude of the craft and the corresponding hydrostatic characteristics, added mass and damping as the speed of the craft varied. He thought the maximum roll angle of 10° considered by the authors might be inadequate, because tests on models of planing vessels showed rolling to 20° to 25° as speeds reduced. He suggested the range of tests should be expanded to include very large roll angles.

Mr Hooft, on behalf of the authors, replied that each variable was changed with changes in draught, at each time step during the simulation. The test programme was organised so that the variables were interdependent and varied accordingly. He emphasised the study was still in its early stages and it was hoped that large angles of heel would be considered eventually.

Mr P Werenskiold opined that the issues surrounding the effect of dynamic instability on safety matters were so complex that they would not be resolved in the foreseeable future. Because of this the requirements of the HSC Code were based on the results of model experiments. He considered the best way of documenting the safety limitations of craft was to define the following items and resolve them by means of model experiments and practical experience.

- Define Critical Factors.

- Requirements.

- Verification Methods.

- Corrective Measures.

- Design Guidelines.

SESSION II - SAFETY IN DESIGN AND OPERATION

In the chair: Mr S Phillips (Seaspeed Technology, Chairman RINA Rapid Marine Transport Group)

PAPER NO 4

DESIGN LIMITATIONS: OPERATING LIMITATIONS THE SAFETY OF HIGH SPEED CRAFT

Presented by M Simpson and R Bryce

Mr A G Blyth reinforced the author's view that the industry should support certifying authorities because these bodies could not be expected to know everything about every type of craft. He suggested that any revision of the HSC Code should be based on performance objectives for particular operating conditions. He believed this would open the way towards consistency of interpretation as well as alternatives to the current prescriptive approach to safety matters.

Mr R Bryce agreed saying an example of this might be the adoption of accelerations as measured on the vessel as an alternative to using the significant wave height ahead of the vessel, bearing in mind the difficulties of assessing wave heights.

Mr D Whittaker (Lloyd's Register of Shipping) said the structural design of high speed craft should be considered in relation to his society's Special Service Craft Rules rather than its Steel Ship Rules. He remarked that scantling requirements for steel ships also varied amongst classification societies and this was not a state of affairs confined to high speed craft.

Mr P Werenskiold opined that classification societies used the significant wave height and vessel speed for structural design purposes, whereas the HSC Code was concerned with more than head seas and structural design. However, performance limitations of high speed must be related to some significant wave height. Because of this the master must be provided with a means of measuring wave height.

PAPER NO 5

CATAMARANS: THE SAFEST WAY TO TRAVEL BY SEA?

Presented by T A Armstrong

Mr I Williams (Australian Maritime Safety Authority, Australia) emphasised the importance of collaboration between the industry and the safety authorities in leading to the formulation of the next HSC Code, otherwise it was likely to be unsatisfactory for all concerned.

The proposed revision of the HSC Code was in response to political concern about the safety of the travelling public. Future revisions had to be soundly based on research if the easy option of prescriptive rules was to be avoided. However it must be borne in mind that any new rules had to be such that they could be interpreted and used by surveyors in their day to day work.

Speaking as Chairman of the Design and Equipment Committee of IMO he said the proposals to IMO so far did not reflect the problems aired at this Symposium, and he repeated his call for greater collaboration from the Industry.

Mr D Fry (Fry Design and Research, Australia) said he was a very strong advocate for the fitting of double bottoms in high speed vehicle catamarans having seen the extensive damage done to many of these craft by striking the Great Barrier Reef. He expressed his fear that large vehicle catamarans were capable of destroying their entire bottom structure on submerged rocks, and would sink unless provision was made in the design for some form of reserve buoyancy. For passenger-only catamarans a watertight subdivided upper structure might be adequate for this purpose.

The author cautioned against attempts to make high speed craft unsinkable by means of design requirements which did not apply to other types of ship.

PAPER NO 6

DESIGNING A SPECIAL PURPOSE SWATH TO THE HSC CODE

Presented by N F Warren and G Rudgely

Mr D Whittaker expressed surprise that the authors originally questioned the need for the vessel to have a rescue boat. However he wondered whether it was necessary for the boat to be capable of manoeuvring liferafts in view of the vessel's area of operation, where rescue operations could be mounted quickly.

He said SOLAS required two means of operation for the engine room CO_2 system in order to prevent the accidental release of the gas whilst personnel were in the space. Also there were requirements for the automatic closure of vents and doors etc. to meet the needs of unmanned engine rooms.

Mr Warren responded saying MoD had required a rescue boat to be fitted, but in any event he believed MSA would have done so in order to meet SOLAS requirements. He remarked that because the CO_2 release systems were sited so close together on this craft, the additional complication of a remote release system was considered to be unnecessary and might even introduce additional hazards.

Mr P Werenskiold said the purpose of a rescue boat was to retrieve people from the sea. He considered the SOLAS requirement that it should be capable of towing a loaded liferaft at a speed of 3 knots to be unrealistic because this would result in the destruction of the liferaft.

Mr Rudgely responded saying the towage of liferafts was not the main purpose of this particular rescue boat which was to standby during the transfer of personnel.

Capt A Esmiley (Marine Safety Agency) emphasised that rescue boats were intended for retrieving people from the water and exemption might be granted to craft slightly greater than 20m in length in special cases.

In response to a query from **Mr T Moore** (Rolls-Royce) concerning the time taken to prepare the Safety Case, Mr Rudgely replied that for this particular vessel about 1500 man hours were needed. The time required varied according to the type of vessel and the scope of the work.

SESSION III - SAFETY APPROACHES

In the chair: Mr S Phillips

PAPER NO 7

FORMAL SAFETY ASSESSMENT AND HIGH SPEED CRAFT

Presented by Jim Peachey

After the presentation of this paper insufficient time was available for discussion which was deferred until the general discussion period.

PAPER NO 8

FORMAL SAFETY ASSESSMENT FOR HIGH SPEED CRAFT: PROPULSION AND MANOEUVRING SYSTEMS RELIABILITY:
AN OUTLINE OF THE START OF A RESEARCH PROJECT

Presented by J M Forestier and R Giribone.

Mr T Hoare expressed surprise at the degree of redundancy suggested by the authors in selecting four propulsion systems instead of two in the craft selected for the project.

On behalf of the authors Mr Giribone said a risk analysis, during which this question would be considered, formed part of the next stage of the project.

Mr P Werenskiold said a risk analysis had been carried out in Norway, on behalf of operators, after a major accident involving a catamaran. From these studies human factors had emerged as the principal risks. In order of magnitude they were Navigational Procedures, Crew Competence, and Training of Personnel. He expressed the view that any safety regulations must take into account these human factors, and not just technical considerations.

He added that it was often said 80% of accidents or failures were due to human factors and statistics showed that all fatalities might be caused by this, ie, collisions, groundings, etc.

The author responded saying human factors which were often related to the selection and training of personnel were affected to some extent by operating economics and it would not be easy for classification societies to take account of them.

Mr J Peachey supported the view that the human element was a very important factor in marine accidents. Early indications from work at MSA suggested that there might be a misdirection of efforts to improve safety which concentrated on design and hardware solutions rather than on human factors.

In response to a query from **Mr A Mulder** (Royal Netherlands Navy, Netherlands) the author said navigational matters were not part of the current project, but the area of operation would be taken into consideration in order to assess the consequences of equipment failure.

Mr S Phillips, from the chair, said a similar project in the UK had developed into a genetic shipping project which took account of ship management, navigation buoys, lighthouses and other environmental factors.

PAPER NO 9

GLOBAL SAFETY APPROACH

Presented by V Farinetti, L Grossi and A Gazzo

Prof D Vassalos asked why the vessel had been designed in accordance with the Stockholm Agreement when there was no need to do so.

Mr Grossi, on behalf of the authors, said they wished to know whether or not the vessel would comply with the Agreement, and in any event such compliance implied a greater degree of safety for passengers.

Mr D Whittaker said the Stockholm Agreement was meant to apply to Ro-Ro ships of conventional design and he expressed the view that many administrations would be inclined to treat SUPERSEACAT under the HSC Code.

In response to a query from **Mr G Gibbons** (Ministry of Defence) concerning the choice of different materials for the two vessels which were nominally similar, the author replied that both vessels were designed for a similar level of safety. The choice of material in each case was made by the owners on the basis of first cost and maintenance considerations.

PAPER NO 10

RECENT DEVELOPMENTS IN FIRE SAFETY FOR HIGH SPEED CRAFT

Presented by T Eidal

In response to a query from **Mr S Phillips,** the author said consideration of the effect of fire on aluminium had not been taken into account in deciding the strength of lightweight structures.

Mr G H Fuller (BMT, Chairman of Council RINA) asked whether any attempt had been made to limit the supply of oxygen during the room corner fire test.

The author said no such attempt had been made and it was believed that because the room was small it represented a more severe situation than a similar fire within a large public room.

Mr A Mulder queried the need for a two shot gas system. The author said there should be a high level of redundancy within a high speed craft. The two systems may be of different types: a vehicle space may be fitted with sprinklers as well as an inert gas system.

In response to a query from **Mr T Moore,** the author said until now DNV approval has been sought for Halotron for use in fire fighting systems. FM 200 has been approved for use in gas turbine machinery spaces but not for general engine room use.

Mr G H Fuller said the London Underground had banned smoking anywhere in the system in an attempt to reduce fire risks. Many airlines also banned smoking in aircraft and he wondered why the practice had not extended to high speed craft.

The author responded saying it was assumed passengers and crew would soon be aware of fires started by smokers and they could then be quickly extinguished. In any event few northern European operators would permit smoking on their craft.

GENERAL DISCUSSION

In the chair: Mr S Phillips

Mr H R J Akerboom (Directorate General of Shipping and Maritime Affairs, Netherlands) indicated that some operators considered the requirement of the HSC Code for Category B craft to have two engine rooms to be onerous. He pointed out that most, if not all Ro-Ro vessels operating under SOLAS, had two separate engine rooms even though they were not required to do so.

Mr J Peachey said the current study by MSA on the application of Formal Safety Assessments to high speed craft was attempting to quantify the risks involved in a variety of situations. The risks of fires in engine rooms and passenger spaces were being assessed and compared with collision risks. It was hoped that by this means it would be possible to identify which were the greatest risks to high speed vessels and to address these in a rational way. What FSA could not do was to compare risks between a lightweight high speed craft and a conventional steel Ro-Ro vessel. It was hoped that at some time in the future it might be possible to do so and to establish the appropriate level of safety for each type of craft.

Prof D Vassalos said relative safety standards could be assessed by comparing the results of model experiments with the results of calculations for the relevant vessels which only just complied with the requirements of, for example, SOLAS '90. But he asked what was really meant by expressions such as safety, relative safety and absolute safety.

Mr V Jenkins (AEA Technology) said a number of industries were addressing, and had addressed, the question of acceptable safety standards in relation to both individuals and the community at large. In the UK the nuclear industry was probably the best known in this connection.

Mr M Starling (BMT Reliability Consultants) said as a result of work done for MSA, risk assessments of Ro-Ro vessels for the past 50 years were known.

Mr N Wells (INCAT, Australia) expressed concern that the incident involving CONDOR 11 was being wrongly used as a basis for the revision of the HSC Code. At the time of the grounding the craft was operating as a private craft on trials, and was not therefore being operated in accordance with the requirements of the HSC Code. The sole injury during the incident was caused by an unlaid roll of carpet, to a person who was lying against it whilst watching TV.

The HSC Code in its current form could work providing that the people approving novel craft were persons of novel approach who could balance commercial realism with common sense. Without such an approach the progress of a very fragile industry would stall, or at worst fail.

He concluded by saying both builders and operators had demonstrated an ability to self-regulate a safe and novel means of transport. However operators needed reassurance that revisions of the HSC Code would not lead to a series of retrospective changes to existing craft, thus imposing an unreasonable economic burden on them.

Mr S Phillips, from the chair, said he hoped the eventual widespread use of the FSA process would enable a cost-benefit analysis to be carried out on proposed safety improvements.

Mr A Blyth said work on FSA techniques was still at an early stage and he wondered when they would be available for general use by the industry. He also expressed regret that it seemed unlikely this would be before the deadline of 1999 set by IMO for the revision of the HSC Code.

Mr J Peachey said the fortuitous choice by MSA of high speed craft for the FSA case study was not linked in any way to the forthcoming revision of the HSC Code. He added that the continuation of the study depended on the availability of funding for the work.

Mr I Williams added to the comments of the previous speaker saying there appeared to be no support amongst administrations for a delay in revising the HSC Code until proven FSA techniques were available.

Prof D Vassalos said the author of Paper 7 defined FSA as a formal method of regulating safety even though there was a current tendency amongst administrations to address safety by means of regulations.

Strathclyde University was a member of an informal group of organisations which looked upon FSA as a link between technological development and design and which hoped to develop a formalised design methodology. However FSA could not be regarded as a panacea when there was much evidence that 80% of marine mishaps were caused by human factors.

Mr N Warren supported the view that human operational factors were more relevant to safety than hull design, or indeed, to the relative safety of monohulls or catamarans.

Mr R Bryce expressed his concern that regulators by concentrating efforts on FSA might become remote from the day to day problems of builders and operators in dealing with the varying interpretations of current safety regulations.

Mr P Werenskiold observed that a risk analysis, FSA by another name, had been used in the development of the Norwegian Operational Code and led to the conclusion that 80% of accidents were caused by human factors. It had also led to improvements in interior design in order to reduce the injuries to passengers during a collision.

Mr S Phillips, from the chair, closed the Symposium and thanked authors and delegates for their attendance. He thanked all who had been concerned with the organisation of what had been a very successful event.

Written Contribution to Discussion

Mr D Fry added to the views he expressed during the discussion of Paper No 5, and provided Fig 2 in which he suggested a relationship between damage length expressed as a percentage of vessel length, and craft speed.

He suggested that structural fire protection was not necessary where

- mechanical and electrical equipment was Installed to standards which limited the cause of fire;

- fire fighting equipment had automatic fast deployment in specified zones;

- an adequate manually operated fire fighting system and equipment was available for deployment by passengers and crew for all zones.

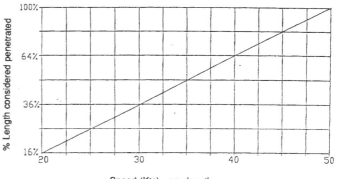

Speed (Kts) - any length

Fig. 2

SEMINAR / STRUCTURED DISCUSSION

Opening Address by Mr W A Graham, Director
Marine Standards Division, Marine Safety Agency, UK

SESSION I - DESIGN ACCELERATIONS

Speakers: K Wiklund, Head of High Speed Light Craft Section,
              Det Norske Veritas, Norway.

              P Werenskiold, Senior Research Engineer, Marintek, Norway.

SESSION II - STRUCTURES & FIRE

Speakers: Professor T Jastrzebski, Faculty of Maritime Technology,
              University of Szczecin, Poland.

              R Curry, Manager of Rule Development, ABS Europe, UK

              A Marchant, Managing Director, CETEC Consultancy Ltd, UK

SESSION III - STABILITY & SUBDIVISION

Speakers: A G Blyth, Director, Blyth Bridges Marine Consultants Ltd, UK

              J Lewthwaite, Manager, IMAA Consultancy Ltd, UK

SESSION IV - LIFESAVING & EVACUATION

Speakers: Geoff Billington, ML Lifeguard Ltd, UK.

              S Phillips, Director, Seaspeed Technology Ltd, UK.

              J Gifford, Managing Director, Griffon Hovercraft Ltd, UK

SUMMARY OF SEMINAR ACTION POINTS

SUMMARY REPORT OF DISCUSSIONS FROM SHANGHAI

INTERNATIONAL SEMINAR

THE SAFETY OF HIGH SPEED CRAFT

7th FEBRUARY 1997

Address by

W A GRAHAM
MARINE SAFETY AGENCY - Marine Standards Division

It is a pleasure for me to be with you today and I am honoured to be invited to give the opening address to this very important symposium. As on other occasions, I have asked myself why I have been selected to undertake this duty and perhaps it is because of my involvement with the formation of the High Speed Craft Advisory Group. As that indeed seems to be the case I will refer at some length to the work of that group later in this address.

Before I give an account of the Advisory Group's work I think it is necessary to put its work in the context of safety generally. As a senior official within the Marine Safety Agency I have noted an understandable tendency to look towards regulation as the means of achieving safety. We all feel safe with regulations because they cannot be made without Parliamentary consent and therefore have near unquestionable authority. There are two serious flaws in that argument. The first is that safety is the primary responsibility of the owner and his employees and regulations can be seen as a means of sharing that responsibility. Secondly, there is no purpose whatsoever in having high standards if they are not enforced and enforceable. There is also the very serious question of how far one can take standards without affecting the viability of a project and therefore bringing those standards into a measure of disrespect or perhaps even disrepute.

The arguments that I have set out on the pros and cons of regulations are particularly important in the context of high speed craft. If they are to be commercially viable then they must, to a certain extent, compete against conventional ferries which are subject to demanding requirements. From the outset they have had to be attractive to passengers who value speed of transit, but also other factors such as comfort and cost, to name but two. It was in that environment that the first generation high speed craft developed and became subject to the somewhat erroneously titled Dynamically Supported Craft code. The main characteristics of those craft were their speed, lightweight construction and relatively small size. It was quite evident that they could not comply with the safety standards for conventional ships and this led to safety standards enshrined in the Dynamically Supported Craft code.

I think it is now accepted that high speed craft are here to stay. One has only to look at the developments in the North Sea and the Irish Sea to recognise this. Indeed, one of the major commercial considerations that affected successful high speed craft operations in the past - the inability to carry vehicles -seems to have been overcome.

To sum up, I think that we can safely say that we are well into the second generation of high speed craft and the recent enactment of a dedicated chapter of the SOLAS Convention underlines that position.

Before I look to the future I would perhaps like to express my personal satisfaction at being involved in the development of safety standards for high speed craft over the years. It has certainly been my experience that the debate on their safety has moved from discussion in the margins of IMO meetings to the forefront of debates at the Maritime Safety Committee where I have had the privilege of leading the United Kingdom delegation. It was from that position that I recognised the limitations of the new Code of Safety dealing with high speed craft. However a judgement had to be made between having a reasonable measure of standards within the international convention or none at all. I think it was generally recognised that it is better to have the requirements as they stand for further development and with that in mind I sought Ministers' permission to establish the High Speed Craft Advisory Group to further that purpose.

The new generation of high speed craft present the world with a serious new safety challenge and a new approach is needed. The international requirements for high speed craft represent only a limited framework for the development of safety and the group is clearly of the mind that there is a need for agreed interpretations of the code and, furthermore, there are some areas where it is in need of amendment. I think I must also say on behalf of the group that we do not see that the requirements are fundamentally flawed or there is need for drastic change. The requirements are such that they do contain a large measure of flexibility and there is nothing wrong with that provided that proper and consistent interpretations are made by administrations and others involved. That, in a nutshell, is the international problem to resolve but there are also problems around our United Kingdom coast which require a sensible and consistent approach to their resolution. The Advisory Group will also deal with those issues.

In order to put the group on a proper footing, I approached Ministers suggesting the formation of the group to establish a balanced forum to provide advice. After a measure of consultation with industry, the following terms of reference were agreed:

- to consider the practical application of the International Code of Safety for High Speed Craft (HSC Code);

- to assist the MSA in its aim to achieve the consistent interpretation and application of safety standards to high speed craft and where necessary suggest equivalent arrangements for consideration and possible deposition at the International Maritime Organization (IMO);

- to consider the need for, and to make proposals for, amendments to the HSC Code to enhance the safety of high speed craft operations; and,

- to assist the Agency in its task to ensure the safe operation of high speed craft in UK and international waters.

As can be seen there is very little restriction on the work of the group in the context of high speed craft safety and as you will see from the following list of its members there is a very wide field of experience and knowledge available to the Group:

Chairman
Director, MSAS
(Mr W A Graham)

Secretariat
Mr R Wilson (MSAS(A))

Chief Surveyor, MSAS(A)
Capt D Thompson

Chief Surveyor, MSAS(B)
Mr T Allan

Chief Surveyor, MSAS(C)
Mr R Smith

Chief Surveyor, MSAS(D)
Mr J Nicholson

Chief Surveyor, MSOS(A)
Mr D Patterson

Chief Examiner, MSOS(B)
Capt A Winbow

Marine Surveyor with responsibility for overview of high speed craft, MSAS(A)
Capt A Esmiley

Ports Division, DoT
Mr D A Burr

Mr C D J Bland	Mr A Blyth
Hovertravel Ltd	Royal Institution of Naval Architects
Mr E J N Brookes	Mr R Curry
Chamber of Shipping	American Bureau of Shipping (Europe)
Mr Goodwin	Mr Hardy
Lloyds Register	Bureau Veritas
Mr A Heath	Capt G R Hicks
Consultant with the CAA	NUMAST

Capt C Jacklin	Capt M Parrott
British Ports Association	Chamber of Shipping
Dr U Petersen	Capt N R Pryke
Germanischer Lloyd	Chamber of Shipping
Mr I Rawlinson	Capt M Ridge
Det Norske Veritas	UK Major Ports Group
Mr B Tolliday	Mr K Usher
Consumers' Association	RMT

Mr N Warren
FMB Marine Ltd

I believe that the group is well on its way to establishing itself as both important and influential, not only in this country but internationally. Indeed, there has been very supportive comment for the work of the group at the International Maritime Organization and elsewhere. This is not surprising because of the broad base upon which the group undertakes its task.

It is absolutely essential for a balanced group to be at the centre of standard setting and the application of those standards so that sensible workable solutions to problems are developed that have regard to the commercial viability of operations. The Marine Safety Agency and its predecessor, the SGO, have been involved in a large number of problems associated with high speed craft over the years and a complete reappraisal of our work was indeed necessary. We had tended to look at high speed craft operations in isolation and any misgivings that we might have had about safety standards tended to be reflected in the permits to operate that were issued for individual craft. This is not surprising given the diversity of the craft involved and a general lack of experience with their operations.

I can well recall the difficulties we had applying consistent standards to different types of dynamically supported craft such as the Boeing Jetfoil and some of the surface piercing foil craft at that time. I think it is fair to say that we achieved an acceptable level of safety only by strict adherence to quite severe operating limitations made effective through a passenger certificate with associated permits to operate. Times have changed and we now have sufficient craft of this type operating to justify an industry-based advisory group to help the Marine Safety Agency uphold its safety responsibilities.

I mentioned permits to operate specifically because of their supreme importance in my view to the safe operation of these craft. Their importance to the Marine Safety Agency is perhaps best epitomised by our insistence during the formulation of the requirements that both the flag state and the port state have some measure of control. To my mind it is absolutely essential that the operation of these craft is monitored by an outside organisation and there can be no doubt what that organisation should be if large numbers of passengers are being carried.

Safety cannot be assured by craft built to internationally accepted standards that are not operated within the limits of their design. This elemental and elementary requirement must be upheld if the high speed craft industry is to prosper. Quite clearly the day-to-day responsibility for the safety of operations, maintenance and all the other aspects of safety rests with the owners, operators and officers. But the industry must also be aware of the opportunity and advantage that could be taken by a less scrupulous owner if any craft was to operate outside the margins of safety ascribed to it.

It is with this in mind that the audience today will be pleased to learn that the Marine Safety Agency will exert such influence as it has and enforce such requirements as are necessary to ensure that safety standards are upheld regardless of the flag state involved. To do otherwise would not be in the interests of the safety of passengers, or be fair in the commercial sense to safety conscious owners and operators. I make no apology for going on at some length about permits to operate because to my mind they are the essential feature of safe high speed craft operation around our coast. I will also confidently predict that the permit principle will emerge as a key safety feature in the MSA research into the application of the Formal Safety Assessment criteria and techniques.

To be fair to its members I think I should give a brief outline of the work of the High Speed Craft Advisory Group thus far and thank them for their involvement. I think that the first meeting in April last year was perhaps the most interesting because we quickly recognised the amount of work that the group had to do and the need to establish priorities. I recall that there was a list of 16 items to be urgently addressed and with the help of that formidable list we established two immediate priorities - stability related matters and fire protection - with further consideration of acceleration levels and the manning and operation of craft as the second rank issues. I am very glad to report that the group attended to its work with such gusto that papers on fire safety and stability have already been presented to the International Maritime Organization with good effect. Furthermore, we have also submitted a paper on acceleration levels for consideration by the Design & Equipment Sub-Committee, whilst the very difficult issues of manning, qualifications, training and fatigue are being actively reviewed within the group.

I do not know if it was by design or accident that the first three sessions that follow this address deal with matters that have gained the attention of the High Speed Craft Advisory Group. Whatever the reason, I look forward to hearing what those experts have to say on these difficult topics and I am sure that I can rely upon members of the group to ask some searching questions. It is not appropriate to delve too far into technical matters during an opening address but I cannot resist the temptation to ask whether various plastic resins should be used for the structure of high speed craft and whether safety criteria such as evacuation standards, that are for discussion later today, could accommodate any shortcomings in those materials.

This speech would not be complete without looking to the future, with particular reference to the work of the High Speed Craft Advisory Group. It should certainly not be

the case that the group's work is constrained to improving the international requirements. The terms of reference go much further than that and I can assure members of the audience that the MSA sees the group as a forum for the discussion of all aspects of the safe operation of high speed craft. I have already made reference to the importance of operations in the context of safety and permits to operate. Others have heard me speak on other occasions on the importance of the International Safety Management code and that, of course, has some bearing on the work of the group. But there is also a wider field for discussion and agreement and that is the position of high speed craft within the sea-going community. We are beginning to hear of problems in the navigational sense where perhaps an element of competition has crept in to establish good transit times. There is also a growing perception that these craft can generate pressure waves which can affect the safety of others.

Surely problems such as these must be addressed positively and sensibly before an accident occurs and I think I can rely upon the membership of the group to do that. I say this because I am well acquainted with the problems that can occur if seafarers are at loggerheads with each other on safety issues. I think there is already the indication that a measure of peaceful co-existence is necessary between the high speed craft community and other users. I would hope that this comes about sooner rather than later and not emulate submariners and fishermen where a tragic accident was the major driving force towards an agreed code of safety. If we need encouragement to think along these lines then just for a moment think about wing-in-ground effect craft of the future travelling at an altitude of one or two metres at a speed of 150 kilometres/hour. I have heard the suggestion that they should be banned but that was also said about steamships.

Mr Chairman, I think I was invited to make this address as Chairman of the High Speed Craft Advisory Group which has a clear duty to advise Ministers on safety matters. That indeed is a serious business which the group has tackled vigorously. It is, in fact, quite remarkable to me that we talked about high speed craft as novel craft a few years ago - now they are not quite commonplace but their presence is becoming increasingly noticeable. Their size has increased beyond recognition and even in my wildest dreams I did not envisage a craft operating carrying 1500 passengers and 300 vehicles at high speed. I think that the group, with the backing of our industry, is rising to the many challenges put forward and that we will continue to address those challenges.

A seminar such as this one organised by the Royal Institution of Naval Architects not only informs those directly concerned but, in a way, epitomises the United Kingdom's position at the centre of the development of high speed craft. Our geographical location as an island off continental Europe underlines the position that we hold. I would hope that in the future we would be able to design and build more of these craft and, if that comes about, I can guarantee that the MSA will do all that it can to further that development. For the moment, I wish the Institution and all of you a very good day.

SEMINAR AGENDA

Chairman Sessions I & II:

Karl Wiklund   Head of High Speed Light Craft
Section, Det Norske Veritas, Norway.

Chairman Sessions III & IV:

Andrew Blyth   Director, Blyth Bridges Marine
Consultants Ltd, UK.

SESSION I

PERFORMANCE/DESIGN ACCELERATIONS

Speakers:

Karl Wiklund   Head of High Speed Light Craft
Section, Det Norske Veritas, Norway.

Per Werenskiold   Senior Research Engineer, Marintek,
Norway.

- General Introduction

- Performance documentation, the ISM and the HSC
Codes.

- HSC performance documentation methods, standards
and criteria:

  - passenger and crew comfort, health and safety;

  - ship seakeeping and structural loads;

  - ship performance in extreme situations;

  - cargo loads and cargo shift;

  - low and high speed manoeuvring;

  - collision and grounding loads.

SESSION II

STRUCTURES AND FIRE

Speakers:

Professor T Jastrzebski

        Faculty of Maritime Technology,
University of Szczecin, Poland.

Bob Curry   Manager of Rule Development, ABS
Europe, UK.

Tony Marchant   Managing Director, CETEC
Consultancy Ltd, UK.

Structures:

- Evaluation of environmental conditions:

  - sea state limit conditions;

  - ice strength conditions for HSC.

- Analysis of loads:

  - analytical and model test predictions and their
uncertainties.

  - what kind of loads should be covered by the
Code?

- Analysis of response:

  - conventional and fast ships.

  - parametric and comparative studies for collecting
design and service data.

- Evaluation of strength:

  - probability approach and reliability analysis -
partial safety coefficients, safety index.

  - calibration of safety levels according to
classification rule standards.

  - design criteria - should the Code have more
detailed requirements?

- Control of Safety:

  - Strength monitoring systems - the influence on
design safety standards.

Classification:

- HSC Code, Chapter 3, Structures

  - very general - performance based;

  - class requirements acceptable.

- Class Requirements

  - length less than 60m to 80m;

  - acceptance criteria based on experience;

  - published rules;

  - additional requirements for length greater than
60m to 80m or speeds exceeding 45-50 knots;

  - F E Analysis for global strength and primary
structure;

- all HSC approved for sea state/speed operating envelope to control vertical acceleration for design strength.

- Structural Materials

  - Aluminium: small-large HSC catamarans;

  - HTS/Aluminium: large HSC (monohulls);

  - FRP: small-medium HSC;

  - Potential use of FRP: all superstructures and deckhouses of HSC.

- Classification Rules Continually Under Development

  - service experience feedback;

  - technology development;

  - new vessel types;

  - statutory regulations.

Materials:

- The HSC Code requirements for "fire-restrictive" materials.

- The tests required for "fire restrictive" materials, ISO 9705, 5660 etc.

- Possible solutions to the last point.

- Other materials - steel and aluminium alloy.

SESSION III

STABILITY AND SUBDIVISION

Speakers:

Andrew Blyth   Director, Blyth Bridges Marine
                 Consultants Ltd, UK.

John Lewthwaite IMAA, Managing Director, IMAA
                 Consultancy Ltd, UK.

- Bottom Damage: The Longitudinal extent of damage covered by the HSC needs urgent review.

- Several Classification Societies now recommend the incorporation of double bottoms in new designs; should this become regulatory?

- Vertical Damage: In the Code bottom damage is assumed to extend vertically to 0.02B or 0.5 metres, whichever is the least. This is likely to be below the waterline, so should this depth be increased?

- Residual stability requirements: these are similar to those applicable to conventional Ro-Ro vessels, should they be more stringent?

- Margin Line/Downflooding angle: these relate to heel angle limits, but there is possibly some confusion between these two parameters.

- Water on deck: SOLAS Regulations now require consideration of the possibility of this. This must be studied with respect to high speed craft.

- Watertight and Weathertight Integrity:

  - High speed craft with bow doors do not have to meet requirements comparable with those for conventional vessels;

  - admissibility and requirements for watertight doors below bulkhead deck;

  - requirements for watertight/weathertight loading doors in the main shell;

  - exterior watertight/weathertight integrity above the bulkhead deck;

  - measures for prevention of downflooding from vehicle spaces.

SESSION IV

LIFESAVING & EVACUATION

Speakers:

Geoff Billington   ML Lifeguard Ltd, UK.

Stephen Phillips   Director, Seaspeed Technology
                     Ltd, UK.

John Gifford   Managing Director, Griffon
                     Hovercraft Ltd, UK.

- The practicality of demonstrating Marine Escape Systems (MES) - particularly for the higher sea states.

- Rescue requirements: What is practical for the large capacity raft where recovery of approximately 1000 passengers is concerned?

- The lifesaving equipment requirements are in the same proportions regardless of craft size.

- Ship-borne rescue vessels: Are they necessary for smaller craft considering the weight and space penalties. Are they of realistic benefit for their perceived purpose?

- International routes may still be "sheltered", but there is no provision for them under the Code.

SUMMARY OF SEMINAR ACTION POINTS

by A G Blyth and S Phillips

International Symposium & Seminar

THE SAFETY OF HIGH SPEED CRAFT

6 - 7 FEBRUARY 1997 LONDON

SEMINAR / STRUCTURED DISCUSSION

AT THE INTERNATIONAL SYMPOSIUM ON THE SAFETY OF HIGH SPEED CRAFT

7TH FEBRUARY 1997

SUMMARY OF ACTION POINTS

The following summary of the principal matters raised during the seminar was prepared by Mr A G Blyth and Mr S Phillips and represents their view of the discussions.

GENERAL

- **Title of the Code:** There is a logical argument that this Code should be called the Restricted Service Code, since it is the operational restrictions that constitute the main difference from conventional SOLAS, the equivalence to which does not change with craft speed.

- **Operational limits:** These are set relative to significant wave height, but how can the Master apply such limits in practice? Limits should be set considering safety not comfort.

- **Navigation:** The use of identified routes for HSC operation should be considered as a means of reducing collision risks.

- **Interpretation:** Means of minimising differences in interpretation by member administrations, and duplication of expensive demonstrations.

- **Interpretation:** Uniformity of interpretation would be aided if each Chapter or Part of a Chapter commenced with a statement of aims and objectives.

- **Other IMO requirements:** Need for consideration of HSC operation when compiling other IMO instruments, eg: MARPOL, Load Line. Possibly develop agreed equivalencies suited to HSC.

- **Small Craft:** Craft under about 30m and/or operating on sheltered international routes have difficulty complying with all the HSC Code. A paragraph clarifying the circumstances under which application of the Code may be relaxed is needed.

- **Retrospective Application:** The extent to which revisions to the Code may be applied retrospectively needs clarification.

STABILITY & SUBDIVISION

- The length of bottom damage currently considered is far too small. A new requirement covering a raking situation must be developed. A prescriptive requirement for double bottoms, although attractive in some ways, would not cover all raking damage scenarios.

- Consequences of damage greater than basic rules should be evaluated, in order to avoid sudden catastrophic behaviour; eg, by requiring that extent of damage resulting in excessive heel angles or sinking be investigated, or by setting secondary extents and residual requirements.

- HSC Ro-Ro watertight integrity requirements should be brought into line with conventional ships; eg, requirement for inner bow doors.

- Requirements regarding watertight and weathertight integrity need to be added, and the admissibility of watertight doors below the bulkhead deck clarified. The advantages of not fitting void spaces with air vents in limiting the degree of flooding after damage should be recognised.

- Model tests should be accepted as an alternative to the current prescriptive requirements, in which case performance based criteria need to be identified.

FIRE

- Statistics and Formal Safety Assessment experience appear to indicate that undue accent is placed on fire aspects compared to the risk for other HSC hazards. Occurrence of fires is relatively low.

- More accent should be placed on fire prevention through limiting the risk of occurrence and good engineering, and less on fire protection and extinguishing.

- Permit alternative balances to be struck between restricting the risk, extinguishing measures and passive fire protection.

- Reconsideration AND clarification of the acceptability of suitable composite materials for hull and superstructure, including:

  - use of ISO 5660 test in lieu of ISO 9705, especially for craft of under 30m;

  - accept non-fire restricting structures in low fire risk areas, such as below waterline.

COLLISION & ACCOMMODATION

- Current requirements for g_{coll} are excessive for smaller craft (sometimes reaching 40g), and are quite impractical to design for. Suggestions include: fixed overall design level; or placing an upper limit of (say) 12g to existing formulation.

- Formula in 4.4.1 is unsatisfactory in practice, producing zones of between 2% and 40% craft length. Suggestions include: fixed length percentage (say) 7%; or empirical formula varying zone length from 5% to 10% with craft speeds up to 50 knots.

- Design accelerations in other directions are needed; eg, if consistency with seat testing requirements is to be addressed.

- Safety of passengers when boarding or disembarking is not considered.

LIFESAVING APPARATUS

- Serious safety issues are arising from the use of A.689(17) MES test requirements, including:

  - danger to personnel when type approving MES in limiting sea state head sea testing is irrelevant to HSC;

  - excessive duration of load test compared to real scenario;

  - excessive wear is occurring to MES due to annual testing & recovery requirement. Crew training would be better conducted on a dedicated rig.

- MES limiting sea state often restricts limits of craft operation. This limit should also consider the feasibility of recovering evacuees from rafts into rescue craft, and recovery of a rescue boat after deployment. Consistency with conventional SOLAS should be borne in mind.

- The requirements for exemption from the need to carry a rescue boat should be extended to apply to craft up to (say) 30m.

- The specification required for rescue boats needs clarification. A lesser standard than current SOLAS may be appropriate for craft under (say) 30m.

- The weight burden of requiring SOLAS standards for rescue boats, liferafts and lifejackets on smaller craft (under about 30m) when operating in restricted circumstances is excessive, and can challenge their viability. Lighter weight alternative standards (eg, aircraft) should be considered for Category A craft.

Written Contribution

Mr A Armstrong (Australian Shipbuilders Association): The following written reply was submitted in response to the above 'action' ponts:

I cannot accept that the action points included *"the length of bottom damage currently considered is far too small"*. Certainly this was put forward by two UK presenters, but there was equally an opinion that the current requirement was all right.

There was no real debate at all during the conference on g_{coll} being too high, (nor the resultant "person free" zone); rather two presenters expressed this opinion, so I do not agree that this was an action point that represents the opinion of the attendees. It was agreed that we did not have enough information available for us to draw any conclusions.

I do not agree with the comment that *"safety of passengers when boarding or disembarking is not considered"*. It does not come under the HSC Code; rather in the UK it comes under the Department of Industry. It is a topical point, given the unfortunate accident at Ramsgate recently in the Courts.

SUMMARY REPORT OF DISCUSSIONS ON PAPERS PRESENTED IN SHANGHAI

by J C Lewthwaite

International Symposium & Seminar

THE SAFETY OF HIGH SPEED CRAFT

14 APRIL 1997 SHANGHAI

SUMMARY REPORT OF DISCUSSIONS ON PAPERS PRESENTED IN SHANGHAI
THE SAFETY OF HIGH SPEED CRAFT SEMINAR

by J C Lewthwaite
IMAA Ltd

Note: Papers were presented in English, with accompanying translations in Mandarin by Chinese interpreters. Questions and discussion were similarly handled.

In the Chair: **Dr A Tang** (Secretary Hong Kong RINA/IMarE Joint Branch)

PAPER 4

DESIGN LIMITATIONS: OPERATING LIMITATIONS THE SAFETY OF HIGH SPEED CRAFT

Presented by Mr Robert Bryce, Hart Fenton & Co Ltd, UK

Ms Hong Qian (China Classification Society) requested more information with regard to the type of accelerometer used as a means of assessing sea state limitations. Mr Bryce stated that the instrument should be capable of measuring low frequency vertical accelerations, not necessarily wave impacts.

Prof Yuan Suishan (Shanghai Society for Pacific Economic Development) endorsed the use of accelerometers to assess limits. He was rather doubtful about a master's ability to judge wave conditions.

Mr Francis Law (Shun Tak Ship Management Ltd), asked whether the limiting conditions were determined by passenger comfort or the impact loading on the structure. Mr Bryce said that generally passenger comfort was more important, but some craft may suffer from structural limitations. The effect of speed was significant. Quite high acceleration levels could be tolerated for short periods, but fatigue was then likely to be a problem.

Mr Chen Guo Quan (China Classification Society), asked how a speed versus limiting wave height curve could be established. Mr Bryce agreed that it was difficult to define such a limitation. Wave conditions should include assessment of period and the effect of this on the response of the craft.

Dr Tang (Chairman) asked whether there had been any feed-back from Classification Societies. Mr Bryce said it was difficult to comment on individual responses from Societies, but that discussions had taken place.

Mr K M Wong (ABS Pacific) again questioned the use of a wave height versus speed curve. Mr Bryce said that it was important that whatever limitations were imposed they should be understandable and comparable. Consistency was important to operators as well as builders to ensure everybody worked within a uniform framework. If not, then certain builders could 'cut corners' by choosing Societies with the least demanding requirements! A healthy debate within Classification Societies was essential in order to resolve these points.

Mr Bryce added that the size of craft used to date in China had been at the lower end of the scale. It was very important that limitation issues were thought about now before the market advanced to the use of larger craft operating in more open sea conditions.

Dr Tang (Chairman) asked if there were any major differences with regard to Classification Society costs. Mr Bryce stated that the cost depended on a whole range of issues, particularly structural, and these therefore influenced the life of the vessel. Most Societies ensured craft were built to a good standard, but equating cost with safety was impossible.

Mr Francis Law (Shun Tak Ship Management Ltd) referred again to the subject of accelerations, mentioning his experience with catamarans. He suggested that 'jerk' (ie, the rate of change of acceleration) should be examined since this was more relevant to high speed craft. Mr Bryce said that the issue of comfort in relation to accelerations was really interesting. Both transverse and longitudinal accelerations were now receiving more attention, especially with regard to the motion of catamarans with their relatively stiff rolling action. Passengers tended to get used to such motions and were able to predict their effects, with reductions in the incidence of motion sickness.

Dr Tang (Chairman) agreed that deck-edge acceleration levels on wide beam catamarans were high. He considered however, that longitudinal and lateral acceleration levels were only really considered by Navy ship designers with regard to the operation of weapon systems.

Mr Mike Porter (Assistant Secretary Technical, RINA) said that he considered that future design criteria should be based on all three acceleration directions. Mr Bryce agreed but thought that such an instrument would probably become part of a total package form rather than a single criterion.

1

Mr Mike Porter also asked how important weather forecasting was in the daily operation of high speed craft. Mr Bryce thought this would become a more significant issue in the future.

In the Chair: Mr Francis Law
                     (Shun Tak Ship Management Ltd)

REVISED REQUIREMENTS FOR CLASSIFICATION OF HIGH-SPEED CRAFT

Presented by Mr Martin Cooper, American Bureau of Shipping, Singapore

Mr Lhu Yong (Chinese Register of Shipping), mentioned his interest in high speed craft regulation. He was particularly interested in the data shown in Figure 6 of the paper, and asked for more explanation. Mr Cooper said that the slamming pressure (Psxx) was based on the equation given in paragraph 4.1, which gave the vertical acceleration along the craft length L. This decreased towards the bow due to the increase in deadrise angle. The side pressure (Ps) could be obtained from the equation given in paragraph 4.3. The pitching pressure (Psf) was based on the length of the craft and the hull geometry at the forward end. **Mr K M Wong** (ABS Pacific) also provided further explanation.

Mr Ge Weizhen (China Ship Research Centre) asked whether the revised rules applied to SWATH vessel types. Mr Cooper said that builders of such vessels generally regarded them as high speed types with reduced motions. ABS analysed certain parts of SWATH vessels under the revised rules.

Mr L Grossi (Fincantieri, Naval Shipbuilding Division) said the equation for vertical acceleration (para. 4.1) was useful for builders, but technology was advancing and for large craft of around 140m in length, it was necessary to work from first principles. He asked if ABS took into account the results from experiments in tank tests. Mr Cooper stated that this was a complicated issue. Anything outside of the Rules (presently limited to 130m monohulls) would be considered. The past building history of the yard was important and how new vessels related to earlier designs. ABS had experience in working with yards on tank test data that could be used to evaluate the structure.

Mr Raymond Toh (Greenbay Marine Pte Ltd) asked why the limits shown in Figure 3 related to 0.6 and 1.0g levels. Mr Cooper explained that the data in the figure related to the performance of a 35m passenger ferry designed to 0.6g (1/100 highest vertical acceleration level). The 1.0g level was shown in the figure for comparison only. He said that crewboats and rescue craft would be designed to higher levels, probably up to 3.0g.

Mr Yang Xin-Fa (Shanghai Shipbuilding Corporation) asked about the impact strength and requirements of FRP. Mr Cooper said that this material would not be treated any differently to either steel or aluminium. There were minimum thickness limits for all materials and GRP/FRP would not present problems.

Mr Cheng Rai-Lin (Navy Equipment Transport Centre) asked about the boundary conditions used in 3-D modelling of structures. Mr Cooper said that this was controversial. The example shown as Figure 8 considered a centreline bulkhead constrained by vertical frames and subjected to slam loading. In such studies it was important to move the boundaries as far away as possible from the area under consideration.

In the Chair: Professor Yuan Suishan

PAPER 10

RECENT DEVELOPMENTS IN FIRE SAFETY FOR FAST CRAFT

Presented by Mr Tormod Eidal, Det Norske Veritas AS, Norway

Ms Hong Qian (China Classification Society) asked if the gas burner arrangement, shown in Figure 1, was a High Speed Code special requirement. Mr Eidal stated that it was a normal test arrangement. The difference from conventional ships where only non-combustible materials were permitted, was that the HSC code considered the use of any Fire Resisting Material (FRM) provided that it complied with MSC.40(64) criteria. The test procedure which was covered by ISO 9705 was used to evaluate such materials.

Ms Hong Qian also asked whether the use of inert gas as specified by the HSC Code resulted in a weight penalty. Mr Eidal explained that such systems have to be of the two-shot type (ie, to have a second discharge capability). However, the weights of the new non-toxic gas systems such as those based on Halotron, FM200 or Envirogel, were a little different to those using Halon. None of these gases constituted dangers to the crew but the newer types were environmentally friendly. All were lighter than the old CO^2 systems which required high gas concentrations. Halotron had now been approved by DnV and Swedish authorities.

In the Chair: Professor Yuan Suishan

PAPER 2

COMPARISON OF TYPICAL DAMAGED STABILITY CHARACTERISTICS OF CATAMARAN AND FAST MONOHULL TYPES

Presented by Mr John Lewthwaite, IMAA Ltd., UK

The Chairman asked for more information regarding the application of 'water-on-deck' to high speed craft. Mr Lewthwaite explained how this was applied in the UK but stated that international agreement within the IMO had not yet been obtained on this issue. The effect of applying 0.5m of 'water-on-deck' to the catamaran and fast monohull types used as examples in the paper was explained (see Figure 7). This resulted in the monohull having insufficient damaged stability but the catamaran could just tolerate this condition.

Professor Yuan Suishan asked Mr Lewthwaite if he believed that the application of 'water-on-deck' to the high speed craft rules was justified. Mr Lewthwaite stated that such matters had to be decided politically between nations. Naval architects would of course be advising their representatives, but the rules would be made by the IMO. However, he believed that it might be necessary to seek a compromise solution, since it appeared that fast monohulls might not be able to cope with such a damaged condition.

Mr Yang Xin-Fa (Shanghai Shipbuilding Corporation) asked how the 0.5m figure had been arrived at. Mr Lewthwaite said that this had been derived by the IMO from experience with conventional Ro-Ro ferries in order to try and overcome the problems that such vessels had had in the past.

Ms Qian Pai-Ying (Chinese Ship Classification Society) gave a detailed review of how the situation of 'water-on-deck' was viewed in China. She said that this had caused many problems and was likely to result in substantial costs. In her opinion the legislation, which was only the result of one accident, was too hasty and should not be applied to all vessels.

Mr Lewthwaite said that the UK regarded this legislation as extremely important and that things were moving ahead as quickly as possible to ensure that all UK ships were as safe as possible.

Professor Yuan Suishan said that with regard to the earlier remarks there was a different opinion in China. Politicians should listen to professional naval architects and form rules which were sensible. Mr Lewthwaite said that was exactly why they were gathered together and

able to voice opinions and present the results of investigations to this assembly.

Mr Lhu Yong (Chinese Register of Shipping) said that while he agreed with the findings in the paper, he believed that these only applied to larger craft. He had carried out some stability calculations for a 40m design and was sure that small craft could not tolerate a doubling of the damaged length, as proposed in the paper. Mr Lewthwaite reminded Mr Lhu that the HSC Code was only intended to be applied to craft operating in international waters and that small craft may not have to meet the full requirements of the Code. In any event he was a little surprised that with appropriate sub-division of the bulkheads it was not possible to tolerate an increase in the damaged length of a 40m long craft.

Mr Zhang Ji-Meng (Shanghai Merchant Ship Research Institute) said the problem of 'water-on-deck' could be avoided by designing the ship so that water drained off quickly, by, for example, increasing the curvature of the main deck. Mr Lewthwaite reminded Mr Zhang that the condition applied to the damaged vessel. Residual freeboard was the key to reducing the amount of 'water-on-deck', and invariably high speed craft tended to have higher freeboards.

Mr Zhang also made the point that it was difficult to design small craft with many sub-divisions. Mr Lewthwaite reminded the assembly of a recent incident in UK waters where a small catamaran sustained considerable damage to one hull and yet stayed afloat, albeit at a severe angle of heel. He said that we really should try and learn from such cases. Finally Mr Lewthwaite said that with regard to damaged length, the IMO was currently reviewing this matter and he believed that it was likely that some increase would be agreed.

In the Chair: Professor Yuan Suishan

PAPER 12

LEGAL & INSURANCE ASPECTS ON HIGH SPEED CRAFT

Presented by Mr Luo Hai, Clifford Chance, Hong Kong and Mr Robert Bryce, Hart Fenton & Co Ltd., UK

Mr M Porter (Assistant Secretary (Technical) RINA) asked how underwriting high speed craft compared with aircraft, especially in relation to costs. Mr Bryce said that the comparison with aircraft was interesting. Premiums and deductibles were higher than for high speed vessels, and it was hoped that costs would not move towards aircraft levels. About US $1000M had been underwritten on high speed craft since 1990 and their safety was in the hands of technicians and operators. It was very important that this was appreciated and safety standards were continually improved.

GENERAL DISCUSSION ON PAPERS

In the Chair: Professor Yuan Suishan

The Chairman said that it had been a very interesting and hard working day. He suggested that high speed craft were also high-tech craft. Because of these new developments a whole range of problems had tended to arise. Discussion had ranged from seakeeping, stability, structural integration and craft management, as well as the legal aspects. The pro's and con's would all be contained in the final Proceedings which provided an excellent source of reference for all concerned.

Mr Trevor Blakeley (Secretary designate RINA) said that the day had been both interesting and useful for all those attending. He had been very surprised and pleased by the number of Chinese delegates attending the sessions. Although numbers had dropped off slightly in the afternoon, he believed that this conference could be counted as being very successful. The subject matter of the papers had been both relevant and appropriate to China at this time.

On behalf of the RINA, Mr Blakeley thanked the speakers for, if possible, an even better performance than in London. He also thanked the chairmen who had played such an important part in sustaining the momentum in the discussions.

In conclusion Mr Blakeley thanked the delegates for attending and playing such an active part in the proceedings. He said that he looked forward to seeing them again at another conference organised by the RINA on an equally relevant topic in the near future.

Professor Yuan thanked the RINA, acknowledging their world famous reputation. He said that the standard of the speakers had been excellent and the delegates had learnt a lot. He thought that the time had come for a closer association between the Chinese shipbuilding authorities and the RINA, and looked forward to future co-operations.